Mathematics Curriculum
Issues, Trends, and Future Directions

Seventy-second Yearbook

Barbara J. Reys
Seventy-second Yearbook Editor
University of Missouri—Columbia
Columbia, Missouri

Robert E. Reys
Seventy-second Yearbook Editor
University of Missouri—Columbia
Columbia, Missouri

Rheta Rubenstein
General Yearbook Editor
University of Michigan—Dearborn
Dearborn, Michigan

NATIONAL COUNCIL OF
TEACHERS OF MATHEMATICS

ISSN 0077-4103
ISBN 978-0-87353-643-1

The National Council of Teachers of Mathematics is a public
voice of mathematics education, supporting teachers to ensure
equitable mathematics learning of the highest quality for all
students through vision, leadership, professional development,
and research.

Contents

Preface

Mathematics Curriculum: Issues, Trends, and Future Directions

Why was *mathematics curriculum* chosen as a theme for the Seventy-second NCTM Yearbook? One explanation might be that mathematics curriculum—

> … was chosen as the central theme because of the present interest in curriculum revision. Since it should be understood that such revision ought to be a continuous process, the discussions herein presented are not final. However, they furnish a basis that will help us to find better ways of determining how the proper content should be selected, arranged, and presented. (Reeve 1927, p. vii)

This is a timely response today, just as it was when it was originally stated by William D. Reeve in 1927 in the preface to the Second NCTM Yearbook, *Curriculum Problems in Teaching Mathematics*. It is a reminder that mathematics curriculum has long been a topic of keen interest in mathematics education. Some things don't change!

One thing is certain today, just as it has been for many decades. Mathematics curriculum remains a central issue in efforts to improve mathematics learning opportunities for students. Although times change, society changes, and people change, for many it is difficult to accept change in the mathematics curriculum. Terms such as *basic, old, new, modern, antiquated, traditional, conservative, liberal, contemporary,* and *reform* are commonly used in society. In fact, these terms are frequently mentioned in the context of mathematics curriculum. Some things don't change!

Returning to history, we find that the developers of the Second Yearbook tried to provide a balanced view of mathematics curriculum, as reflected in their statement—

> The Committee tried to obtain contributors holding many different points of view and representing as widely separated sections of the country as possible. The result can be labeled neither liberal nor conservative. (Reeve 1927, p. vii)

Nearly a century ago, the Yearbook Editorial Committee believed that it needed to provide a balance between whatever was considered conservative and liberal. Some things don't change!

Most controversy about mathematics curriculum centers on either the need for change or the lack of change. The need for change, along with visions for change, has long been reflected by NCTM in such publications as *An Agenda for Action* (1980), *Curriculum and Evaluation Standards for School Mathematics* (1989), *Principles and Standards for School Mathematics* (2000), *Curriculum Focal Points for Prekindergarten through Grade 8 Mathematics* (2006), and *Focus in High School Mathematics: Reasoning and Sense Making* (2009). These publications have called for curricular change, and several have been met with mixed reactions. Although many strongly support the vision of school mathematics outlined by NCTM, some think the recommendations have gone too far in outlining changes, whereas others think they have not gone far enough.

Change in any period of time is difficult and creates challenges. In schools, mathematics curriculum change affects teachers, students, administrators, and parents. Change, particularly for parents, teachers, and administrators, has always been difficult. This concern is documented in one of the papers in the Fourth NCTM Yearbook (Reeve 1929, p. 132):

> Tradition has been a hard factor to overcome in modernizing the curriculum in mathematics. The difficulty being largely a matter of clinging to the hazy and invalid objectives used in teaching the mathematics of many generations ago.

Tradition continues to maintain inertia that is difficult to overcome in changing mathematics curriculum. As a result, debates about the direction of mathematics curriculum in schools and cities throughout the world continue to this day. Some things don't change!

This Yearbook continues in a long line of NCTM Yearbooks, dating back to 1927, that have addressed various facets of the changing mathematics curriculum. Although some factors such as tradition can inhibit significant change, other factors such as policy (e.g., federal No Child Left Behind legislation), societal needs (mathematically literate graduates), and technological advances (computer software, calculators) foster and accelerate the need for change.

This Yearbook, *Mathematics Curriculum: Issues, Trends, and Future Directions,* was developed during a period of major curriculum change. The past two decades have seen an era of unprecedented mathematics curriculum development across grades K–12. In the past year alone, a major state-initiated process for developing "common core standards" is underway (NGA and CCSSO 2009). With forty-eight states (all but Texas and Alaska) and several territories participating in the articulation of "college and career-ready" high school graduation expectations and common grades K–12 standards in mathematics and language arts,

2010 promises to be a landmark year of discussion and dialogue about mathematics curriculum.

This Yearbook reflects some of the many issues that the field is currently discussing, so it serves as both a record of current advances and a summary of challenges regarding curriculum. We hope that it will both guide and stimulate thinking about where we have been, where we are, and where we need to go.

The Yearbook is organized to acknowledge the various forms of curriculum that shape the grades K–12 mathematics program, including the following:

> *The Intended Curriculum*—Curriculum authorities at the local, state, and national level specify particular learning expectations, often delineated by grade, for school mathematics instruction. Often called "curriculum standards," these learning expectations furnish guidance regarding what should be taught and when various mathematical content and processes should receive emphasis in the school program. They also guide the development of textbooks and assessments designed to monitor school programs.

> *The Written (Textbook) Curriculum*—Publishers use curriculum standards to design textbooks and other instructional materials to implement the intended curriculum. These materials include textbooks typically developed to support the day-to-day teaching of mathematics over a school semester or academic year of study. They also include modules focusing on smaller amounts of mathematical content, workbooks, and computer software.

> *The Implemented Curriculum*—Individual teachers make decisions every day regarding if and how they will use district-adopted curriculum materials. Therefore students, for example, using the same textbook may, in fact, have differing opportunities to learn mathematics. The implemented curriculum refers to the mathematics that students have an opportunity to learn, which is often a function of the district-adopted textbook and the individual teacher's preferences.

Together, these different forms of curriculum have a direct impact on teachers' decisions and students' opportunities to learn. Each has been a focus of intense work over the past three decades (since the publication of *An Agenda for Action* in 1980) as each has served as a lever for school improvement.

So here we are today, one-tenth of the way through the twenty-first century, wrestling to improve students' learning opportunities. This Yearbook includes articles focusing on the full range of curriculum issues, as well as articles that offer insight into the impact of curriculum on students' and teachers' learning. Specifically, the articles are organized into the following sections:

Access to Historical Documents on Mathematics Curriculum

In addition to sharing information and provoking discussion with the printed articles in this Yearbook, the Editorial Panel, under the direction of Tom Romberg, has assembled a set of sixty-eight articles, chapters, and relevant publications provided in an accompanying CD. These reflect issues and trends in the mathematics curriculum in the United States and Canada for the period 1843–1993. The articles are organized by time period: nineteenth and early twentieth century, mid-twentieth century, modern math era, post–modern math era, and standards-based era. (No articles more recent than 1993 were considered for inclusion in the CD.) For each era, the features of schools are briefly described. Then, as warranted, each era's documents have been organized by issues or topics of concern at that time, such as arithmetic, college-preparatory mathematics, and mathematics for all.

The Editorial Panel strove to set forth a broad, meaningful set of resources on the CD to offer significant perspectives on mathematics education curriculum philosophy and history. For the past century and a half, a constant dilemma faced by those choosing the mathematical content for the school mathematics curriculum has involved how one caters to the needs of the college-bound students who will study mathematics at universities (particularly those who will become professional mathematicians) and at the same time teaches other students the mathematical skills they will need to be productive citizens in a changing society. The selected articles reflect how each era dealt with this dilemma on the basis of the structure of schools and the social issues of that era.

Summary

For more than a century, mathematics curriculum has been changing, and these changes have generated much discussion. In fact, the past thirty years have witnessed an unprecedented focus on school mathematics in the United States. In 2009–2010, the momentum is building, with the "common core standards" initiative (NGA and CCSSO 2009) well underway. Prompted by national reports and international assessments, attention has focused on the need to raise the quality of school mathematics programs for grades K–12 students to be more successful so as to compete in the global economy. Curriculum has been central to many of the recent school mathematics improvement efforts. As a result, grades K–12 students are studying more mathematics, often at an early grade, with a focus on conceptual understanding as well as skill development and problem solving. We hope the discussion stimulated by this Yearbook will advance our thinking and support continued reflection and productive work on the mathematics curriculum.

Acknowledgments

This Yearbook resulted from an open call for papers. On behalf of the Editorial Panel, we thank the authors for their contributions and working with us throughout the review process. Their willingness to accept suggestions, respond to queries, and meet deadlines was both exemplary and greatly appreciated. Behind the scenes and shaping this Yearbook have been authors, reviewers, members of the Editorial Panel, the NCTM staff, the General Editor, and the Yearbook coeditors all working together to write, review, edit, revise, lay out, and produce a set of papers addressing a wide range of issues related to mathematics curriculum.

This is the last in a series of NCTM Yearbooks (2008 to 2010) being shepherded by Rheta Rubenstein as General Editor. Rheta has done a stellar job advising, counseling, editing, and working to help in every way possible throughout the development of these yearbooks. On behalf of previous editors and the coeditors of this book, we thank Rheta for a job well done.

The members of the Editorial Panel reflect a deep knowledge about mathematics curriculum along with experience addressing a wide range of curricular issues. Their rich backgrounds served the yearbook development process well. Additionally, they worked tirelessly throughout all stages of the yearbook development process, and their contributions are greatly appreciated. The Seventy-second Yearbook Editorial Panel consisted of the following:

> Randall Charles, Carmel, California
> Kathleen Cramer, University of Minnesota—Twin Cities
> Diana V. Lambdin, Indiana University Bloomington
> Thomas A. Romberg, University of Wisconsin—Madison
> James W. Wilson, University of Georgia

Yearbook Coeditors
> Barbara J. Reys, University of Missouri—Columbia
> Robert E. Reys, University of Missouri—Columbia

General Editor
Rheta Rubenstein, University of Michigan—Dearborn

REFERENCES

National Council of Teachers of Mathematics (NCTM). *An Agenda for Action*. Reston, Va.: NCTM, 1980.

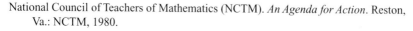. *Curriculum and Evaluation Standards for School Mathematics*. Reston, Va.: NCTM, 1989.

———. *Principles and Standards for School Mathematics*. Reston, Va.: NCTM, 2000.

———. *Curriculum Focal Points for Prekindergarten through Grade 8 Mathematics*. Reston, Va.: NCTM, 2006.

———. *Focus in High School Mathematics: Reasoning and Sense Making*. Reston, Va.: NCTM, 2009.

National Governor's Association (NGA) and Council of Chief State School Officers (CCSSO). *College and Career Readiness Standards for Mathematics: Draft for Review and Comment, September 21, 2009*. http://www.CoreStandards.org/Standards/index.htm (accessed September 25, 2009).

Reeve, William David, ed. *Curriculum Problems in Teaching Mathematics*, Second Yearbook of the National Council of Teachers of Mathematics. New York: Bureau of Publications: Teachers College, Columbia University, 1927.

———. "United States." In *Significant Changes and Trends in the Teaching of Mathematics throughout the World since 1910*, Fourth Yearbook of the National Council of Teachers of Mathematics, edited by William David Reeve, pp. 132–86. New York: Bureau of Publications: Teachers College, Columbia University, 1929.

Introduction to the CD Collection: Classic Publications on the Mathematics Curriculum

Thomas A. Romberg

The compact disc (CD) that accompanies the 2010 NCTM Yearbook of the National Council of Teachers of Mathematics (NCTM), *Mathematics Curriculum: Issues, Trends, and Future Directions,* contains a set of sixty-eight articles that reflect issues and trends in the mathematics curriculum in the United States and Canada for the past approximately 150 years. The articles were selected by the Editorial Panel as important references on the mathematics curriculum published before 1993.

All societies create educational institutions—schools, apprentice programs, and so on—to teach students "something." That "something" may be a collection of concepts and skills related to a particular topic in a discipline (e.g., rational numbers in mathematics, the Bill of Rights in American history), a common social context (e.g., carpentry, tailoring), a valued cultural aspect (e.g., writing poetry, playing a musical instrument), and so forth. In each instance the "something" to be learned is considered by adults, employers, or society to be an important feature of the culture, which needs to be passed on to students so they have the opportunity to be productive citizens. The assumption is that if students participate in the activities of the institution, they will learn that "something" with understanding. Thus, the focus in this set of papers is on the issues surrounding the selection of that "something" with respect to mathematics (the mathematical content) that students have been expected to learn. The issues include such questions as what topics should be included, how the topics should be sequenced, and who decides on the content.

The Editorial Panel is aware that additional issues, such as the learning of mathematics, how students are assessed, teacher preparation, curriculum implementation, and others, influence the mathematical content that students experience and are expected to learn. However, for this CD, articles on these issues were generally not included. The exceptions are a few seminal articles by four psychologists on the learning of mathematics—John Dewey, Edward L. Thorndike, Merl Wittrock, and James Greeno. Generally in articles on the learning of mathematics, content is not an issue. Instead, instruction is the issue. If the curriculum is a path involving the mathematical content that society wants students to learn, instruction focuses on how students are to travel that path. Lauren Resnick and Wendy Ford's (1981) *The Psychology of Mathematics for Instruction* is a good summary of the history of this line of work.

The Curriculum Papers on the CD

The following two complementary documents by George Stanic and Jeremy Kilpatrick provide background for the CD. These authors present an overall historical perspective about mathematics curricula.

> Stanic, George M. A., and Jeremy Kilpatrick. "Historical Perspective on Problem Solving in the Mathematics Curriculum." In *The Teaching and Assessing of Mathematical Problem Solving: Research Agenda for Mathematics Education,* edited by Randall Charles and Edward A. Silver, pp. 1–22. Reston, Va.: National Council of Teachers of Mathematics, 1988.

> Stanic, George M. A., and Jeremy Kilpatrick. "Mathematics Curriculum Reform in the United States: A Historical Perspective." *International Journal of Educational Research* 17, no. 5 (1992): 407–17.

The remainder of the CD has been organized by time period: nineteenth and early twentieth centuries, mid-twen-tieth century, modern math era, post–modern math era, and standards-based era. For each era, the features of schools are briefly described. Then within those eras, as warranted, the documents have been organized by issues or topics of concern at that time, such as arithmetic, college-preparatory mathematics, and mathematics for all.

Nineteenth and Early Twentieth Centuries

In this period, most students attended a common school for six or eight years as a consequence of industrial expansion. It was assumed that only a very few students would go on to high school. In the common schools, it was assumed that all students needed to study arithmetic (the third "R"). Measurement and "shop-keeper" computational skills were emphasized. The issues were what and how arithmetic should be taught. The following article traces features of the arithmetic curriculum from 1850 to 1928:

> West, Roscoe L., Charles E. Greene, and William A. Brownell. "The Arithmetic Curriculum." In *Report of the Society's Committee on Arithmetic,* Twenty-ninth Yearbook of the National Society for the Study of Education, edited by Guy M. Whipple, pp. 64–142. Bloomington, Ill.: Public School Publishing Co., 1930.

In this era high schools focused on preparing a small number of students for college. The central issue was whether mathematics courses should be offered, and if they were offered, what topics were included. The following article portrays how mathematics for high schools became a unified, closed, scientific system in mid-nineteenth-century German schools rather than a collection of tools to be used to analyze and understand our world. University mathematicians wanted young students to understand the discipline rather than how mathematics is used in other fields. Thus, the focus was on the perceived needs of students who eventually would become professional mathematicians. This concern was prevalent in North America at that time and remains an issue to this date.

> Jahnke, Hans N. "Origins of School Mathematics in Early Nineteenth Century Germany." *Journal of Curriculum Studies* 18, no. 1 (1983): 85–94.

In the United States, the first major call to standardize the secondary school mathematics curricula was made in the following "Committee of Ten" report:

> National Education Association. "Mathematics." In *Report of the Committee of Ten on Secondary School Studies,* pp. 104–16. New York: American Book Co., 1894.

Nevertheless, the following article by George Stanic demonstrates the important ideological battles in this era that focused on the justification of whether mathematics was an integral part of school learning:

> Stanic, George M. A. "The Growing Crisis in Mathematics Education in the Early Twentieth Century." *Journal for Research in Mathematics Education* 17, no. 3 (May 1986): 190–205.

At the secondary school level, E. H. Moore's presidential address in 1903 to the Mathematical Association of America (MAA) had both immediate and long-term influence on the development of curriculum. Among his recommendations was a call for the unification of mathematics in a coherent four-year course around the idea of function and the rejection of a completely axiomatic system at the secondary school level.

> Moore, Eliakim H. "The Foundations of Mathematics." *School Review* 11, no. 6 (1903): 521–38.

Based on Moore's address, the following article discussed the various factors that can influence the content and design of a high school algebra course. It offered general principles for deciding what content should be included in the first year of algebra and in the second year of algebra.

> Slaught, Herbert E. "What Should Be Emphasized and What Omitted in the High-School Course in Algebra?" *School Review* 16, no. 8 (1908): 503–16.

The importance of geometry in relation to Moore's address is discussed in the following article:

> Betz, William. "The Teaching of Geometry in Its Relation to the Present Educational Trend." *School Science and Mathematics* 8 (1908): 625–33.

The following article is a summary of changes in secondary school mathematics curriculum in the first quarter of the twentieth century.

> Smith, David E. "A General Survey of the Progress of Mathematics in Our High Schools in the Last Twenty-five Years." In *The First Yearbook,* First Yearbook of the National Council of Teachers of Mathematics, edited by Charles M. Austin, pp. 1–31. New York: Bureau of Publications, Teachers College, Columbia University, 1926.

Finally, in this era the following three works reflect the contrast of psychological thinking between progressive and behavioral perspectives. The two articles by John Dewey contended that the child and the curriculum are in conflict with one another. He offered divergent viewpoints between the studies of subject matter and the child's experience.

> Dewey, John. "The Psychological Aspect of the School Curriculum." *Educational Review* 13 (1897): 356–69.

> Dewey, John. *The Child and the Curriculum.* Chicago: University of Chicago Press, 1902.

Edward L. Thorndike presented the behavioral perspective, which has had considerable impact on arithmetic instruction.

Thorndike, Edward L. "The Constitution of Arithmetical Abilities." In *The Psychology of Arithmetic,* pp. 51–140. New York: Macmillan Co., 1922.

Mid-Twentieth Century

The period following World War I, encompassing the Great Depression, and ending in the post–World War II years was characterized by a gradual but dramatic change in the structure of schools.[1] It was the era when the Scholastic Aptitude Test and standardized tests were created. As more students continued schooling beyond grade 8, junior high schools, then middle schools, and community colleges were created. The high school became what has been called "the shopping mall school," offering a variety of courses for college-bound and non-college-bound students. Thus, although the mathematics for college-bound students was still crucial in secondary schools, concern was growing for the mathematical needs of general students.

Arithmetic skills were still the focus in elementary schools. The following article demonstrated that there had been only minor changes in the arithmetic curriculum since the article by West, Green, and Brownell some twenty years earlier:

Horn, Ernest. "Arithmetic in the Elementary School Curriculum." In *The Teaching of Arithmetic,* Fiftieth Yearbook of the National Society for the Study of Education, Part 2, edited by Nelson B. Henry, pp. 6–21, Chicago: University of Chicago Press, 1951.

However, change in instruction was being examined following progressive notions in the era. In the following article, William Brownell asserted that meaning and skill in arithmetic are both important. He defined *meaningful habituation* as the skills that are firmly based on understanding and described how this can be accomplished by first developing understanding and then converting that understanding to efficient skill.

Brownell, William A. "Meaning and Skill—Maintaining the Balance." *Arithmetic Teacher* 3, no. 4 (1956): 129–36.

Also, this period saw what is now considered the "traditional mathematics curriculum" become standard in secondary schools. The following document was an attempt to standardize the mathematics for students in junior and senior high schools preparing to attend college. The notion of a general mathematics program for grades 7 and 8 followed by the "layer cake" of algebra and geometry

---

1. An excellent summary of schools in this era is Lawrence A. Cremin, The *Transformation of the School,* New York: Vintage Books, Random House, 1961.

for all secondary school students, and advanced algebra, analytic geometry, and trigonometry for mathematics and science students, was recommended. Differential tracks of mathematics courses became common in this era.

> National Committee on Mathematical Requirements. *The Reorganization of Mathematics in Secondary Education.* Washington, D.C.: Mathematical Association of America, 1923.

Also, during the Great Depression, many students were kept in secondary schools with no intent of going on to higher education—to keep them off the job market. The following article is typical of many that describe mathematics for non-college-bound students in this era:

> Reeve, William D. "General Mathematics for the High School: Its Purpose and Content." *Educational Administration and Supervision* 6 (1920): 258–73.

It is interesting to note that mathematics as a discipline was still the primary focus for college-bound students, whereas a variety of applications became the focus for non-college-bound and community college students.

To summarize the curriculum notions of this era, NCTM and MAA prepared the following curriculum report. This report addressed such practical considerations as consumer mathematics, business mathematics, and shop mathematics, as well as courses for college-bound students.

> National Council of Teachers of Mathematics (NCTM). *The Place of Mathematics in Secondary Education: Report of the Joint Commission of the Mathematical Association of America and the National Council of Teachers of Mathematics.* New York: Bureau of Publications, Teachers College, Columbia University, 1940.

Modern Math Era

In the post–World War II and early Cold War era, the organization and structure of university mathematics was changed, with emphasis placed on calculus and modern algebra. Internationally these changes reflected the work of the French Bourbaki group, who had created a systematic description for presenting and teaching mathematics in universities.[2] As universities made changes, calls came for change in the college-preparatory curriculum in mathematics, so that more

---

2. A good discussion of this approach to mathematics can be found in Geoffrey Howson, Christine Keitel, and Jeremy Kilpatrick, *Curriculum Development in Mathematics*, Cambridge: Cambridge University Press, 1981, pp. 100–104.

students would be ready to study contemporary mathematics.

The following article typifies the argument for curriculum change of the time. Carl Shuster introduced his paper by writing, "In our present scientific, mechanistic, industrial civilization, mathematics is vastly more important than it ever was in any former age." Also, he argued for higher standards and against the plague of soft pedagogy.

> Shuster, Carl N. "A Call for Reform in High School Mathematics." *American Mathematical Monthly* 55, no. 8 (October 1948): 472–75.

The following article by Morris Kline reflects the typical issues about mathematical content of the school curriculum being addressed early in this era:

> Kline, Morris. "The Ancients versus the Moderns: A New Battle of the Books." *Mathematics Teacher* 51 (October 1958): 418–27.

The document that was central to the emergence of "modern math" materials was produced by a commission of the College Entrance Examination Board (CEEB), established in 1955. Drafts of the report were widely discussed at professional meetings during the 1950s. Although it is similar to the 1923 MAA document in mathematical courses, it emphasized developing basic competence in all students and adding the structural aspects of mathematics.

> Commission on Mathematics. *Program for College Preparatory Mathematics.* New York: College Entrance Examination Board, 1959.

NCTM, in support of the Commission on Mathematics, recommended the use of set theory throughout all courses, attention to geometry throughout all courses but with emphasis on deductive plane geometry in tenth grade, and the formation of courses differentiated according to students' ability.

> National Council of Teachers of Mathematics, Secondary-School Curriculum Committee. "The Secondary Mathematics Curriculum." *Mathematics Teacher* 52, no. 5 (May 1959): 389–417.

The catalyst for reform in this era was the "beeping" of the Russian satellite *Sputnik* in 1957. As a consequence the federal government, through the National Science Foundation (NSF), allocated funds for the development of new curriculum materials that reflected these recommendations and for appropriate teacher retraining in summer and academic institutes.

Five articles from the 1970 National Society for the Study of Education (NSSE) Yearbook describe the mathematical content in the "modern math" curricula:

> Wilder, R. L. "Historical Background of Innovations in Mathematics Curricula." In *Mathematics Education,* Sixty-ninth Yearbook of the

National Society for the Study of Education, Part 1, edited by Edward G. Begle and Herman G. Richey, pp. 7–12. Chicago: University of Chicago Press, 1970.

Kelley, John L. "Number Systems." In *Mathematics Education,* Sixty-ninth Yearbook of the National Society for the Study of Education, Part 1, edited by Edward G. Begle and Herman G. Richey, pp. 75–130. Chicago: University of Chicago Press, 1970.

Dean, Richard A. "Algebraic Systems." In *Mathematics Education,* Sixty-ninth Yearbook of the National Society for the Study of Education, Part 1, edited by Edward G. Begle and Herman G. Richey, pp. 131–66. Chicago: University of Chicago Press, 1970.

Moredock, H. Stewart. "Geometry and Measurement." In *Mathematics Education,* Sixty-ninth Yearbook of the National Society for the Study of Education, Part 1, edited by Edward G. Begle and Herman G. Richey, pp. 167–235. Chicago: University of Chicago Press, 1970.

Buck, R. Creighton. "Functions." In *Mathematics Education,* Sixty-ninth Yearbook of the National Society for the Study of Education, Part 1, edited by Edward G. Begle and Herman G. Richey, pp. 236–59. Chicago: University of Chicago Press, 1970.

The two principal secondary school curricula that were developed at that time were by the University of Illinois Committee on School Mathematics (UICSM) and the School Mathematics Study Group (SMSG). The following two articles describe these programs:

Beberman, Max. "An Emerging Program of Secondary School Mathematics." In *New Curricula,* edited by Robert W. Heath, pp. 9–34. New York: Harper & Row, 1964.

Wooten, William. "The History and Status of the School Mathematics Study Group." In *New Curricula,* edited by Robert W. Heath, pp. 35–53. New York: Harper & Row, 1964.

Three other important documents clarifying the recommended changes in this era were the following:

Educational Development Center. *Goals for School Mathematics: The Report of the Cambridge Conference on School Mathematics.* Boston: Houghton Mifflin Co., 1963.

Buck, R. Creighton. "Goals for Mathematics Instruction." *American Mathematical Monthly* 72, no. 9 (1965): 949–56.

Buck, Charles. "What Should High School Geometry Be?" *Mathematics Teacher* 61, no. 5 (1968): 466–71.

Finally, toward the end of the era, Robert Davis described the richness of the work of that era and the variety of pressures that were influencing the mathematics curriculum. The pressures included technology (computers, TV, tape recorders, and so on), nonachieving students (dropouts, culturally disadvantaged, and so on), the awareness of similar issues in other countries, and revolt against the primitive pedagogy in most classrooms (little beyond blackboard, chalk, pen, paper, and textbook).

> Davis, Robert B. *The Changing Curriculum: Mathematics.* Washington,
> D.C.: Association for Supervision and Curriculum Development,
> 1967.

The following are two summaries of the modern math era. First, in the United States, S. Irene Williams examined the degree to which the recommendations by the Commission on Mathematics appeared in the courses of study of a select group of college-bound students.

> Williams, S. Irene. "A Progress Report on the Implementation of the
> Recommendations of the Commission on Mathematics." *Mathematics
> Teacher* 63, no. 6 (1970): 461–68.

Second, Geoffrey Howson, Christine Keitel, and Jeremy Kilpatrick's (1981) *Curriculum Development in Mathematics* is an excellent summary of curriculum development internationally in this era and foreshadowed the standards-based era a decade later. Unfortunately, NCTM was unable to secure permission to include this book on this CD.

Post–Modern Math Era

By the early 1970s there was disillusionment over the impact of modern math, and the pressures mentioned by Robert Davis[3] became stronger. Morris Kline's *Why Johnny Can't Add,* published in 1973, was highly critical of the modern math approach to mathematics, and in many minds spelled the end of that era. Unfortunately, we were unable to get permission to include this book on this CD.

Reaction to Kline's book and many other articles culminated in a "back to the basics" movement. Also at this time, criticisms of the NSF-supported humanities program *Man: A Course of Study* because of its emphasis on questioning aspects of life, including belief and morality, led to the political cutoff of NSF funds for all curriculum development and teacher education.

The dynamics of the modern math era, and the subsequent movement toward basic skills, was examined in the following NACOME Report. It also highlighted

---

3. See *The Changing Curriculum Mathematics* (Davis 1967) earlier in this listing.

the overall impact of the curricula in schools.

> National Advisory Committee on Mathematical Education (NACOME). "Overview and Analysis of School Mathematics, K–12." Washington, D.C.: Conference Board of the Mathematical Sciences, 1975.

This post–modern math era raised such questions as what statistics should be in the curriculum, given its growth as a consequence of computers; how the use of computers should be incorporated in the curriculum; and whether students should have access to and use the inexpensive handheld calculator in classrooms. At the same time, new research information about learning was becoming available. We had discovered the contrasting works of such psychologists as Jean Piaget and Lev Vygotsky, which led to notions about social cognition and constructivist psychology. The article by Merl Wittrock illustrates the growing evolution from behaviorism to cognitivism in educational psychology at that time.

> Wittrock, Merl C. "A Generative Model of Mathematics Learning." *Journal for Research in Mathematics Education* 5, no. 4 (November 1974): 181–96.

This era saw educational research centers founded, new mathematics education research journals established, and a mathematics education research community evolve. Finally, the era saw achievement data indicating that far too many students were not learning and, instead, were dropping out of school.

Many interesting articles dealing with specific issues about mathematics were published in this era. First, the following three examples address issues of basic skills:

> Scheffler, Israel. "Basic Mathematical Skills: Some Philosophical and Practical Remarks." In *National Institute of Education Conference on Basic Mathematical Skills and Learning,* vol. 1, pp. 182–89. Euclid, Ohio: National Institute of Education, 1975.

> Denmark, Thomas, and Henry Kepner, Jr. "Basic Skills in Mathematics: A Survey." *Journal for Research in Mathematics Education* 11, no. 2 (March 1980): 105–23.

> Hill, Johnny, William Rouse, and James Wesson. "Mathematics Education: Reactionary Regression or Responsible Reform?" *Elementary School Journal* 80, no. 2 (November 1979): 76–79.

Second, at the elementary school level during the modern math era, the structural ideas based on set theory gradually reached some texts. However, traditional arithmetic was still the basic content for the elementary school curricula. But fresh ideas were beginning to surface. For example, Hans Freudenthal argued for a practical approach to early mathematics, and the work of the Nuffield Foundation in the United Kingdom was beginning to be noticed by mathematics educators.

Freudenthal, Hans. "Why Teach Mathematics So As to Be Useful?" *Educational Studies in Mathematics* 1, nos. 1–2 (May 1968): 3–8.

Rappaport, David. "The Nuffield Mathematics Project." *Elementary School Journal* 71, no. 6 (March 1971): 295–308.

Third, one theme during this era involved calls for mathematics—*not* general mathematics—for all students. The following are two articles on the topic:

Damerow, Peter, and Ian Westbury. "Mathematics for All: Problems and Implications." *Journal of Curriculum Studies* 17, no. 2 (February 1985): 175–86.

Romberg, Thomas A. "A Common Curriculum for Mathematics." In *Individual Differences and the Common Curriculum,* edited by Gary Fenstermacher and John Goodlad, pp. 121–59. Chicago: National Society for the Study of Education, 1983.

By 1980 the growing international mathematics education community seriously examined the curriculum development efforts of the past two decades. An international conference jointly organized by the Institute for the Didactics of Mathematics (IDM) and the International Mathematics Committee of the Second International Mathematics Study Group of the International Association for the Evaluation of Educational Achievement (IEA) was held in 1980 to examine the fact that, in spite of the rhetoric for change, little change was evident in students' achievement. The following four articles reflect the emerging international concerns about curriculum change and stability:

Westbury, Ian. "Change and Stability in the Curriculum: An Overview of the Questions." In *Comparative Studies of Mathematics Curricula: Change and Stability 1960–1980,* edited by Hans Steiner, pp. 12–36. Bielefeld, Federal Republic of Germany: Institut für Didaktik der Mathematik der Universität Bielefeld, 1980.

van der Blij, Frederik, Sven Hilding, and Ari I. Weinzweig. "A Synthesis of National Reports on Changes in Curricula." In *Comparative Studies of Mathematics Curricula: Change and Stability 1960–1980,* edited by Hans Steiner, pp. 37–54. Bielefeld, Federal Republic of Germany: Institut für Didaktik der Mathematik der Universität Bielefeld, 1980.

Robitaille, David F. "Intention, Implementation, Realization: Case Studies of the Impact of Curriculum Reform." In *Comparative Studies of Mathematics Curricula: Change and Stability 1960–1980,* edited by Hans Steiner, pp. 90–107. Bielefeld, Federal Republic of Germany: Institut für Didaktik der Mathematik der Universität Bielefeld, 1980.

Fey, James T. "The United States' NSF Studies of Mathematics Education."

In *Comparative Studies of Mathematics Curricula: Change and Stability 1960–1980,* edited by Hans Steiner, pp. 108–22. Bielefeld, Federal Republic of Germany: Institut für Didaktik der Mathematik der Universität Bielefeld, 1980.

The following two important documents are on issues and recommendations about what needed to be done:

National Council of Teachers of Mathematics (NCTM). *An Agenda for Action: Recommendations for School Mathematics of the 1980s.* Reston, Va.: NCTM, 1980.

Hill, Shirley A. "Recommendations for School Mathematics Programs of the 1980s." In *Selected Issues in Mathematics Education,* edited by Mary M. Lindquist, pp. 258–68. Chicago: McCutchan Publishing Corporation, 1980.

The next three articles present critiques of the curricula in that era.

Freeman, Donald J., Theresa M. Kuhs, Andrew Porter, Robert Floden, William Schmidt, and John Schwille. "Do Textbooks and Tests Define a National Curriculum in Elementary School Mathematics?" *Elementary School Journal* 83, no. 5 (May 1983): 501–13.

Flanders, James R. "How Much of the Content in Mathematics Textbooks Is New?" *Arithmetic Teacher* 35, no. 1 (September 1987): 18–25.

Porter, Andrew. "A Curriculum out of Balance: The Case of Elementary School Mathematics." *Educational Researcher* 18, no. 5 (June/July 1989): 9–15.

In response to such recommendations and criticisms, several articles posed issues and examples of what could be done. The following four articles represent the variety of curricular suggestions at that time:

Freudenthal, Hans. "Mathematics Starting and Staying in Reality." In *Proceedings of the USCMP Conference on Mathematics Education on Development in School Mathematics Education around the World,* edited by Izaak Wirszup and Robert Street, pp. 279–95. Reston, Va.: National Council of Teachers of Mathematics, 1987.

Wheeler, David. "Mathematization Matters." *For the Learning of Mathematics* 3, no. 1 (1982): 45–47.

Pollak, Henry O. "The Mathematical Sciences Curriculum K–12: What Is Still Fundamental and What Is Not." Report from The Conference Board of the Mathematical Sciences. Washington, D.C.: National Science Foundation, 1983.

Hilton, Peter. "Current Trends in Mathematics and Future Trends in Mathematics Education." *For the Learning of Mathematics* 4, no. 1 (February 1984): 2–8.

Standards-Based Era

Although there were recommendations and suggestions about reforming the mathematics curricula, the actual catalysts that led to the development of curricular standards for mathematics were two reports published in 1983 by federal agencies. Both reports called for reform in school mathematics: National Commission on Excellence in Education, *A Nation at Risk: The Imperative for Educational Reform* (1983) and National Science Board Commission on Precollege Education in Mathematics, Science and Technology, *Educating Americans for the 21st Century* (1983). Economic competitiveness was the underlying concern. This concern reflected an awareness of the international data-driven demands of contemporary businesses.

The following articles were produced by the mathematics and mathematics education communities as responses to these documents:

> Conference Board of the Mathematical Sciences (CBMS). *New Goals for Mathematical Sciences Education.* Washington, D.C.: CBMS, 1984.

> Romberg, Thomas A. *School Mathematics: Options for the 1990s.* Chairman's Report of a Conference. Washington, D.C.: U.S. Government Printing Office, 1984.

One consequence of these reports, and the responses, was the creation of the Mathematical Sciences Education Board (MSEB) of the National Academy of Sciences to oversee and make recommendations about the mathematics curriculum. During the next decade MSEB produced several reports, such as *Everybody Counts: A Report to the Nation on the Future of Mathematics Education* (1990a) and *Reshaping School Mathematics: A Philosophy and Framework of Curriculum* (1990b). Unfortunately, NCTM was unable to secure permission to include these documents in this CD.

Zalman Usiskin's article reflected the calls for change in the secondary school curriculum.

> Usiskin, Zalman. "We Need Another Revolution in School Mathematics." In *The Secondary School Mathematics Curriculum,* 1985 Yearbook of the National Council of Teachers of Mathematics (NCTM), edited by Christian R. Hirsch, pp. 1–21. Reston, Va.: NCTM, 1985.

To complement the calls to reform the secondary school mathematics curriculum, the following two articles examine the elementary school curriculum:

> Lindquist, Mary M. "The Elementary School Mathematics Curriculum: Issues for Today." *Elementary School Journal* 84, no. 5 (May 1984): 595–608.

Coburn, Terry G. "The Role of Computation in the Changing Mathematics Curriculum." In *New Directions for Elementary School Mathematics,* edited by Paul R. Trafton, pp. 43–56. Reston, Va.: National Council of Teachers of Mathematics, 1989.

Also, although the Cockroft Report from Great Britain focused on the United Kingdom, it pointed toward similar reform needed in the United States.

Committee of Inquiry into the Teaching of Mathematics in Schools. *Mathematics Counts (The Cockroft Report).* London: Her Majesty's Stationery Office, 1982.

Chapter 6: "Mathematics in the Primary School" (pp. 83–108)

Chapter 9: "Mathematics in the Secondary School" (pp. 128–57)

Chapter 11: "Mathematics in the Sixth Form" (pp. 169–82)

However, the NCTM *Standards* was the primary curriculum document that brought about curricular reform.

National Council of Teachers of Mathematics (NCTM). *Curriculum and Evaluation Standards for School Mathematics.* Reston, Va.: NCTM, 1989.

"Introduction" (pp. 1–12)

"Curriculum Standards for Grades K–4" (pp. 15–21)

"Curriculum Standards for Grades 5–8" (pp. 65–73)

"Curriculum Standards for Grades 9–12" (pp. 123–36)

"Next Steps" (pp. 251–58)

Four interesting features of this report make it quite different from those in previous eras. First, it was produced by a teachers' organization, not by mathematicians, although mathematicians were involved. Second, its focus was on all students, not just college-bound students. Third, the focus in grades K–8 was on mathematics, not just arithmetic. And finally, statistics and probability were included in the curriculum standards along with number, algebra, measurement, and geometry.

One consequence of this report was that the federal government, through the National Science Foundation, again provided funds for the development of new curriculum materials that reflected these recommendations. All descriptions of these programs and their effects are post-1993, our end date for the CD. However, many such issues are discussed in this 2010 Yearbook.

The following article is a summary of the curricular issues being faced in this era:

> Romberg, Thomas A. "Problematic Features of the School Mathematics Curriculum." In *Handbook on Research on Curriculum*, edited by Paul Jackson, pp. 749–87. New York: Macmillan, 1992.

Many papers have been published on aspects of the impact of this era since 1993. However, the following three articles should be of interest:

> Kamens, David H., and Aaron Benavot. "Elite Knowledge for the Masses: The Origins and Spread of Mathematics and Science Education in National Curricula." *American Journal of Education* 99, no. 2 (February 1991): 137–80.

> Steffe, Leslie P. "Mathematics Curriculum Design: A Constructivist's Perspective." In *Transforming Children's Mathematics Education: International Perspectives,* edited by Leslie P. Steffe and Terry L. Wood, pp. 389–98. Hillsdale, N.J.: Lawrence Erlbaum Associates, 1990.

> Wheeler, David. "Knowledge at the Crossroads." *For the Learning of Mathematics* 13, no. 1 (1993): 53–54.

To complement the NCTM Curriculum Standards, James Greeno presented a contemporary view of the psychology of mathematics instruction. He argued that instruction will help students develop understanding when a mathematical domain is thought of as an environment, with resources at various places in the domain. In this metaphor, "knowing" is knowing your way around in the environment and knowing how to use its resources.

> Greeno, James. "Number Sense as Situated Knowing in a Conceptual Domain." *Journal for Research in Mathematics Education* 22, no. 3 (March 1991): 170–218.

Summary

The Editorial Panel for the 2010 NCTM Yearbook strove to provide a broad, meaningful set of resources on the CD to provide significant perspectives on the philosophy and history of the curriculum for mathematics education. For the past century and a half, the dilemma facing those faced with choosing the mathematical content for the school mathematics curriculum involves how one caters to needs of the college-bound students who will study mathematics at universities (particularly those who will become professional mathematicians) and at the same time provides the general student with the mathematical skills he or she will need to be a productive citizen in a changing society. The selected articles reflect how this dilemma was dealt with during five eras on the basis of the structure of schools and the social issues of that era. We hope that readers find it useful.

REFERENCES

Cremin, Lawrence A. *The Transformation of the School.* New York: Vintage Books, Random House, 1961.

Howson, Geoffrey, Christine Keitel, and Jeremy Kilpatrick. *Curriculum Development in Mathematics.* Cambridge: Cambridge University Press, 1981.

Kline, Morris. *Why Johnny Can't Add.* New York: St. Martin's Press, 1973.

Mathematical Sciences Education Board. *Everybody Counts*: *A Report to the Nation on the Future of Mathematics Education.* Washington, D.C.: National Academy Press, 1990a.

―――. *Reshaping School Mathematics: A Philosophy and Framework of Curriculum.* Washington, D.C.: National Academy Press, 1990b.

National Commission on Excellence in Education. *A Nation at Risk: The Imperative for Educational Reform.* Washington, D.C.: U.S. Government Printing Office, 1983.

National Science Board Commission on Precollege Education in Mathematics, Science and Technology. *Educating Americans for the Twenty-first Century.* Washington, D.C.: National Science Foundation, 1983.

Resnick, Lauren B., and Wendy W. Ford. *The Psychology of Mathematics Instruction.* Hillsdale, N.J.: Lawrence Erlbaum Associates, 1981.

ARTICLES ON THE CD

Beberman, Max. "An Emerging Program of Secondary School Mathematics." In *New Curricula,* edited by Robert W. Heath, pp. 9–34. New York: Harper & Row, 1964.

Betz, William. "The Teaching of Geometry in Its Relation to the Present Educational Trend." *School Science and Mathematics* 8 (1908): 625–33.

Brownell, William A. "Meaning and Skill—Maintaining the Balance." *Arithmetic Teacher* 3, no. 4 (1956): 129–36.

Buck, Charles. "What Should High School Geometry Be?" *Mathematics Teacher* 61, no. 5 (1968): 466–71.

Buck, R. Creighton. "Goals for Mathematics Instruction." *American Mathematical Monthly* 72, no. 9 (1965): 949–56.

―――. "Functions." In *Mathematics Education,* Sixty-ninth Yearbook of the National Society for the Study of Education, Part 1, edited by Edward G. Begle and Herman G. Richey, pp. 236–59. Chicago: University of Chicago Press, 1970.

Coburn, Terry G. "The Role of Computation in the Changing Mathematics Curriculum." In *New Directions for Elementary School Mathematics,* edited by Paul R. Trafton, pp. 43–56. Reston, Va.: National Council of Teachers of Mathematics, 1989.

Commission on Mathematics. *Program for College Preparatory Mathematics.* New York: College Entrance Examination Board, 1959.

Committee of Inquiry into the Teaching of Mathematics in Schools. *Mathematics Counts (The Cockroft Report).* London: Her Majesty's Stationery Office, 1982. Chapter 6, "Mathematics in the Primary School," pp. 83–108; Chapter 9, "Mathematics in the Secondary School," pp. 128–57; Chapter 11, "Mathematics in the Sixth Form," pp. 169–82.

Conference Board of the Mathematical Sciences (CBMS). *New Goals for Mathematical Sciences Education.* Washington, D.C.: CBMS, 1984.

Damerow, Peter, and Ian Westbury. "Mathematics for All: Problems and Implications." *Journal of Curriculum Studies* 17, no. 2 (February 1985): 175–86.

Davis, Robert B. *The Changing Curriculum: Mathematics.* Washington, D.C.: Association for Supervision and Curriculum Development, 1967.

Dean, Richard A. "Algebraic Systems." In *Mathematics Education,* Sixty-ninth Yearbook of the National Society for the Study of Education, Part 1, edited by Edward G. Begle and Herman G. Richey, pp. 131–66. Chicago: University of Chicago Press, 1970.

Denmark, Thomas, and Henry Kepner, Jr. "Basic Skills in Mathematics: A Survey." *Journal for Research in Mathematics Education* 11, no. 2 (March 1980): 105–23.

Dewey, John. "The Psychological Aspect of the School Curriculum." *Educational Review* 13 (1897): 356–69.

———. *The Child and the Curriculum.* Chicago: University of Chicago Press, 1902.

Educational Development Center. *Goals for School Mathematics: The Report of the Cambridge Conference on School Mathematics.* Boston: Houghton Mifflin Co., 1963.

Fey, James T. "The United States' NSF Studies of Mathematics Education." In *Comparative Studies of Mathematics Curricula: Change and Stability 1960–1980,* edited by Hans Steiner, pp. 108–22. Bielefeld, Federal Republic of Germany: Institut für Didaktik der Mathematik der Universität Bielefeld, 1980.

Flanders, James R. "How Much of the Content in Mathematics Textbooks Is New?" *Arithmetic Teacher* 31, no. 1 (January 1987): 18–25.

Freeman, Donald J., Theresa M. Kuhs, Andrew Porter, Robert Floden, William Schmidt, and John Schwille. "Do Textbooks and Tests Define a National Curriculum in Elementary School Mathematics?" *Elementary School Journal* 83, no. 5 (May 1983): 501–13.

Freudenthal, Hans. "Why Teach Mathematics So As to Be Useful?" *Educational Studies in Mathematics* 1, nos. 1–2 (May 1968): 3–8.

———. "Mathematics Starting and Staying in Reality." *Proceedings of the USCMP Conference on Mathematics Education on Development in School Mathematics Education around the World,* edited by Izaak Wirszup and Robert Street, pp. 279–95. Reston, Va.: National Council of Teachers of Mathematics, 1987.

Greeno, James. "Number Sense as Situated Knowing in a Conceptual Domain." *Journal for Research in Mathematics Education* 22, no. 3 (March 1991): 170–218.

Hill, Johnny, William Rouse, and James Wesson. "Mathematics Education: Reactionary Regression or Responsible Reform?" *Elementary School Journal* 80, no. 2 (November 1979): 76–79.

Hill, Shirley A. "Recommendations for School Mathematics Programs of the 1980s." In *Selected Issues in Mathematics Education*, edited by Mary M. Lindquist, pp. 258–68. Chicago: McCutchan Publishing Corporation, 1980.

Hilton, Peter. "Current Trends in Mathematics and Future Trends in Mathematics Education." *For the Learning of Mathematics* 4, no. 1 (February 1984): 2–8.

Horn, Ernest. "Arithmetic in the Elementary School Curriculum." In *The Teaching of Arithmetic,* Fiftieth Yearbook of the National Society for the Study of Education, Part 2, edited by Nelson B. Henry, pp. 6–21. Chicago: University of Chicago Press, 1951.

Jahnke, Hans N. "Origins of School Mathematics in Early Nineteenth-Century Germany." *Journal of Curriculum Studies* 18, no. 1 (1983): 85–94.

Kamens, David H., and Aaron Benavot. "Elite Knowledge for the Masses: The Origins and Spread of Mathematics and Science Education in National Curricula." *American Journal of Education* 99, no. 2 (February 1991): 137–80.

Kelley, John L. "Number Systems." In *Mathematics Education,* Sixty-ninth Yearbook of the National Society for the Study of Education, Part 1, edited by Edward G. Begle and Herman G. Richey, pp. 75–130. Chicago: University of Chicago Press, 1970.

Kline, Morris. "The Ancients versus the Moderns: A New Battle of the Books." *Mathematics Teacher* 51 (October 1958): 418–27.

Lindquist, Mary M. "The Elementary School Mathematics Curriculum: Issues for Today." *Elementary School Journal* 84, no. 5 (May 1984): 595–608.

Moore, Eliakim H. "The Foundations of Mathematics." *School Review* 11, no. 6 (1903): 521–38.

Moredock, H. Stewart. "Geometry and Measurement." In *Mathematics Education,* Sixty-ninth Yearbook of the National Society for the Study of Education, Part 1, edited by Edward G. Begle and Herman G. Richey, pp. 167–35. Chicago: University of Chicago Press, 1970.

National Advisory Committee on Mathematical Education. "Overview and Analysis of School Mathematics, K–12." Washington, D.C.: Conference Board of the Mathematical Sciences, 1975.

National Committee on Mathematical Requirements. *The Reorganization of Mathematics in Secondary Education.* Washington, D.C.: Mathematical Association of America, 1923.

National Council of Teachers of Mathematics (NCTM). *The Place of Mathematics in Secondary Education: Report of the Joint Commission of the Mathematical Association of America and the National Council of Teachers of Mathematics.* New York: Bureau of Publications, Teachers College, Columbia University, 1940.

———. *An Agenda for Action: Recommendations for School Mathematics of the 1980s.* Reston, Va.: NCTM, 1980.

———. *Curriculum and Evaluation Standards for School Mathematics.* Reston, Va.:

NCTM, 1989. "Introduction," pp. 1–12; "Curriculum Standards for Grades K–4," pp. 15–21; "Curriculum Standards for Grades 5–8," pp. 65–73; "Curriculum Standards for Grades 9–12," pp. 123–36; "Next Steps," pp. 251–58.

National Council of Teachers of Mathematics, Secondary-School Curriculum Committee. "The Secondary Mathematics Curriculum." *Mathematics Teacher* 52, no. 5 (May 1959): 389–417.

National Education Association. "Mathematics." In *Report of the Committee of Ten on Secondary School Studies,* pp. 104–16. New York: American Book Co., 1894.

Pollak, Henry O. "The Mathematical Sciences Curriculum K–12: What Is Still Fundamental and What Is Not." Report from the Conference Board of the Mathematical Sciences. Washington, D.C.: National Science Foundation, 1983.

Porter, Andrew. "A Curriculum out of Balance: The Case of Elementary School Mathematics." *Educational Researcher* 18, no. 5 (June/July 1989): 9–15.

Rappaport, David. "The Nuffield Mathematics Project." *Elementary School Journal* 71, no. 6 (March 1971): 295–308.

Reeve, William D. "General Mathematics for the High School: Its Purpose and Content." *Educational Administration and Supervision* 6 (1920): 258–73.

Robitaille, David F. "Intention, Implementation, Realization: Case Studies of the Impact of Curriculum Reform." In *Comparative Studies of Mathematics Curricula: Change and Stability 1960–1980,* edited by Hans Steiner, pp. 90–107. Bielefeld, Federal Republic of Germany: Institut für Didaktik der Mathematik der Universität Bielefeld, 1980.

Romberg, Thomas A. "A Common Curriculum for Mathematics." In *Individual Differences and the Common Curriculum,* edited by Gary Fenstermacher and John Goodlad, pp. 121–59. Chicago: National Society for the Study of Education, 1983.

———. *School Mathematics: Options for the 1990s.* Chairman's Report of a Conference. Washington, D.C.: U.S. Government Printing Office, 1984.

———. "Problematic Features of the School Mathematics Curriculum." In *Handbook on Research on Curriculum,* edited by Paul Jackson, pp. 749–87. New York: Macmillan, 1992.

Scheffler, Israel. "Basic Mathematical Skills: Some Philosophical and Practical Remarks." In *National Institute of Education Conference on Basic Mathematical Skills and Learning,* vol. 1, pp. 182–89. Euclid, Ohio: National Institute of Education, 1975.

Shuster, Carl N. "A Call for Reform in High School Mathematics." *American Mathematical Monthly* 55, no. 8 (October 1948): 472–75.

Slaught, Herbert E. "What Should Be Emphasized and What Omitted in the High-School Course in Algebra?" *School Review* 16, no. 8 (1908): 503–16.

Smith, David E. "A General Survey of the Progress of Mathematics in Our High Schools in the Last Twenty-five Years." In *The First Yearbook,* First Yearbook of the National Council of Teachers of Mathematics, edited by Charles M. Austin, pp. 1–31. New York: Bureau of Publications, Teachers College, Columbia University, 1926.

Stanic, George M. A. "The Growing Crisis in Mathematics Education in the Early Twentieth Century." *Journal for Research in Mathematics Education* 17, no. 3 (May 1986): 190–205.

Stanic, George M. A., and Jeremy Kilpatrick. "Historical Perspective on Problem Solving in the Mathematics Curriculum." In *The Teaching and Assessing of Mathematical Problem Solving: Research Agenda for Mathematics Education,* edited by Randall Charles and Edward A. Silver, pp. 1–22. Reston, Va.: National Council of Teachers of Mathematics, 1988.

———. "Mathematics Curriculum Reform in the United States: A Historical Perspective." *International Journal of Educational Research* 17, no. 5 (1992): 407–17.

Steffe, Leslie P. "Mathematics Curriculum Design: A Constructivist's Perspective." In *Transforming Children's Mathematics Education: International Perspectives,* edited by Leslie P. Steffe and Terry L. Wood, pp. 389–98. Hillsdale, N.J.: Lawrence Erlbaum Associates, 1990.

Thorndike, Edward L. "The Constitution of Arithmetical Abilities." In *The Psychology of Arithmetic,* pp. 51–140. New York: Macmillan Co., 1922.

Usiskin, Zalman. "We Need Another Revolution in School Mathematics." In *The Secondary School Mathematics Curriculum,* 1985 Yearbook of the National Council of Teachers of Mathematics, edited by Christian R. Hirsch, pp. 1–21. Reston, Va.: NCTM, 1985.

van der Blij, Frederik, Sven Hilding, and Ari I. Weinzweig. "A Synthesis of National Reports on Changes in Curricula." In *Comparative Studies of Mathematics Curricula: Change and Stability 1960–1980,* edited by Hans Steiner, pp. 37–54. Bielefeld, Federal Republic of Germany: Institut für Didaktik der Mathematik der Universität Bielefeld, 1980.

West, Roscoe L., Charles E. Greene, and William A. Brownell. "The Arithmetic Curriculum." In *Report of the Society's Committee on Arithmetic,* Twenty-ninth Yearbook of the National Society for the Study of Education, edited by Guy M. Whipple, pp. 64–142. Bloomington, Ill.: Public School Publishing Co., 1930.

Westbury, Ian. "Change and Stability in the Curriculum: An Overview of the Questions." In *Comparative Studies of Mathematics Curricula: Change and Stability 1960–1980,* edited by Hans Steiner, pp. 12–36. Bielefeld, Federal Republic of Germany: Institut für Didaktik der Mathematik der Universität Bielefeld, 1980.

Wheeler, David. "Mathematization Matters." *For the Learning of Mathematics* 3, no. 1 (1983): 45–47.

———. "Knowledge at the Crossroads." *For the Learning of Mathematics* 13, no. 1 (1993): 53–54.

Wilder, R. L. "Historical Background of Innovations in Mathematics Curricula." In *Mathematics Education,* Sixty-ninth Yearbook of the National Society for the Study of Education, Part 1, edited by Edward G. Begle and Herman G. Richey, pp. 7–12. Chicago: University of Chicago Press, 1970.

Williams, S. Irene. "A Progress Report on the Implementation of the Recommendations of the Commission on Mathematics." *Mathematics Teacher* 63, no. 6 (1970): 461–68.

Wittrock, Merl C. "A Generative Model of Mathematics Learning." *Journal for Research in Mathematics Education* 5, no. 4 (November 1974): 181–96.

Wooten, William. "The History and Status of the School Mathematics Study Group." In *New Curricula,* edited by Robert W. Heath, pp. 35–53. New York: Harper & Row, 1964.

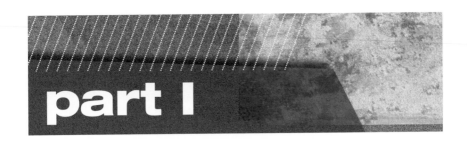

Curriculum Matters:
Looking Back,
Looking Forward

1

The Current State of the School Mathematics Curriculum

Zalman Usiskin

ECENTLY, I was speaking at a conference in Los Angeles and rented a car to get from the airport to the conference hotel. In preparation, two days earlier I had downloaded directions from Google Maps. But I had even more guidance than that, for with me was a global positioning system (GPS) that I had recently received as a present. Before I left home I had looked over the GPS quickly and realized that it was quite easy to use. So, in the parking lot, sitting in my rental car, I entered the hotel address. Then, immediately, I was faced with a dilemma. The GPS advice for the first turn out of the parking lot was in a different direction from the advice given me by Google Maps. Google Maps had shown a reasonably familiar route—from one freeway to another to a third—but I had some time, and so I decided to follow the GPS directions. The GPS took me on a zigzag route through main streets, never more than 1.7 miles on any street. I was afraid that the GPS did not know my destination, but it kept me going generally in the direction of the hotel. Ultimately, I arrived at the hotel without ever being on a freeway, in very close to the optimal time that Google had estimated.

How similar that situation is to working with new curriculum materials in schools! Both situations sometimes involve taking new paths to get to places we want to go. Sometimes we are familiar with our destination; sometimes not.

Mathematics is a multidimensional universe, and those who write curriculum materials are engineers, building roads through that universe. Curriculum supervisors are travel agents, planning trips on those roads. Teachers are bus drivers on these roads, and students are the bus passengers. As bus drivers, teachers can make the bus stop and look at sites, or they can whiz by them. Teachers may be under the authority of school officials who decide what things are important enough for students to get out and touch and what things might be bypassed. Many curriculum materials authors simply repave roads that were first constructed decades, if not centuries, ago. Some of the roads we take, however—for instance into the world of statistics—are new roads. At times they are uneven because they are unpaved or pass through uncharted territory. Some of the materials used to pave the roads, such as spreadsheets, interactive geometry systems, and computer algebra systems (CAS), are also new. Many people think riding over roads using those materials is a smoother ride and enables students to see and touch more of the mathematical countryside. Others believe that a rough ride helps one appreciate the landscape.

There are many possible roads through the world of mathematics, and despite our search for better pathways, choices still remain. Some students need to spend time on things that other students do not. Some students benefit from detours that motivate and capture their attention. Furthermore, just as there are individual differences among students, there are individual differences among teachers, and what works for one teacher may not work for another. In designing and implementing curriculum—as in building roads—we need to have enough instructional options, enough stops along the way, enough side trips or detours so that a teacher can choose what she or he deems best for the students.

How do we decide what roads to take through this world of mathematics? In many states, schools and teachers pay attention to their state's mathematics framework because high-stakes state-level tests are based on that framework. Compared with other subjects in the school curriculum, these state frameworks have quite a bit in common. A ninth-grade teacher of mathematics in any state can be sure that her students have studied whole numbers, fractions, decimals, percent, and basic units of measurement. Compare this situation with a ninth-grade science teacher, who typically cannot predict with assurance that her students have studied any particular topic. Yet, as Reys (2006) pointed out, substantial differences exist in the mathematics frameworks among the fifty states and the District of Columbia.

Given these differences, in a search for regularity it is natural to examine documents at the national level. The most prominent documents have come from the National Council of Teachers of Mathematics (2000, 2006, 2009). Project Achieve, a Washington, D.C.–based group with backing from governors of many states, has also developed detailed standards for grades K–8 and high school. The American Statistical Association has published *Guidelines for Assessment and Instruction in Statistics Education* (GAISE) (Franklin et al. 2007), a set of recommendations for all the grades K–12. The College Board (2006) has produced standards for high school mathematics. The National Mathematics Advisory Panel (NMAP 2008), supported by the U.S. Department of Education, has made recommendations for school mathematics, giving particular attention to getting students ready for algebra.

These national reports have influenced state frameworks and textbooks to different degrees. Some states have realigned their grades K–8 frameworks on the basis of NCTM's *Curriculum Focal Points* (2006). Some have based their frameworks on the Project Achieve model. But, like the state documents they influence, these national reports do not always agree with one another, and some of the disagreements are major. For instance, the GAISE recommendations assume technology, whereas the NMAP recommendations eschew technology. Sometimes even two documents from the same group do not agree. For example, Achieve's test after second-year algebra follows quite different guidelines than its recommended high school curriculum (Achieve, Inc. 2004, 2008).

It is ironic that the mathematics curriculum is perhaps the most consistent curriculum of all subjects in schools (with the possible exception of foreign languages), yet its variations cause disputes that often are acrimonious. All mathematics teachers are beleaguered by conflicting expectations from their district or school's syllabus, the adopted textbook, state tests, parental expectations, local customs, and their own judgments. Teachers at higher levels can add to these the variety of expectations of college entrance tests and college placement tests. Add to these the individual differences students *and teachers* bring in background, achievement, and motivation, and it is easy to understand why the analysis of the ideal or intended curriculum is as much an art as a science.

In this environment, we would naturally expect to find a variety of curriculum materials. Although as this essay is being written, the United States has only three large publishers of school mathematics materials[1], a mathematics teacher can obtain textbooks and other materials from a number of smaller publishers[2], from software and hardware manufacturers[3], and from a host of nonprofit organizations. In addition to the basal textbook offerings, these curricular materials may be designed for specific purposes: skill remediation, test preparation, competitions, problem-solving practice, software enhancement, and hands-on activities. They may be in print form; on CDs; or downloadable from, or reachable only on, the Internet. At no time in history has a greater variety of curriculum materials been available.

---

1. They are McGraw-Hill (including Macmillan, Glencoe, SRA, Everyday Learning, Laidlaw, Merrill, Open Court, Wright Group); Houghton Mifflin/Harcourt (including also McDougal-Littell, Heath, Holt, Saxon, Heinemann); and Pearson (including Scott Foresman, Prentice Hall, Addison-Wesley, Ginn, Silver Burdette, Dale Seymour, and Globe-Fearon).

2. For example, ETA/Cuisenaire, Heinemann, It's About Time, Kendall/Hunt, Key Curriculum Press, Scholastic, and William Sadlier.

3. For example, Cabrilog, Casio, Hewlett-Packard, and Texas Instruments.

Making Sense of a Complex Situation

When results in mathematics conflict, we know that they must have originated from different assumptions. The sum of the measures of a triangle is 180° in Euclidean geometry but greater than 180° in spherical geometry, so spherical geometry must work from different assumptions than Euclidean geometry does. If one statistical analysis shows that sample A outperforms sample B, and another analysis of the same data shows the opposite, then the two analyses must be using different procedures. One way to try to make sense of the complex nature of today's national reports, state frameworks, textbooks, and other materials is to examine the assumptions underlying them.

As a curriculum developer, I realize that the decisions I make about what should be in the mathematics curriculum—and how that content should be organized, presented, and taught—are based on my beliefs about the nature and purposes of schooling, about the roles of teachers, about students, and about curriculum. These beliefs are sometimes based on data and sometimes on experience. Yet sometimes they are so strong that data will not influence them. Virtually all individuals and organizations charged with trying to improve the mathematics curriculum operate in the same way. Prior to beginning the work, the group follows the belief that either we are on the right track and need to continue what we are doing, or (more often, because it is easier to sway policy by asserting there is a disaster) we are performing horribly and the security and well-being of our nation are at stake.

How can one group think that we are on the right track while another thinks we have gone astray? Why can some people be adamant in wanting to emphasize basic skills while others wish to devote most of the time to solving problems? Why are many people in favor of using calculators in elementary school and CAS in high school while others abhor the use of these devices in school? I would like to offer four reasons:

1. Conflicting views of what is appropriate school mathematics
2. Conflicting beliefs about the purpose of schooling and the roles of the teacher
3. Differing views of past and current mathematics education reform efforts
4. The difficulty of deciding which curriculum is better or best

Each of these reasons is itself complex.

Conflicting Views of What Is Appropriate School Mathematics

Six conflicts are identified here. They run to the very heart of the subject.

Pure versus Applied Mathematics

Which should take priority, abstract (pure) mathematics or its applications? Pure mathematics is one of the most beautiful of all areas of study. This beauty is found in the geometric pictures of fractals or rose curves; in the elegance of structures (groups, fields, rings, etc.) that permeate higher algebra and analysis; in the astounding properties of numbers, figures, and functions; and in the interrelationships among the various areas of mathematics. But mathematics is a fixture of the school curriculum not because of its beauty but because of its applications. Mathematics arose from a need to count and measure real phenomena, from the areas of lands to the prediction of eclipses, and mathematics remains one of the most applicable of school subjects in everyday life and in the workplace. Pure mathematics provides results that may apply to many situations, but many of those situations are inaccessible to grades K–12 students. Applications focus on specific contexts, but if they are not generalized, a student will not see the power of the underlying mathematics. Curricula differ significantly on the relative importance given to pure versus applied mathematics.

Deduction versus Induction versus Statistical Inference

What relative importance should be given to (formal) deduction, (informal) induction, and statistical (probabilistic) reasoning? Deduction is the hallmark of mathematical thinking and provides results with 100% certainty. For example, we know there are infinitely many primes not because we have made a list of them (we cannot do so) but because we (or others we trust) have *proved* there are infinitely many primes. Induction, though not valid for proving propositions, gives specific examples from which we conjecture results and, for many young students, is more believable than a deductive proof. We tabulate the number of primes from 1 to 10^n and find that there continue to be primes among the larger numbers. Statistical inference, even in a theoretical sense and in its best manifestation, offers results with a probability of belief. We sample some large numbers at random, test them for primality, and find there are some primes. Each of these ways of thinking is important. Curricula differ in the relative attention they give to these ways.

From Algorithms to Creative Problem Solving

What relative emphasis should be placed on teaching algorithms versus teaching creativity? For many decades, psychologists have used mathematics as a context when they want to study simple, well-defined tasks such as short-term memory, as in recalling random digits, or when they want to study rule following and algorithms. Mathematics is filled with algorithms; its history includes finding simpler ways to do operations with arithmetic, more efficient procedures for solving equations, and thousands of formulas for calculating everything from areas to mortgage costs. Additionally, psychologists have used mathematics when they want to study problem solving and creativity, for no discipline is so filled with well-identified problems and in no discipline are there more difficult problems than in mathematics. People need to be able to follow algorithms, and people also need to be creative and attack problems they have not seen before. To what extent should curricula focus on simple, well-defined mathematical tasks as opposed to emphasize problems unfamiliar to students?

Fluency versus Flippancy

Can we achieve fluency without flippancy? The NMAP panel and the National Research Council report *Adding It Up* (2001) emphasize the need for fluency and automaticity in the application of skills. *Fluency* refers to knowing when to apply an algorithm and being able to apply it flexibly, accurately, and efficiently. *Automaticity* is the execution of a procedure "without conscious thought" (National Research Council 2001, p. 351). This supports the view of three contemporary mathematicians, who wrote, "The ultimate goal of mathematics is to eliminate all need for intelligent thought" (Graham, Knuth, and Patashnik 1989, p. 56). Yet we also know that when students apply algorithms without thinking, they do not realize when they come up with nonsense results. Fluency without thinking is flippancy; how can we best attain fluency without grooming people who do not understand what they are doing?

Culture Free versus Culture Dependent

How much should the curriculum reflect our culture(s)? Mathematics is a universal language. Visit a mathematics classroom in China or Italy or Algeria or Brazil, and you will likely be able to understand what mathematics is being taught even if you cannot understand the written or spoken everyday language. But you will not see inches or ounces or others of the measurements used in the United States; you are unlikely to see examples from American football or from mortgages, but you will likely see subtle and not-so-subtle differences in the algorithms children use in arithmetic. You are sure to see differences in the definitions of common mathematical terms, for these differences occur even within the same country (Usiskin and Griffin 2008). To what extent should mathematics materials reflect the mathematics unique to a particular country or to the ethnicities of its students?

Hard versus Easy

Is mathematics inherently difficult, or is a major goal of mathematics to make things easy? Some curricula emphasize difficult tasks more than others. Must mathematics be hard in order to be good? Those who use today's powerful calculator and computer technology believe that use helps students by making difficult problems more accessible. Others believe technology use hurts students by shortcutting the routes by which those problems can be solved. Are these technological developments merely the current manifestations of a long history of the development of algorithms in mathematics to make it easier to get answers to problems, or are they new developments deleterious to the entire discipline because they enable students to obtain answers without work? Calculators first appeared almost forty years ago and are still not a staple of elementary school classrooms. Today's CAS technology provides the algebra equivalent. Curricula around the world differ significantly in the extent to which they employ technology.

Conflicting Beliefs about the Purpose of Schooling and the Roles of the Teacher

Attitudes toward the purposes of public schooling vary widely. A small but significant minority of parents fear public schooling not because of concerns for the physical safety of their children, but because of what the children might learn in school. Many parents send their children to religious or other day schools because they do not want their children to learn about other religions and practices that differ from their beliefs. Other parents homeschool their children for the same reason. Some parents do not have that choice, and they press their local public schools not to deal with such issues as sex education or evolution.

For these parents, the school exists to transmit the best of the learned culture. Schools do not exist to expand students' minds because such expansion is dangerous, leading to unwise behaviors (sex, drugs, etc.) and heresy. This belief plays out in the mathematics classroom in a desire not to have students invent new procedures or engage in creative activities. It is a major reason why schools run by fundamentalists in almost any religion tend to focus on learning algorithms rather than on creative problem solving, and why constructivism is a dirty word in some places.

Is the purpose of schooling to bring all students to approximately the same level of performance, focusing more on those who need more help, or is the purpose of schooling to nurture those who are likely to perform better? Is the

In general, the standards revolution brought algebra and some data analysis into the elementary school, algebra into grade 8 and earlier for many students, applications into the algebra and geometry curricula, graphing calculators into the study of functions, and a major increase in the number of high school students taking calculus. It promoted active learning, classroom discourse, alternate algorithms, and multiple ways of approaching problems.

Virtually all evidence is that, overall, the NCTM Standards *improved* performance and led to significant increases in the amount and level of mathematics taken by high school students. From 1990 to 2004, the National Assessment average scale score of 9-year-olds on its longitudinal assessment increased from 230 to 241; of 13-year-olds, from 270 to 281. National Assessment scores of 17-year-olds changed from 305 to 307, an insignificant increase, but mean mathematics scores of seniors on the SAT mathematics test increased from 501 in 1990 to peak at 520 in 2005, and on the ACT increased from 19.9 in 1990 to 20.7 in 2005 despite increases in the percent of the age group taking those tests.

Certainly some of this improvement is due to the startling increases in enrollment in college-preparatory mathematics courses that began in the 1980s and carried through the 1990s, as seen in table 1.1.

Table 1.1
Percent of High School Graduates Who Completed Different Levels of Mathematics Courses in 1982, 1992, and 2004

Level of mathematics	1982	1992	2004
No math or low academic math	24.9	12.9	5.2
Algebra 1/plane geometry	30.6	22.6	18.1
Algebra 2	19.2	26.4	25.7
Algebra 2/trigonometry/analytic geometry	15.6	16.4	18.0
Precalculus	4.8	11.0	18.9
Calculus	5.9	10.7	14.1

Source: Dalton et al. 2007, p. 13

An examination of table 1.1 shows that the kinds of students who would finish their high school mathematics with algebra 1 or a geometry course in 1982 were *all* taking algebra 2 in 2004; students who finished with algebra 2 in 1982 were *all* taking precalculus in 2004, and some were taking calculus. Experienced teachers of the later high school courses who asserted that their students were not like the students of years gone by are accurate, and it is no wonder that the content or difficulty of these courses was modified by schools and teachers to fit a larger percent of the population.

The rebellion to the standards revolution, leading to what has been called the "math wars," was strikingly similar to the back-to-basics rebellion of the 1970s, even though these two revolutions were quite different in their origins and in what they brought to the mathematics classroom. Both rebellions espoused the view that the most important aspects of school mathematics are paper-and-pencil arithmetic skills at the elementary school level and algebraic skills at the high school level. Both rebellions ignored, if not decried, the use of technology in the learning of mathematics. Both rebellions viewed a foreign country as having implemented a curriculum that ostensibly shows that performance can be improved[4]. Both rebellions viewed mathematics as culture-free and wanted applications to be studied *after* skills are developed, not used to develop the skills. Both took advantage of concurrent movements to atomize the goals of school mathematics.[5]

The Difficulty of Deciding Which Curriculum Is Better or Best

The situations in which schools make decisions about which curriculum materials (e.g., textbooks) are best vary significantly from place to place (Hudson, Lahann, and Lee 2009). In many state-adoption states and in some large school districts, the broad (and sometimes the specific) thrusts of the curriculum have been determined: the materials for course X must have *this* content; they cannot have *that* content; etc. Then a school's decision regarding which curriculum is best for its students is not made on beliefs like those mentioned earlier but on which books or other materials best implement the beliefs imposed by the state. In other locales, schools have the option of choosing any materials they wish, and they have to consider what might constitute an ideal curriculum.

In all instances, schools must decide on some curriculum to implement and some materials to purchase, usually based on a textbook. These decisions are always difficult to make. Rarely have any of the curricula been tested, since the length of time between the announcement of state adoption guidelines and the deadline for submitting materials is seldom even close to the three-year minimum that it takes to write materials, give them a year of testing, and revise them based on that testing (Reys and Reys 2006). Thus, the only materials that are tested before publication tend to be those funded by noncommercial ventures that are then picked up by a publisher for commercial publication. Consequently, the evidence that exists to make a decision is most often just belief supported by

---

4. The Soviet Union in the time of new math; Singapore currently.

5. In the back-to-basics era, the atomization came from a desire for behavioral objectives; in the current era, the atomization has come from provisions of the No Child Left Behind statute.

anecdote. As a result, teachers are often asked to teach using materials that no one has tested, following guidelines that reflect dreams more than reality. Only teaching and testing can determine whether explanations are clear, material is organized in a cohesive manner, questions are appropriate, and the teacher' edition gives enough suggestions for the diverse sets of students likely to use the materials, or whether the additional materials available provide the support for which they are intended.

A decade ago, the number of studies that compared identifiable curricula was astonishingly small (Usiskin 1999). This lack of studies existed even though in those years there had been more textbook development activity than perhaps any decade previously. Instead, there were many studies of graphing calculators, a number of studies of geometry drawing programs, some of symbol manipulators. But these are tools, not curricula. They have no definite sequence and an unclear scope, and there is no reason to expect that different teachers would use these tools in anything resembling a consistent manner, nowhere near the consistency we get from textbook use.

Ironically, a number of studies were conducted on "cooperative learning," a "technology-rich" curriculum, or a "constructivist-based" curriculum, but not on specific textbooks. Such singular emphasis ignores the fact that any of these ideas can be implemented in many ways. A particular method of implementing an idea may be so poor that it results in poor performance, but another implementation of the same idea may be quite effective. Researchers tended to avoid studies of textbooks, where the treatments are roughly replicable, and instead studied instructional techniques, where the treatments are seldom replicable. As a result, little was learned that could be passed on to others.

The results from studies of textbook use are likely to be more consistent than the results of studies of specific instructional practices. But even that approach is problematic. Our experience, based on at least twenty University of Chicago School Mathematics Project studies from 1985 to 2007 involving multiple classes in six to twenty schools each, is that classes differ far more than would be expected by chance, and teachers and schools differ on so many different variables that a textbook or curriculum that works better in one place cannot be predicted with certainty to work better in another.

Comparative curriculum research is complex. When studying curriculum, the treatments may have substantially different goals; for example, one curriculum may spend a great deal of time on statistics whereas another ignores statistics completely. For students who have encountered significantly different content, no test of comparison is fair. The decision about which curriculum is better must again be made on belief rather than statistical evidence.

Given such difficulties, could we possibly statistically determine that one curriculum is better than another? Due to the variety of student populations, samples would have to be larger than just a few classes or a few schools. The natural place to collect such data would be in conjunction with the National Assessment of Educational Progress, because samples are typically of classroom size in every school in which there is testing, and as students' data are collected, so too are data on their classrooms, their teachers, and their schools. However, the National Assessment Governing Board (NAGB) has refused to collect data on the textbooks used by the students in its assessments. So, despite more than three decades of data collection, we have no definitive statements about the textbooks used in the United States or any causal or even correlational connections between particular textbooks and students' performance. As a result, in both the new math and the standards eras, some observers believed that the newer curricula were not really being implemented in schools, whereas others reported the occurrence of major changes, and some believed that changes in student performance were due to changes in curriculum, whereas others believed that no conclusive evidence was found to tie these changes to any particular curriculum. The situation is akin to examining whether vitamins can reduce incidence of cancer in a population by recording the incidence of cancer but not recording who in the sample has taken which vitamins. We will never be able to determine the relative merits or deficits of various curricula until we are willing to attach the best performance data we have accumulated to the specific curricular materials in use by those being tested.

Conclusion

What can we say is the current state of the school mathematics curriculum? In the United States, the answer is that it is one in which beliefs about what should be in the curriculum have overridden what evidence there is about successful curricula. Teachers and students are taking many different roads through the mathematical universe despite efforts in many states and at the national level to put all the buses on the same road. Most of the time these roads lead almost all students through the same itinerary, but some roads are charting new, exciting, different territories using new kinds of transports. If the history of the rebellions against the new math era tells us anything about the corresponding rebellion against the standards era, it suggests that attempts to reach consensus on common goals will continue. We can only hope that that our visions regarding what is best for our students and our societies are broad enough to encompass the extraordinary universe of mathematics in which our students find themselves.

REFERENCES

Achieve. *Mathematics Benchmarks, Grades K–12*. Washington, D.C.: Achieve, 2004. http://www.utdanacenter.org/k12mathbenchmarks/, September 3, 2008.

————. *Algebra 2 Test Overview*. Washington, D.C.: Achieve, 2008. http://www.achieve .org/node/842, September 12, 2008.

College Board. *College Board Mathematics and Statistics Standards for College Success*. New York: College Board, 2006. http://www.collegeboard.com/ prod_downloads/about/association/academic/mathematics-statistics_cbscs.pdf, September 3, 2008.

Dalton, Ben, Steven J. Ingels, Jane Downing, and Robert Bozick. *Advanced Mathematics and Science Course Taking in the Spring High School Senior Classes of 1982, 1992 and 2004*. NCES 2007-312. Washington, D.C.: National Center for Education Statistics, Institute of Educational Sciences, U.S. Department of Education, 2007.

Deans, Edwina. *Elementary School Mathematics: New Directions*. Washington, D.C.: U.S. Department of Health, Education, and Welfare, 1963.

Franklin, Christine, Gary Kader, Denise Mewborn, Jerry Moreno, Roxy Peck, Mike Perry, and Richard Scheaffer. *Guidelines for Assessment and Instruction in Statistics Education Report: A Pre-K–12 Curriculum Framework*. Alexandria, Va.: American Statistical Association, 2004. http://www.amstat.org/education/gaise/, September 3, 2008.

Graham, Ronald L., Donald E. Knuth, and Oren Patashnik. *Concrete Mathematics*. Reading, Mass.: Addison-Wesley Publishing Co., 1989.

Hirsch, Christian R., ed. *Perspectives on the Design and Development of School Mathematics Curricula*. Reston, Va.: NCTM, 2007.

Hudson, Rick A., Paula Elmer Lannan, and Jean S. Lee. "Considerations in the Review and Adoption of Mathematics Textbooks." In *Mathematics Curriculum: Issues Trends, and Future Directions,* Seventy-second Yearbook of the National Council of Teachers of Mathematics (NCTM), edited by Barbara Reys and Robert Reys, pp. 213–29. Reston, Va.: NCTM, 2010.

National Commision on Excellence in Education. *A Nation at Risk*. Washington, D.C.: U.S. Department of Education, 1983.

National Council of Teachers of Mathematics. *Curriculum and Evaluation Standards for School Mathematics*. Reston, Va.: NCTM, 1989.

————. *Professional Standards for Teaching Mathematics*. Reston, Va.: NCTM, 1991.

————. *Principles and Standards for School Mathematics*. Reston, Va.: NCTM, 2000.

————. *Curriculum Focal Points for Prekindergarten through Grade 8 Mathematics: A Quest for Coherence*. Reston, Va.: NCTM, 2006.

————. *Focus in High School Mathematics: Reasoning and Sense Making*. Reston, Va.: NCTM, 2009.

National Mathematics Advisory Panel (NMAP). *Foundations for Success: The Final Report of the National Mathematics Advisory Panel*. Washington, D.C.: U.S. Department of Education, 2008. http://www.ed.gov/about/bdscomm/list/mathpanel/ report/final-report.pdf, June 11, 2009.

National Research Council. *Everybody Counts: A Report to the Nation on the Future of Mathematics Education*. Washington, D.C.: National Academy Press, 1989.

————. *Adding It Up: Helping Children Learn Mathematics.* Washington, D.C.: National Academy Press, 2001.

Reys, Barbara, ed. *The Intended Curriculum as Represented in State-Level Curriculum Standards: Consensus or Confusion.* Charlotte, N.C.: Information Age Publishing, 2006.

Reys, Barbara, and Robert Reys. "The Development and Publication of Elementary Mathematics Textbooks: Let the Buyer Beware!" *Phi Delta Kappan* 87, no. 5 (2006): 377–83.

Senk, Sharon L., and Denisse R. Thompson, eds. *Standards-Based School Mathematics Curricula: What Are They? What Do Students Learn?* Mahwah, N.J.: Lawrence Erlbaum Associates, 2003.

Usiskin, Zalman, ed. *Reforming the Third R: Changing the School Mathematics Curriculum.* Special issue, *American Journal of Education* 106 (November 1997): 1.

————. "Which Curriculum Is Best?" *UCSMP Newsletter* 24 (Winter 1999): 3–10.

Usiskin, Zalman, and Jennifer Griffin. *The Classification of Quadrilaterals: A Study of Definition.* Charlotte, N.C.: Information Age Publishing, 2008.

Wu, Hung-Hsi. "The Mathematician and Mathematics Education Reform." *Notices of the American Mathematical Society* 43 (1996): 1531–37.

2

Technology and the Mathematics Curriculum

James T. Fey
Richard M. Hollenbeck
Jonathan A. Wray

T HE FUNDAMENTAL goal of school mathematics is to help students develop the understandings, skills, and dispositions that are required for applying mathematical reasoning effectively to the tasks of future study, work, and personal living. In the past, mathematics programs reflected expectations that a relatively small number of students should be prepared for mathematics-intensive collegiate study in physical science or engineering and that most students need only modest understanding of practical arithmetic and geometry for the limited demands of work and daily life. However, the rapid mathematization of work in almost all areas of business, industry, personal decision making, and the social and life sciences dictates that most students learn more and different mathematics than school mathematics programs provide. Without doubt, the most important factor in this transformation of demands for school mathematics has been the infusion of computer tools for calculation, visualization, and data management in all facets of our work and personal lives.

Computer tools enable users to effortlessly handle complex computations. Using such tools presents opportunities to interconnect mathematical topics in dynamic and interactive ways. And they make accessible the study of new and different mathematical subjects. Without technology, asking students to do such things as analyze sizeable quantities of real data, use simulations to estimate probabilities, work with recursive relationships, precisely measure areas of irregularly shaped figures, solve large systems of linear equations, and examine and apply encryption algorithms is impractical. Many mathematics curriculum materials already take advantage of the capabilities of technology by giving students opportunities to explore topics and investigate problems that could not be done without technology. For example, the Connected Mathematics Project (Lappan et al. 2006) has developed a series of interactive Java applets (connectedmath .msu.edu/CD/) that allow users to investigate mathematical patterns and relationships to solve problems that would be unfeasible to pose without access to these computer programs.

Over the past several decades, the emergence of electronic tools has transformed the ways that people can explore mathematical ideas and solve mathematical problems. Calculators, notebook computers, and even cellular telephones and other handheld devices offer instant access to powerful options for numeric, graphical, and symbolic calculation and to the information resources of the World Wide Web. Many mathematics classrooms already present students with an impressive array of technological tools for doing and learning mathematics. But access to tools is the easy part of transforming mathematics education. Figuring out how to use the tools effectively and appropriately is a far greater challenge. If teachers and students had full use of even the existing mathematical and communication tools, how would such capability change the content objectives of mathematics courses? How would it change the way teachers teach mathematics in elementary, middle, or high school?

In this article, we elaborate the questions raised by the emergence of technology-rich mathematics classrooms and workplaces. Our objective is to stimulate thinking and experimentation by individual teachers, groups of teachers in the same school or district, teacher educators, curriculum and test developers, researchers, and educational policymakers about the need for, and direction of, change in the school mathematics curriculum.

Technology and Content of the Mathematics Curriculum

Calculators and computers and their various hardware and software programs are particularly well suited to the logical and algorithmic operations of numeric, graphical, and symbolic calculation that are essential in mathematical work. Numeric tools perform exact and approximate arithmetic on whole numbers, fractions, and decimals, as well as on irrational and complex numbers. Graphical tools display and help with analysis of data and functions. They also display, measure, and transform geometric figures that satisfy prescribed conditions. Computer algebra systems solve equations, transform expressions, and test conjectured identities.

What does this current and emerging access to tools for mathematical work imply about our content goals in school mathematics? Do we still need to emphasize proficiency in the standard computational algorithms of arithmetic for all elementary and middle grades students? Do we still need to emphasize proficiency in routine algebraic operations on expressions, equations, and inequalities for all middle and high school students? How is statistical practice transformed by access to sophisticated data-analysis tools?

Arithmetic in the Future

In mathematics classrooms of the precalculator era, a large portion of instructional time was devoted to training all students in procedures for adding, subtracting, multiplying, and dividing whole numbers, common fractions, and decimals and for calculating with proportions and percents. The primary responsibility for developing those skills was assigned to educators at the elementary and early middle grades.

If we look at the way arithmetic is done by most of us in even the current technologically rich environment, we might easily be skeptical of the claim that honing students' skill in use of standard arithmetic algorithms is an appropriate use of precious class time and students' interest. Suppose that we make the reasonable assumption that anyone who finds a need to do arithmetic calculation of even modest complexity has access to a variety of tools for that work. Then we need sensible answers to the following questions about the impact of technology on curricular expectations in arithmetic:

- What arithmetic understandings and personal procedural skills remain important in practical problem solving and learning of advanced mathematical topics?

- How does proficiency in students' performance of standard arithmetic algorithms contribute to the essential skill of deciding which operations will resolve quantitative reasoning tasks?

- How can arithmetic curricula and instruction effectively develop students' skills in the kind of arithmetic estimation that is useful in judging the reasonableness of calculator results?

Of course, these questions are not new in mathematics education or in the public discourse about technology and mathematics curricular goals. But the infusion of calculating tools in all aspects of contemporary life makes timely a reconsideration of our educational objectives in arithmetic.

Algebra in the Future

The case for developing students' proficiency with arithmetic operations and standard algorithms is often justified by the argument that those skills are essential for success in learning algebra. Indeed, if one thinks about algebra as a collection of syntactic rules for manipulating expressions, equations, and inequalities into equivalent forms, the importance of skill in generalized arithmetic procedures is obvious. However, once again, almost anyone who needs to operate on algebraic expressions, equations, and inequalities in technical work has access to tools that perform those tasks.

The use of graphing-calculator table and graph routines to solve equations and inequalities by numeric or graphical estimation is now widely known and applied. For example, suppose that one faces the following algebraic problem:

> Officials of Major League Lacrosse need to decide which ticket prices for the league all-star game will lead to maximum revenue.

Market research and analysis of business conditions might suggest that income, expenses, and profit are related to average ticket price by such functions as the following:

Income: $\qquad\qquad\quad I(x) \;=\; 5000x - 65x^2$
Operation Expenses: $\; E(x) \;=\; 45{,}000 - 260x$
Profit: $\qquad\qquad\quad P(x) \;=\; -65x^2 + 5260x - 45{,}000$

Tables of values or graphs for the functions $I(x)$, $E(x)$, and $P(x)$ show that the optimal average ticket price is approximately \$40 and that the break-even points occur at ticket prices of about \$10 and \$70 (see fig. 2.1).

The optimal ticket prices can also be found by methods of elementary calculus and algebra—taking the derivatives of $I(x)$ and $P(x)$ and solving the equations $I'(x) = 0$ and $P'(x) = 0$. But those results can also be obtained by CAS commands, for example,

$$\text{solve(d(5000x} - 65x^2, \text{x}) = 0, \text{x})$$

and

$$\text{solve(d(}-65x^2 + 5260x - 45000, \text{x}) = 0, \text{x}).$$

The break-even points for the game can also be calculated by solving the equation $5{,}000x - 65x^2 = 45{,}000 - 260x$. This result can be obtained exactly with the CAS command

$$\text{solve(5000x} - 65x^2 = 45{,}000 - 260x, \text{x}).$$

In fact, CAS can do much more of the standard algorithmic calculation that is developed over considerable instructional time in traditional algebra courses.

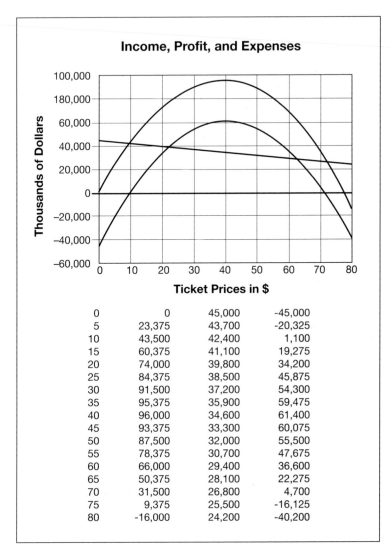

Income, Profit, and Expenses

0	0	45,000	-45,000
5	23,375	43,700	-20,325
10	43,500	42,400	1,100
15	60,375	41,100	19,275
20	74,000	39,800	34,200
25	84,375	38,500	45,875
30	91,500	37,200	54,300
35	95,375	35,900	59,475
40	96,000	34,600	61,400
45	93,375	33,300	60,075
50	87,500	32,000	55,500
55	78,375	30,700	47,675
60	66,000	29,400	36,600
65	50,375	28,100	22,275
70	31,500	26,800	4,700
75	9,375	25,500	-16,125
80	-16,000	24,200	-40,200

Fig. 2.1. Value tables and graphs of income, profit, and cost functions

In this problem situation, the numeric and graphical methods actually lead to valuable insight into the problem that is not available from the standard approaches using methods of algebra and calculus. For instance, although one can locate the maximum income and profit points by taking derivatives and finding zeroes of those functions algebraically, the numeric and graphical displays show how those specific points fit into the overall patterns relating income, expenses, and profit to ticket price. The graph and table reveal that changes in price of as much as $10 from the optimal value will have only a modest negative effect on income and profit from the game.

The capabilities of universally available computer algebra tools suggest the following deep questions about the goals of school algebra instruction:

- Does focusing instruction on manipulating symbolic expressions, equations, and inequalities provide students with the most useful algebraic understanding and skill?

- Is there a productive connection between learning the manipulative skills of algebra and developing the ability to identify and represent problem conditions in the algebraic forms to which spreadsheet, graphical, and computer algebra system software can be applied?

- Because only a modest number of students will eventually enter disciplines that might require personal proficiency in algebraic manipulations, might we be able to provide that technical skill training as an extension of curricula that focus first on basic concepts and technology-assisted problem solving?

The answers to these questions can be found only by thoughtful analysis of curricular goals, by empirical studies that test the limits of turning routine mathematical work over to technology, and by designing experiments that explore instructional strategies for developing students' understanding of core mathematical ideas through the application of computing tools.

Data Analysis and Probability in the Future

In much the same way that calculators and computers raise questions about curricular goals that focus on procedural skills in arithmetic and algebra, tools that perform calculations in data analysis and probability suggest rethinking the goals of those important strands in grades K–12 mathematics. Widely available statistical software allows students to calculate summary statistics and to display the data with such graphics as line plots, histograms, box plots, and scatter plots. Probability software helps students simulate experiments with random processes and do the combinatorial calculations implied by theoretical analysis of those situations.

The fact that such tools for data analysis and probability calculations are now available to, and used by, nearly everyone who needs them for problem solving and decision making raises the following questions about the probability and statistics strand of school mathematics:

- How much time should be devoted to developing students' skill in statistical calculation and graphing and how much to interpreting the results of those procedures?

- What experience with paper-and-pencil calculation and graphing is essential as a foundation for understanding basic concepts and thoughtful use of statistical tools?

- What is the optimal mix of hands-on experiments and simulations in learning basic probability concepts?

Again, these questions can be resolved only by careful analysis of curricular goals and by empirical studies that explore the advantages and limitations of focusing instruction on conceptual understanding more than computational proficiency.

Geometry and Trigonometry in the Future

Although most people probably think of computers first of all as tools for high-speed numeric operations, some of the most impressive displays of computing power are the dynamic graphics that have become commonplace in video games, animated cartoons, and special effects of movies. Computer visualization tools and robots are also used throughout design and manufacturing processes of almost all industries.

Preparing students to participate in this digital visualization world—as either producers or insightful consumers—requires an array of geometric understandings and skills that Euclid could not have imagined. Digital production of images requires the application of such mathematical ideas as vectors, coordinate systems, matrices, and transformations. Interpreting the typical two-dimensional representations of three-dimensional objects requires an understanding of perspective and the ways that color and shading are used to indicate geometric properties of visual objects.

In the classroom, interactive geometry software packages provide students with opportunities to construct and explore properties of geometric figures. A powerful feature of this software is the ability to make measurements and manipulate geometric objects while preserving the properties of construction. Through visualization and repeated empirical measurement, students can gain insight into important geometrical concepts. All of this raises questions about the geometry strand of school mathematics.

- Should geometric topics in the curriculum be developed in ways that emphasize coordinate representation and transformations of figures in lieu of, or in addition to, traditional synthetic methods?

- What balance and interplay of experience and learning about two- and three-dimensional geometry is important for most students?

- What sequence of learning experiences with hands-on objects, drawings, and computer displays will furnish students with essential geometric understandings and skills?

- What is the appropriate interplay of inductive learning through computer-based explorations and deductive proof of geometric principles?

As is true in considering curricular implications of technology for number, algebra, and statistics, these questions about the future of geometry can be answered only by careful analytic and empirical studies. We need to know much more about the ways students can learn to use and understand technology-based visualization tools and effects.

Conclusions

New and emerging technologies will continually transform the mathematics that is available to students and redefine ways that it can be taught. Mathematics educators will need to respond to these technological advances in ways that help students develop the mathematical understanding and reasoning skills necessary to be productive members of society, for example:

- How will advances in cell phones and other handheld devices affect ways that students access mathematics?

- When should interactive electronic textbooks with sophisticated search engines and dynamically connected, readily accessible graphing and calculation tools replace hard-copy versions of textbooks?

- How can digital gaming systems and interactive virtual worlds be used to enhance mathematical learning opportunities?

- What role will podcasts have in supporting mathematics classrooms?

- What opportunities will an ever-changing World Wide Web present for teachers and learners of mathematics?

The calculating and computing tools already pervasive in work situations that require mathematical reasoning and problem solving have been enhanced and adapted to serve as impressive tools for teaching mathematics in elementary, middle, and high school grades. Appropriate use of those instructional tools and appropriate revision of curriculum priorities to reflect the changes in how mathematical work is done in a technology-rich environment will require extensive and thoughtful study and experimentation. Curriculum specialists and other interested parties should carefully examine objectives to determine whether technology can enhance students' learning of mathematics. However, technology should not be an add-on to curricula. Using technology to cover mathematical topics that are just as accessible though other approaches may actually interfere with learning and undermine the benefits of technology. Given the urgency of providing strong mathematical preparation for students who will enter and live in a technologically sophisticated society and workplace, such study and experimentation by all involved in the enterprise of mathematics teaching should be a high priority for our field.

REFERENCES

Lappan, Glenda, James T. Fey, William M. Fitzgerald, Susan N. Friel, and Elizabeth D. Phillips. *Connected Mathematics Project*. Boston: Pearson Prentice Hall, 2006.

National Standards: Lessons from the Past, Directions for the Future[1]

Margaret E. Goertz

THE REAUTHORIZATION of the No Child Left Behind (NCLB) Act renewed calls by organizations across the political spectrum for national standards. The bipartisan Commission on No Child Left Behind (NCLB 2007) recommended the development of voluntary model national content and performance standards and tests in reading and language arts, mathematics, and science based on the National Assessment of Educational Progress (NAEP) frameworks. Groups as ideologically diverse as Education Trust and the Fordham Foundation supported these recommendations. In 2009, forty-eight states agreed to take part in the Common Core State Standards Initiative, a joint effort by the National Governors Association and the Council of Chief State School Officers to develop common K–12 and college- and career-readiness standards in mathematics and language arts. Adoption of these standards will be voluntary, but the U.S. Department of Education will provide some financial incentives for states to accept them.

The arguments in support of national standards today echo those of the past: they will promote democracy, equity, and economic competitiveness. The arguments against national standards are also familiar: they will lead to the establishment of a national curriculum; one size does not fit all; and local communities,

---

1. This paper is based on the article "Standards-Based Reform: Lessons from the Past, Directions for the Future" by Margaret E. Goertz in *Clio at the Table,* edited by Kenneth Wong and Robert Rothman (New York: Peter Lang Publishing, 2008).

not the federal government, know what is best for their students. The context for the debate, however, differs from that in earlier years. The extent of the federal government's involvement in elementary and secondary school education is unprecedented. Professional organizations in several disciplines, such as the National Council of Teachers of Mathematics (NCTM), have developed standards that address students' learning goals, assessment, and instruction (NCTM 1989, 1991, 1995, 2000, 2006). NAEP's proficiency levels have become de facto national performance standards, benchmarks against which the performance of states is judged (or confirmed). Indeed, the disparity between state and NAEP proficiency standards has been a driving force in the current push for national standards.

If the nation already has de facto content and performance standards, the adoption of voluntary national standards would appear to be a logical next step in federal education policy. Yet, the same underlying issues bedevil the adoption of national standards now as in the past: what kinds of standards, whose standards, and with what effect? More specifically, policymakers must reach consensus on the type, content, and specificity of the standards; determine who will develop the standards; and facilitate the implementation of the standards.

This chapter discusses what we have learned over the years about standards and their implementation in an attempt to guide and improve future policy. Although the concept of "standards" encompasses a range of education policies and practices in the mathematics education community (e.g., curriculum: NCTM [1989, 2000, 2006]; appropriate teaching: NCTM [1991]; and assessment: NCTM [1995]), I use the term to reflect *content* and *performance* standards for students, the focus of current policy debates about national standards. *Content standards* are broad descriptions of knowledge and skills that students should acquire and be able to do in a particular subject area. They indicate the topics and skills that should be taught at various grades or grade spans and are intended to guide public school instruction, curriculum, teacher preparation, and assessment. *Performance standards,* in contrast, provide explicit definitions and examples of what students must demonstrate to show that they have mastered the content standards. Performance standards delineate how good is "good enough." As a practical matter, however, performance standards are expressed in the form of "cut scores" on standardized tests.

This chapter begins with a very brief overview of the history of standards in the United States. Its second section discusses the implementation and effect of the standards-based reform movement over the past thirty years. The final section raises a set of issues facing policymakers who advocate national standards—or any standards—as the keystone of education reform in the years to come.

A Brief History of Education Standards

Education standards have been expressed through laws, common curriculum and textbooks, and entrance requirements for more than 200 years. The type (content, performance, input), target (students—all or differentiated; teachers; schools; districts) and use (improving educational quality, increasing educational opportunity, monitoring, gatekeeping) of the standards, however, have changed over time.

One could argue that the founding fathers in the United States delineated the first education standards in their writings about the purpose of education and in the education clauses of early state constitutions. Ravitch (1995) argues that schools in the nineteenth century had common content and performance standards as defined by relatively similar curricular materials (e.g., readers, geography books), grading systems, and, for high schools, college admission requirements and examinations.

In 1893, the Committee of Ten sought to improve high school curriculum and standardize preparation for college by establishing high standards for *all* high school students, whether college bound or workforce bound. Similar to guiding bodies in the current standards movement, they recommended what should be taught in each subject area, how students' knowledge should be assessed, and how teachers should be prepared to teach the content. These standards affected few students, however, because only one in ten youth were enrolled in high school at the turn of the twentieth century. In contrast, the *Cardinal Principles of Education,* issued by the National Education Association's Commission on the Reorganization of Secondary Education (CRSE 1918), called for a curriculum that would adapt the school program to individual differences in interest and ability. This approach seemed well suited for the expanding population of high school students who came from working-class and immigrant families, but resulted in differentiated program and content standards. The principles of the Committee of Ten and college admission standards defined the content of the academic track in high schools, whereas those of CRSE applied to the general and vocational tracks (Ravitch 1995). The equity and excellence movements of the second half of the twentieth century, and the current debate over national standards, are attempts to reconcile these very different visions for educating our youth.

The equity movement of the late 1960s directed new attention to inequities in schools, particularly in poor and minority communities. Concerns about students' inability to read and compute (c.f., Kline [1973]) led many states to implement testing and other policies in the 1970s to hold educators accountable for the operation and performance of their schools and to hold students accountable for the mastery of basic skills through high school graduation tests. When states instituted minimum competency tests in the 1970s, teachers paid attention to the competencies and prepared students for the tests. This emphasis on basic skills, coupled with federal funding for compensatory education through the Elementary and Secondary Education Act, increased the achievement of minority students and, to a lesser extent, students from educationally disadvantaged families (Smith and O'Day 1991). Concerns were raised then, however, as now, that teachers narrowed the curriculum to the tested content, which was low-level mathematics and reading.

Success in raising basic skills was not matched by a commensurate rise in student performance on higher-order skills or in performance that was on par with the country's international competitors. This situation triggered the next round of education reform—one focused on more stringent input standards and, increasingly, on more rigorous content and performance standards. The standards-based reform movement emerged in the late 1980s and early 1990s through the work of a group of education leaders, governors, businessmen, researchers, and professional organizations such as NCTM and the American Association for the Advancement of Science. Under the theory of standards-based reform, states establish challenging content and performance standards for all students and align primary state policies affecting teaching and learning—curriculum and curriculum materials, preservice and in-service teacher training, and assessment—with these standards. States then give schools and school districts greater flexibility to design appropriate instructional programs in exchange for holding schools accountable for students' performance (Smith and O'Day 1991).

These ideas were incorporated into federal policy, beginning with the Improving America's Schools Act of 1994, which required states to develop challenging content standards in at least reading and mathematics, create high-quality assessments to measure performance against these standards, and have local districts identify low-performing schools for assistance. The Goals 2000 legislation and such programs as the National Science Foundation's State and Urban Systemic Initiatives provided funds for states and localities to design the components of a standards-based system and to build the capacity of local districts to implement these reforms. With the enactment of the NCLB Act of 2001, the federal government expanded its role significantly, requiring states to test more frequently and set more ambitious and uniform improvement goals for their schools, and prescribing sanctions for schools that fail to meet these goals. The substance of academic content and proficiency standards, however, remains the responsibility of states. States are constitutionally responsible for education, and federal law forbids its agencies from mandating, directing, or controlling the specific instructional content, curriculum, programs of instruction, or academic achievement standards and assessments of states, school districts, or schools (Fuhrman 2004).

In summary, calls by some for "national standards" have many things in common with the past. Periodic pushes have been made over the centuries for common standards and for higher standards for all students. A new factor, however, is that the talk of high standards takes places in a context in which all students are expected to attend and complete high school. Accountability for the outcomes of schooling has shifted from students to schools and school districts, and the purposes of assessment have expanded from placing and promoting students to generating indicators of performance of the education system and motivating educators to consider changes in their instructional content and strategies.

Implementing Standards

Has the articulation of specific content and performance standards made a difference? Studies of standards-based reform conducted at the end of the twentieth and the early twenty-first century show that standards and accountability systems are driving educational change.

Standards Matter

Although the public is divided in its support of the NCLB Act (Rose and Gallup 2007), the concept of higher academic content and performance standards is generally accepted among the public, educators, and policymakers. Most parents support continuing to raise standards, and most students say that requiring them to meet higher standards for promotion and graduation is a good idea (Johnson, Arumi, and Ott 2006). Teachers also believe in the intrinsic value of standards. They believe that state standards identify what their students should know and be able to do, that the standards are compatible with good educational practice, and that the public should hold students and educators to account for meeting certain outcomes. Teachers find standards useful for bringing focus and consistency of instruction within and across schools. They also find standards helpful for guiding their own instruction and aligning their instruction with them, although they believe that standards include more content than they can cover in a year, and are, in some instances, too vague to give useful guidance (Kannapel et al. 2001; Massell et al. 2005; Johnson, Arumi, and Ott 2006; Stecher et al. 2008).

The perceived legitimacy of state assessment systems, however, is much lower, particularly among teachers. Teachers do not believe that state tests are necessarily a good measure of their students' mastery of content, and many raise concerns about the lack of alignment among standards, curriculum, and assessment. But teachers report that they align instruction with assessment and focus more on standards (Goertz and Massell 2005; Stecher et al. 2008). Teachers, schools, and districts are also paying attention to the data generated by assessments. Teachers review assessment results to identify students who need additional help, topics that require more emphasis, and gaps in curriculum and instruction. Districts and schools are increasing their use of annual and interim student test data to plan for school improvement, to change curriculum and instructional materials, and to focus professional development (Massell 2001; Padilla et al. 2006; Stecher et al. 2008).

Incentives to Use Standards Matter

Accountability has gotten people's attention, for better or worse. Educators are responding to the press of performance-based accountability even though they believe that accountability and assessments narrow the curriculum and constrain their teaching approaches, and even when they do not feel an immediate threat from sanctions or see the possibility of rewards (Goertz 2001; Kelley et al. 2000; Massell et al. 2005; Stecher et al. 2008). Stronger accountability has also focused educators' attention on traditionally underserved populations of students. Although some educators still question whether all students can attain high standards, their expectations for these students are considerably higher than in the past. Teachers report that they search for more effective teaching methods, focus more on standards and on topics and formats emphasized in assessments, and change some elements of their instructional practice in response to state assessments (Goertz and Massell 2005; Kannapel et al. 2001). Districts have responded to the accountability press by providing assistance to schools, although not always the kinds of intensive support envisioned under NCLB (Center on Educational Policy 2007; Padilla et al. 2006; Stecher et al. 2008).

Consequences, however, are not sufficient in and of themselves to encourage action consistently across districts or schools. Staff members in some low-performing schools feel little pressure and react only minimally. An important factor in staff responsiveness is whether their district leaders take a strong stand on accountability, mandating or in other ways encouraging their schools to take action. Professional pride and the acceptance of the intent of reform are other factors that explain changes in teacher behaviors (Goertz and Massell 2005).

Researchers have identified negative consequences of increased accountability pressure as well. High-stakes accountability has led to more time spent on test-preparation activities, narrowing of the curriculum, and increased attention to "bubble kids," or children who are performing at just below the pass rates of mandated assessments (c.f., Booher-Jennings [2005]; Firestone, Schorr, and Monfils [2004]; McMurrer [2008]; Shepard and Dougherty [1991]; Stecher et al. [2008]). Concern over the negative impact of more difficult tests on students, particularly students of color and English language learners, has slowed the development of new high school tests aligned with higher standards and led some states to delay the requirement of students' passage of these tests for high school graduation (Fuhrman, Goertz, and Duffy 2004). And, under the press of NCLB sanctions, states have called for changes in ways that schools are identified for improvement, such as increasing subgroup sizes, incorporating confidence intervals in the measurement of proficiency, and using growth models.

Who Sets Standards and Incentives Matters Even More

States use different processes for setting and updating academic content standards, setting proficiency standards, and designing accountability systems. Who sets standards can affect the legitimacy of standards among educators and the public.

Teachers are more likely to support standards set by other educators or their professional associations than by government. Although professional organizations such as NCTM have used consensus processes to develop standards, consensus over the content of standards remains elusive both within and outside the education community. States have faced philosophical battles over what should be taught (e.g., evolution, social science content) and how (e.g., different approaches to teaching mathematics and reading). For example, the teaching of mathematics became the subject of heated controversy in California and other states, with traditionalists (including some university mathematics professors) battling reformers over appropriate pedagogy (teacher-directed versus student-constructed knowledge) and curricular emphasis—process (problem solving and mathematical reasoning) versus content (facts, computation, and algorithms). The resulting standards placed greater emphasis on basic skills and traditional pedagogy and assessment formats (c.f., Smith, Heinecke, and Nobel [1999]; Wilson [2003]).

These battles are not new. Schoenfeld (2004) argues that the underlying issues being contested in mathematics education are more than a century old. Is mathematics for the elite or for the masses? Should mathematics be studied because it develops the ability to reason, for its cultural value, or for its economic value? Standards-based reform has shifted the venue for these battles, however, from local school boards to state boards of education and state legislatures. Although skirmishes continue in local communities and debates rage in the academic and practitioner communities, combatants now mobilize to influence the content of state curriculum frameworks, and, in many states, the selection of instructional materials.

Standards Are Necessary but Not Sufficient to Change Teaching and Learning

Rigorous standards may require teachers to teach different content and to teach that content differently. As recognized in the NCTM *Standards* (1989, 2000), building teachers' knowledge and skills is a crucial component of the change process, and the theory of action underlying both standards-based reform and NCLB assumes that states and local school districts possess, or can develop, the capacity to assist school improvement efforts, to bring all students to proficiency, and to pay for these efforts.

Districts have been aligning curriculum and instruction for more than a decade, both vertically with state standards and horizontally with other elements of district and school policies and procedures. Many districts have taken additional steps to align instruction by developing more specific local standards; publishing curriculum guides with standards, frameworks, and pacing sequences; and issuing documents that map the content of required textbooks to standards and assessments (c.f., Massell and Goertz [2002]; Padilla et al. [2006]). Most districts with schools identified as needing improvement report using other strategies, such as school improvement planning; the use of data and research to guide instruction; increasing the quantity or quality or professional development; providing extra time for, and more intensive academic instruction to, low-performing students; and increasing instructional time in reading and mathematics, particularly in elementary schools. Districts are also restructuring the elementary school day to teach core content areas in greater depth (Center on Educational Policy 2007; Padilla et al. 2006).

States and districts lack capacity, however, to provide *intensive* support to low-performing schools and students, the kind of support they need to meet the high academic standards as envisioned under NCLB. Only half the districts with schools in need of improvement report that they have school support teams, and only one-third provide additional full-time school-level staff to support teacher development, mentors, or coaches for the principal (Center on Educational Policy 2007; Padilla et al. 2006). Furthermore, the availability and intensity of support varies by the size of districts. This variability in level of support is worrisome because most technical assistance comes from school districts. Districts, in turn, report they turn to their state departments of education and education service agencies for help (Center on Educational Policy 2006). As with districts, however, resource-intensive state assistance covers only a portion of low-performing schools (Padilla et al. 2006). States with large or growing numbers of schools and districts identified for improvement are focusing support on their most challenged schools, leading to calls for differentiated treatment of, and consequences for, schools under NCLB.

Considering National Standards

Education policy in the United States has changed considerably in the past twenty years. All states have content standards, assessments, and accountability systems that include all students and focus attention on students' learning. In most states, the rigor of standards is higher than in the past, although many stakeholders argue that current standards are not rigorous enough. If low standards are the problem, then the solution lies in generating higher-quality academic standards (perhaps national standards), encouraging states to adopt them, and supporting schools and districts in implementing more-challenging curricula. The push for reform based on national standards raises five issues for policymakers, however.

First, what is the nature of the problem? Are standards too lax? Are they too general? Are they too incoherent? Critics charge that standards in most states are not as challenging as those in high-performing nations and that too few students are gaining the knowledge and skills they need to succeed in college and the workplace. In contrast with other countries, our state academic standards are unfocused, lack coherence, and have led to a curriculum in the United States that is "a mile wide and an inch deep" (c.f., Schmidt, McKnight, and Raizen [1997]; Rothman [2004]). Or, have we established suitable standards but set our expectations for students' performance too low? States vary widely in the percent of students who are proficient on their state standards, ranging from 87 percent in Mississippi to 34 percent in Missouri (U.S. Department of Education 2006). Is this range due to variation in content standards or in proficiency standards? Is the quality and coverage of state assessments problematic? If we establish national standards, must we also create national assessments and proficiency standards (such as NAEP) to accurately measure what students know and are able to do?

Second, what constitutes good standards? How specific should they be? What learning trajectories should they incorporate? Should they include assessment frameworks? Instructional strategies? What research exists on the most effective characteristics of standards? Have any states benchmarked their standards against international standards and, if so, with what effect on teaching and students' learning? Do we (and how do we) know whether one state's standards are superior to another's? How can research on how students' learning typically proceeds over time in specific content areas guide the design of standards?

Third, who should develop national standards? Should this function be the purview of federal organizations, such as the National Assessment Governing Board; national bodies, such as the National Academy of Science; professional organizations in the disciplines, such as NCTM; or consortia of states, such as the American Diploma Project? What should be the relative roles and contributions of academics, practitioners, parents, business, and the public in the development of standards? As discussed previously in this chapter, these decisions have both normative and political implications.

Fourth, what are the incentives for states to adopt new standards? Would a federal requirement of states to benchmark their standards against national, international, or multistate standards as a condition of receiving Title I funds be politically feasible? Previous attempts to do so have failed. The Goals 2000 Act of 1994 created a federal agency, the National Education Standards and Improvement Council, with the responsibility of certifying voluntary national content and performance standards and certifying that state standards "are comparable to or higher in rigor and quality than national standards" (Ravitch 1995). The following year, the new Republican majority in Congress repealed this provision of Goals 2000, and the federal government now approves each state's standard-setting process, not the content of its standards. The publication of NAEP scores is intended to serve as a check on state assessments, enabling the public to compare state proficiency standards and confirm changes in students' performance. We do not know, however, whether publicizing discrepancies between performance on states' own assessments and NAEP has led any states to consider raising their standards.

Fifth, what kinds of support do states, districts, schools, and teachers need to improve failing schools and raise students' performance? Who will provide the needed resources and support? Is it fair to hold students and schools accountable for meeting more-rigorous academic standards if they are not given the opportunity to learn the tested content? Because a high school diploma is a property right, courts require states to ensure that high school students have sufficient opportunity to learn the skills assessed on a test required for graduation. These include teaching the tested skills ("curricular validity") and any evidence of successful remediation attempts. This principle does not apply, however, to other policies involving education accountability, and the concept of opportunity-to-learn standards remains controversial and not well defined. Although NCLB's requirement that all schools have "highly qualified" teachers is intended to address one inequity in the delivery of educational services, large disparities in education spending across as well as within states remain a major barrier to ensuring equal access to a high-quality education.

In conclusion, the adoption of national standards would appear to address concerns about the quality and equity of elementary and secondary school education in the United States. Frameworks for national standards already exist in several disciplines. Experience with current standards suggests that national standards could make some difference in what is taught and in what students learn. Yet, they are not a panacea for what ails American education. As with most public policy, the devil is in the details of the design and implementation of national standards. Proposals for national standards raise the ever-present issue of who controls our educational system. Although the federal government expanded its role significantly under NCLB, states remain constitutionally, fiscally, and substantively responsible for education, and schools and their staffs ultimately determine how standards are enacted in the classroom. Can national standards alone bring coherence to our highly decentralized and fragmented educational system?

REFERENCES

Booher-Jennings, Jennifer. "Below the Bubble: 'Educational Triage' and the Texas Accountability System." *American Educational Research Journal* 42 (Summer 2005): 231–68.

Center on Education Policy. *From the Capitol to the Classroom: Year 4 of the No Child Left Behind Act*. Washington, D.C.: Center on Education Policy, 2006.

———. *Moving beyond Identification: Assisting Schools in Improvement*. Washington, D.C.: Center on Education Policy, 2007.

Commission on No Child Left Behind (NCLB). *Beyond NCLB: Fulfilling the Promise to Our Nation's Children*. Washington, D.C.: Aspen Institute, 2007. http://www .aspeninstitute.org/policy-work/no-child-left-behind/background-materials.

Commission on the Reorganization of Secondary Education (CRSE). *Cardinal Principles of Education*. Washington, D.C: National Education Association, 1918.

Firestone, William A., Robert Y. Schorr, and Lora F. Monfils. *The Ambiguity of Teaching to the Test*. Mahwah, N.J.: Lawrence Erlbaum Associates, 2004.

Fuhrman, Susan H. "Less Than Meets the Eye: Standards, Testing, and Fear of Federal Control." In *Who's in Charge Here? The Tangled Web of School Governance and Policy,* edited by Noah Epstein, pp. 131–63. Washington, D.C.: Brookings Institution, 2004.

Fuhrman, Susan H., Margaret E. Goertz, and Mark C. Duffy. "'Slow Down, You Move Too Fast': The Politics of Making Changes in High-Stakes Accountability Policies for Students." In *Redesigning Accountability Systems for Education,* edited by Susan H. Fuhrman and Richard F. Elmore, pp. 245–73. New York: Teachers College Press, 2004.

Goertz, Margaret E. "Standards-Based Accountability: Horse Trade or Horse Whip?" In *From the Capitol to the Classroom: Standards-Based Reform in the States,* One Hundredth Yearbook of the National Society for the Study of Education, Part 2, edited by Susan H. Fuhrman, pp. 39–59. Chicago: University of Chicago Press, 2001.

Goertz, Margaret E., and Diane Massell. "Holding High Hopes: How High Schools Respond to State Accountability Policies." *CPRE Policy Brief RB-42.* Philadelphia: University of Pennsylvania, Consortium for Policy Research in Education, 2005.

Johnson, Jean, Ana Maria Arumi, and Amber Ott. "Is Support for Standards and Testing Fading?" *Reality Check 2006,* no. 3, July 20, 2006. http://www.publicagenda.org/ reports/reality-check-2006-issue-no-3, June 16, 2009.

Kannapel, Patricia J., Lola Aagaard, Pamela Coe, and Cynthia Reeves. "The Impact of Standards and Accountability on Teaching and Learning in Kentucky." In *From the Capitol to the Classroom: Standards-Based Reform in the States,* One Hundredth Yearbook of the National Society for the Study of Education, Part 2, edited by Susan H. Fuhrman, pp. 242–62. Chicago: University of Chicago Press, 2001.

Kelley, Carolyn, Allan R. Odden, Anthony Milanowski, and Herbert Heneman III. "The Motivational Effects of School-Based Performance Awards." *CPRE Policy Brief RB-29.* Philadelphia: University of Pennsylvania, Consortium for Policy Research in Education, 2000.

Kline, Morris. *Why Johnny Can't Add: The Failure of the New Mathematics.* New York: St. Martin's Press, 1973.

Massell, Diane. "The Theory and Practice of Using Data to Build Capacity: State and Local Strategies and Their Effects." In *From the Capitol to the Classroom: Standards-Based Reform in the States,* One Hundredth Yearbook of the National Society for the Study of Education, Part 2, edited by Susan H. Fuhrman, pp. 148–69. Chicago: University of Chicago Press, 2001.

Massell, Diane, and Margaret E. Goertz. "District Strategies for Building Instructional Capacity." In *School Districts and Instructional Renewal,* edited by Amy M. Hightower, Michael S. Knapp, Julie A. Marsh, and Milbrey W. McLaughlin, pp. 43–60. New York: Teachers College Press, 2002.

Massell, Diane, Margaret E. Goertz, Gail Christensen, and Matthew Goldwasser. "The Press from Above, the Pull from Below: High School Responses to External Accountability." In *Holding High Hopes: How High Schools Respond to State Accountability Policies,* edited by Bethany Gross and Margaret E. Goertz, pp. 17–41. Philadelphia: University of Pennsylvania, Consortium for Policy Research in Education, 2005.

McMurrer, Jennifer. *Instructional Time in Elementary Schools.* Washington, D.C.: Center on Education Policy, 2008.

National Council of Teachers of Teachers of Mathematics (NCTM). *Curriculum and Evaluation Standards for School Mathematics.* Reston, Va.: NCTM, 1989.

———. *Professional Standards for Teaching Mathematics.* Reston, Va.: NCTM, 1991.

———. *Assessment Standards for School Mathematics.* Reston, Va.: NCTM, 1995.

———. *Principles and Standards for School Mathematics.* Reston, Va.: NCTM, 2000.

———. *Curriculum Focal Points for Prekindergarten through Grade 8 Mathematics: A Quest for Coherence.* Reston, Va.: NCTM, 2006.

Padilla, Christine, Heidi Skolnik, Alejandra Lopez-Torkos, Katrina Woodworth, Andrea Lash, Patrick A. Shields, Katrina Laguarda, and Jane L. David. *Title I Accountability and School Improvement from 2001 to 2004.* Washington, D.C.: U.S. Department of Education, Office of Planning, Evaluation and Policy Development, Policy and Program Studies Service, 2006.

Ravitch, Diane. *National Education Standards in American Education: A Citizen's Guide.* Washington, D.C.: Brookings Institution Press, 1995.

Rose, Lowell C., and Alec M. Gallup. "The 39th Annual Phi Delta Kappan/Gallup Poll of the Public's Attitudes toward the Public Schools." *Phi Delta Kappan* 89 (September 2007): 33–48.

Rothman, Robert. "Benchmarking and Alignment of State Standards and Assessments." In *Redesigning Accountability Systems for Education,* edited by Susan H. Fuhrman and Richard F. Elmore, pp. 96–137. New York: Teachers College Press, 2004.

Schmidt, William H., Curtis McKnight, and Senta Raizen. *A Splintered Vision: An Investigation of U.S. Science and Mathematics Education.* Boston: Kluwer, 1997.

Schoenfeld, Alan. "The Math Wars." *Educational Policy* 18 (January 2004): 253–86.

Shepard, Lorrie A., and Katharine C. Dougherty. *Effects of High-Stakes Testing on Instruction.* Chicago: Spencer Foundation, 1991.

Smith, Marshall S., and Jennifer O'Day. "Systemic School Reform." In *The Politics of Curriculum and Testing,* edited by Susan H. Fuhrman and Betty Malen, pp. 233–67. London: Falmer Press, 1991.

Smith, Mary Lee, Walter Heinecke, and Audrey J. Nobel. "Assessment Policy and Political Spectacle." *Teachers College Record* 101, no. 2 (1999): 157–91.

Stecher, Brian M., Scott Epstein, Laura S. Hamilton, Julie A. Marsh, Abby Robyn, Jennifer Sloan McCombs, Jennifer Russell, and Scott Nafital. *Pain and Gain: Implementing No Child Left Behind in Three States, 2004–2006.* Santa Monica, Calif.: RAND Corporation, 2008.

U.S. Department of Education. *National Assessment of Title 1: Interim Report to Congress.* Washington, D.C.: U.S. Department of Education, Institute of Education Sciences, 2006.

Wilson, Suzanne M. *California Dreaming: Reforming Mathematics Education.* New Haven, Conn.: Yale University Press, 2003.

4

Recommendations for Statistics and Probability in School Mathematics over the Past Century

Dustin Jones
James E. Tarr

DURING the course of the current school year, most students in the United States are likely to have had an opportunity to study topics in statistics or probability, regardless of their grade level. Historically, this has not always been true, because statistics and probability are relatively new to the grades K–12 mathematics curriculum. The first major call for reform in mathematics education in the late nineteenth century, the *Report of the Committee of Ten on Secondary School Studies* (National Education Association 1894), made no mention of statistics or probability. However, beginning in the late 1950s, national organizations began to argue that a stand-alone course should be devoted to statistics and probability in the final year of secondary school. Over time, topics in statistics and probability have expanded into the earlier grades, including elementary and middle school (e.g., National Council of Teachers of Mathematics [NCTM] 1989, 2000).

This article highlights significant recommendations for including statistics and probability in the school mathematics curriculum—the recommendations for what students in prekindergarten through grade 12 should have the opportunity to learn. (The timeline in figure 4.1 depicts several pivotal recommendations.) The history of statistics and probability in the school mathematics curriculum over the past century has been distinct from that of other mathematical content strands, such as arithmetic or algebra. Its progression has been a journey from relative insignificance, reserved for the most able students in high school, to prominence as a fundamental component recommended for all students at all grade levels. After including a brief historical overview of the evolution of statistics and probability in grades K–12 mathematics education, we present a rationale for the increasing presence of statistics and probability in the mathematics curriculum.

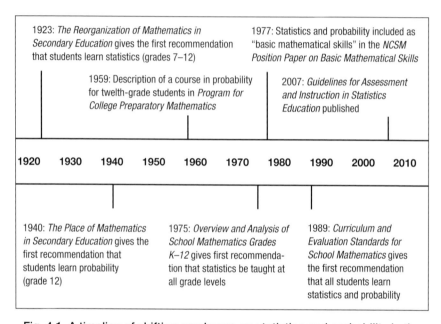

Fig. 4.1. A timeline of shifting emphases on statistics and probability in the grades K–12 school curriculum

Recommendations for Attention to Statistics and Probability in the School Curriculum

Initial Recommendations for Secondary School

In 1923, the National Committee on Mathematical Requirements of the Mathematical Association of America (MAA) made one of the earliest recommendations for including statistics in the school mathematics curriculum in *The Reorganization of Mathematics in Secondary Education*. The report focused on mathematics courses for grades 7–12, and at that time, arithmetic was the major emphasis. The committee asserted that every individual would need a knowledge of additional mathematical topics—as a citizen, in the workplace, and in college. For example, the committee stated that students should learn to create and interpret various types of graphs in grades 7–9. Other elementary statistical concepts, such as measures of central tendency, were recommended components of an elective high school course.

Attention to both statistics and probability were included in *The Place of Mathematics in Secondary Education* (Joint Commission of the MAA and the NCTM 1940). The authors emphasized the growing role of mathematics in daily life and the need for students to learn mathematics needed across different professions. For example, the report recommended that students be able to create and interpret graphical representations of actual data from business, social studies, and science. The recommendations also included proposals for semester-long courses for students in grade 12. Measures of central tendency, measures of variation, and correlation were included in the description of a course on socioeconomic arithmetic. In a proposed college algebra course, the committee mentioned that probability could be included alongside topics from algebra. These recommendations were, on the whole, not implemented as the nation turned its attention toward World War II.

In 1944, NCTM formed the Commission on Post-War Plans, which in turn produced three reports related to the future structure of the secondary mathematics curriculum. The third report, known as the "Guidance Report" (NCTM 1947), targeted high school students and described the mathematics needed for personal use, trained workers, and professional workers. Essentially, the authors sought to answer the question that students often ask: "When will I ever use this?" According to the commission, students needed statistical knowledge for personal use, such as the "intelligent reading of newspapers, magazines, and bulletins" (p. 317). Further, they recommended that trained workers, such as bookkeepers, clerical workers, craftsmen, farmers, and nurses, take a semester-long course in statistics in high school before entering the workforce.

Statistics and Probability for a Wider Audience

In 1959, the College Entrance Examination Board (CEEB) made the first widely accepted recommendation to include probability as a topic for study in school mathematics. The board stated that the theory of probability is "of great importance for our modern technological society" (CEEB 1959, p. 31), citing the increased role of probability in the physical and social sciences and in mathematical applications, as well as the use of statistics in daily life and occupations. Consequently, its recommendation was a semester-long course on probability with statistical applications. Because of the mathematical sophistication of the proposed course, the board advised that it be offered to students in grade 12, and urged teachers to become familiar with the topics outlined.

In the 1960s, the National Science Foundation funded the development of several mathematics curricula, which came to be collectively known as the "new math." In 1975, the Conference Board of the Mathematical Sciences's (CBMS) National Advisory Committee on Mathematical Education (NACOME) evaluated the impact of these curricula. Its report stated that, although materials and courses related to statistics and probability were present, the implementation appeared to fall short of the ideal. The NACOME report recommended that statistics units be taught in all grade levels, stating that these topics were "important in the life of every citizen" (NACOME 1975, p. 45) to critically evaluate such everyday matters as advertisements, public opinion polls, weather reports, and public policy issues. The report endorsed offering a one-semester course in probability for twelfth-grade students who demonstrated the mathematical preparation and desire to do the work required. However, the NACOME report also proposed the creation of a high school course in statistics and probability for students with little or no preparation in algebra. This was a landmark development, moving from endorsing a course for the best and brightest to suggesting a course for *all* students.

As noted elsewhere, the "new math" curriculum materials produced during the 1960s were met with opposition (Kline 1973). A concern emerged from elementary school teachers and the general public that students using these new materials were unable to accurately perform arithmetical computations (Payne 2003). This growing concern blossomed into a full-fledged reactionary movement that focused students on the fundamental, or basic, mathematical skills.

In an effort to define "basic mathematical skills," the National Institute of Education (NIE) organized the Conference on Basic Mathematical Skills and Learning. The report issued from this conference (NIE 1975) stated that the practical uses of statistics and probability (e.g., organizing and interpreting data, understanding and using measures of center, interpreting weather reports, and evaluating gambling scenarios) qualified them as basic mathematical skills. Shortly after this conference, the National Council of Supervisors of Mathematics (NCSM) released the "NCSM Position Paper on Basic Mathematical Skills" (NCSM 1977). This document was influenced by the recommendations of the Conference on Basic Mathematical Skills and Learning, but it was much more widely disseminated. NCSM desired to expand the definition of "basic skills" beyond, yet still including, computation. They included statistics and probability as two areas that were needed in the contemporary technological society. In *An Agenda for Action,* NCTM (1980) stated that knowledge of statistics and probability was "essential to meaningful and productive citizenship, both immediate and future" (p. 5). As an outgrowth of the recommendations by the NCSM and NCTM, the CBMS declared that students in elementary and middle school needed "direct experience with the collection and analysis of data" (1983, p. iv) and called for the existing high school curriculum to be streamlined to make room for the new, fundamental topics of statistics and probability.

Standards for Statistics and Probability across All Grade Levels

Until the late 1980s, probability had been almost exclusively recommended for study in high school. This all changed, however, when NCTM recommended treating statistics and probability as a grades K–12 curriculum strand (NCTM 1989). Specifically, the Council argued that the use of data for prediction and decision making is abundant in a society based on communication and technology, and that students must be prepared to make sense of such data to "enhance [their] social awareness and career opportunities" (p. 167). Furthermore, it contended that statistics and probability was "used to make marketing, research, business, entertainment, and defense decisions, and … to communicate results" (p. 171). It recommended that statistics and probability receive increased attention in each of three grade bands: K–4, 5–8, and 9–12, with the level of sophistication increasing across grade bands.

In the 1990s, NCTM revised and updated its *Curriculum and Evaluation Standards*. The result, *Principles and Standards for School Mathematics* (NCTM 2000), intentionally connected the topics of statistics and probability in the Data Analysis and Probability content strand. In this document, NCTM reasserted that the ability to reason statistically was necessary for "informed citizens and intelligent consumers" (p. 48) faced with the abundance of data available in consumer surveys, polls, and experiments. Furthermore, it argued for the inclusion of statistics and probability in the school mathematics curriculum because those topics involve reasoning that is often counterintuitive and therefore not easily developed without instruction. Compared with the aforementioned documents, *Principles and Standards for School Mathematics* contained the most detailed and coherent set of recommendations for all students.

In recent years, several organizations have argued that to follow the spirit of *Principles and Standards for School Mathematics*, the school mathematics curriculum needs to be reorganized. In *Curriculum Focal Points for Prekindergarten through Grade 8 Mathematics* (NCTM 2006), data analysis and probability are connected with the focal points for seven of the nine grade levels. For grades 6–12, the College Board (2006) listed "data and variation" and "chance, fairness, and risk" as two of eight central mathematical topics to prepare students for "success in college, opportunity in the workplace, and effective participation in civic life" (p. ix).

Most recently, the American Statistical Association (ASA) published *Guidelines for Assessment and Instruction in Statistics Education (GAISE) Report: A Pre-K–12 Curriculum Framework* (Franklin et al. 2007). This document was intended to complement *Principles and Standards for School Mathematics*. The report contains a comprehensive description of various levels of statistical understanding, a framework used to guide the development and assessment of statistics education, and detailed sets of activities illustrating the application of the framework in a classroom setting. The authors asserted, "Every high-school graduate should be able to use sound statistical reasoning to intelligently cope with the requirements of citizenship, employment, and family and to be prepared for a happy, healthy, and productive life" (p. 1). Additionally, because statistical reasoning skills take time to develop, students should have opportunities to reason statistically throughout all grade levels. Further, the authors made a case that statistics is not a subset of mathematics. Instead, they argued that although these are related disciplines, the focus on variability sets statistics apart from mathematics, with some portions of probability used as tools for statistics.

The framework described in the GAISE report includes objectives for the four components of the statistical problem-solving process: formulate questions, collect data, analyze data, and interpret results. For each component, the framework provides three levels of increasing awareness and ability to make the *statistics question distinction,* defined as "a question with an answer based on data that vary versus a question with a deterministic answer" (Franklin et al. 2007, p. 37). Students at the highest level are able to—

> formulate questions that can be answered with data; devise a reasonable plan for collecting appropriate data through observation, sampling, or experimentation; draw conclusions and use data to support these conclusions; and understand the role random variation plays in the inference process. (Franklin et al. 2007, p. 61)

These abilities increase over time by developing proficiency at lower levels of the framework.

Rationale for Studying Statistics and Probability

An examination of the school mathematics curriculum over the past century reveals that its specific composition is dynamic rather than static, because it is responsive to the ever-changing needs of society. The rationale for including particular topics, however, has been remarkably stable. Specifically, three common themes for studying statistics and probability span the reform documents of the past century—citizenship, workplace, and college.

The argument for statistical literacy as a required element for productive *citizenship* is a consistent message made in every document described in this article. Consider the striking similarities of the rationale in the following two passages, written eighty-three years apart:

- "The development of the ability to understand and interpret correctly graphic presentations of various kinds … will also be recognized as one of the necessary aims in the education of every individual. This applies to the representation of statistical data which are becoming increasingly important in the consideration of our daily problems." (National Committee on Mathematics Requirements, MAA 1923, p. 7).

- "The present and emerging uses of statistics and probability in our society have made these fields a part of the 'new basics' for all students. Such knowledge is critical for students' success in quantitatively based college courses, as well as effective participation in civic life" (College Board 2006, p. 16).

Additionally, the prevalence of statistics and probability as essential in the American *workplace* is commonly cited in nearly every set of recommendations, from 1923 to the present. The argument that coursework in probability and statistics prepares students for success in *college* is evident in reform documents of 1923, 1959, and 2006. Despite commonalities in rationale for studying statistics and probability, variations in the scope of study and placement of topics within the school mathematics curriculum are evident across time.

Trends in the Treatment of Statistics and Probability in the Curriculum

Broadly speaking, changes in the role and treatment of statistics and probability are evident across three distinctive eras. First, the period spanning 1923–1959 was one characterized by *limitations* in students' opportunity to study probability and statistics. During this time, statistics was recommended for inclusion in the curriculum but probability was conspicuously absent. The reasons behind excluding probability from the school mathematics curriculum remain unclear; at the time, some mathematical topics were tagged for "decreased emphasis," but probability was simply not listed at all. In comparison, statistics was identified as important content during this era but in a limited capacity. The study of statistics focused almost exclusively on measures of central tendency and the creation and interpretation of data displays, especially tables and graphs. Further limitations resulted from the perception that only advanced students could understand advanced statistical topics.

In the wake of the *Sputnik* launch, reform documents of the 1960s were characterized by calls for a more rigorous school mathematics curriculum. During this era, recommendations called for *earlier* placement of mathematics topics and, for the first time, inclusion of such *advanced topics* as probability. In this second era, spanning 1959–1980, statistics and probability began to emerge as appropriate components of the junior high and even elementary school curriculum, therefore enabling the study of advanced topics in secondary schools. Separate coursework in probability and statistics was recommended as an elective for advanced students in junior high and high school, respectively. However, not until the 1970s was coursework in statistics recommended for *all* high school students instead of only the most able, and did the notion that probability and statistics are essential skills become widely accepted.

During the 1980s, as problem solving became the focus of school mathematics curricula, statistics and probability provided both *relevant problem contexts* and *tools for solving problems*. Reform documents of this era called for school mathematics curricula in which *all* students are afforded opportunities to learn probability and statistics across the grades. Statistics and probability not only began to appear in popular curricular materials (Jones 2004) but also became commonly featured in state curriculum frameworks, beginning as early as kindergarten. Moreover, high-stakes tests have reflected the prevalence of statistics and probability in the school mathematics curriculum. In fact, these topics now comprise 10, 15, and 25 percent of the 2009 National Assessment of Educational Progress in grades 4, 8, and 12, respectively (National Assessment Governing Board 2008).

Essential Content in School Mathematics

The rise of statistics and probability from obscurity to prominence in school mathematics is truly remarkable. In the Curriculum Principle, NCTM (2000, p. 14) states, "A curriculum is more than a collection of activities: it must be coherent, focused on important mathematics, and well articulated across the grades." Statistics and probability are indeed essential elements of the integrated whole, and *Curriculum Focal Points* (NCTM 2006) provides numerous examples of how such content connects with related mathematics topics in the school mathematics curriculum.

Cobb and Moore (1997, p. 801) argue that "the need for [statistics] arises from the *omnipresence of variability*," and so it follows that the study of statistics be structured around this important principle. The important content in statistics can be organized around the components of statistical problem solving, which are each related to variability. Probability topics span the entire statistical problem-solving process.

1. *Formulate questions.* ASA recommends students begin to *anticipate variability* as a foundation on which to formulate statistics questions. For example, children might ponder, "How does sunlight affect the

growth of a plant?" and anticipate that this question necessitates the collection of data that vary.

2. *Collect data.* Data collection designs should *acknowledge variability*, and students should determine how data could be collected to provide answers. Random sampling can reduce the differences between sample and population, and larger samples typically offer less variability.

3. *Analyze data.* Students should come to learn that the primary purpose of statistical analysis is to give an *accounting of variability* in the data. Distributions of data can be represented in a variety of graphical displays (e.g., line plots, box plots, or histograms). Numerical summaries can describe characteristics of the distribution. When examining the center and spread of a distribution, students might use the mode and range, the median and interquartile range, or the mean and standard deviation, depending on grade level.

4. *Interpret data.* Statistical interpretations are made in the presence of *allowing for variability*. Children might argue that results of their class survey are likely to be different from results for a different class, middle school students might argue why the median is a more appropriate measure of center than mean, and high school students might learn that the results of an election poll should be interpreted as an estimate that is likely to vary from one sample to the next.

5. *Probability.* Given the omnipresence of variability, probability should be considered an essential tool for statistics that serves to quantify uncertainty. Children can learn that probability can be used to predict what is likely to happen in the long run, middle school students can develop the concept of independence, and high school students can realize that predictions based on data involve some degree of error.

Rather than pigeonhole these five components into particular grades or grade bands, these processes should be interwoven throughout the school mathematics curriculum, in increasing depth through the years, with the development of statistical literacy as the ultimate goal.

Looking Back and Looking Forward

Over the past century, statistics and probability have moved from relative obscurity in the mathematics curriculum to important, fundamental topics that should be studied by all students at each grade level. The importance of statistical literacy has been emphasized and reemphasized in documents dating back several decades, especially following World War II. Nevertheless, evidence shows that classroom implementation has lagged behind these recommendations

(Jones, Langrall, and Mooney 2007). One possible explanation is the underpreparation of teachers to teach statistics. The disciplines of statistics and mathematics, although related, are different, requiring different ways of thinking. Although mathematical knowledge may be necessary to learn and teach statistics, it is not sufficient. Despite the emergence of probability and statistics in the modern school mathematics curriculum, many teachers may not be affording students opportunities to learn because, ironically, "many prospective teachers have not encountered the fundamental ideas of modern statistics in their own K–12 mathematics courses" (CBMS 2001, p. 114). To break from this cycle, we must devote more effort to the statistical education of teachers if we wish to increase students' knowledge and understanding of statistics and probability.

As we look to the future, statistics and probability are likely to continue to play an important role in the mathematics curriculum for all grade levels. They are widely recognized as important topics for students to study and learn. Research confirms that young children are able to understand topics within the strands of probability and statistics, although understanding develops gradually. In addition, statistics and probability naturally connect with other important areas of the school mathematics curriculum, such as counting, measurement, rational number, and algebra.

A century ago, we heard a recurring debate whether geometry should be included in the school mathematics curriculum. Today, all students at every grade level study geometry. Over the next few decades, we hope to see statistics and probability take a similar place as a staple in the school mathematics curriculum enacted by teachers.

REFERENCES

Cobb, George W., and David S. Moore. "Mathematics, Statistics, and Teaching." *American Mathematical Monthly* 104 (November 1997): 801–23.

College Board. *College Board Standards for College Success: Mathematics and Statistics.* New York: College Board, 2006.

College Entrance Examination Board (CEEB). *Program for College Preparatory Mathematics.* New York: CEEB, 1959.

Conference Board of the Mathematical Sciences (CBMS). *The Mathematical Sciences Curriculum K–12: What Is Still Fundamental and What Is Not.* Washington, D.C.: CBMS, 1983.

_____. *The Mathematical Education of Teachers.* Providence, R.I.: American Mathematical Society, 2001.

Franklin, Christine, Gary Kader, Denise Mewborn, Jerry Moreno, Roxy Peck, Mike Perry, and Richard Scheaffer. *Guidelines for Assessment and Instruction in Statistics Education (GAISE) Report: A Pre-K–12 Curriculum Framework.* Alexandria, Va.: American Statistical Association, 2007.

Joint Commission of the Mathematical Association of America and the National Council of Teachers of Mathematics (NCTM). *The Place of Mathematics in Secondary Education*, Fifteenth Yearbook of the NCTM. New York: Bureau of Publications, Teachers College, Columbia University, 1940.

Jones, Dustin. "Probability in Middle Grades Mathematics Textbooks: An Examination of Historical Trends, 1957–2004." Ph.D. diss., University of Missouri, 2004.

Jones, Graham A., Cynthia W. Langrall, and Edward S. Mooney. "Research in Probability: Responding to Classroom Realities." In *Second Handbook of Research on Mathematics Teaching and Learning,* edited by Frank K. Lester, Jr., pp. 909–55. Charlotte, N.C.: Information Age Publishing, 2007.

Kline, Morris. *Why Johnny Can't Add: The Failure of the New Math*. New York: St. Martin's Press, 1973.

National Advisory Committee on Mathematical Education (NACOME). *Overview and Analysis of School Mathematics Grades K–12*. Reston, Va.: NCTM, 1975.

National Assessment Governing Board. *Mathematics Framework for the 2009 National Assessment of Educational Progress*. Washington, D.C.: United States Government Printing Office, 2008.

National Committee on Mathematical Requirements, Mathematical Association of America (MAA). *The Reorganization of Mathematics in Secondary Education*. Washington, D.C.: MAA, 1923.

National Council of Supervisors of Mathematics (NCSM). "NCSM Position Paper on Basic Mathematical Skills." NCSM, 1977. http://www.ncsmonline.org/docs/PositionPapers/NCSMPositionPaper01_1977.pdf, November 29, 2007.

National Council of Teachers of Mathematics (NCTM). "Guidance Report of the Commission on Post-War Plans." *Mathematics Teacher* 40 (November 1947): 315–49.

_____. *An Agenda for Action: Recommendations for School Mathematics of the 1980s*. Reston, Va.: NCTM, 1980.

_____. *Curriculum and Evaluation Standards for School Mathematics*. Reston, Va.: NCTM, 1989.

_____. *Principles and Standards for School Mathematics*. Reston, Va.: NCTM, 2000.

_____. *Curriculum Focal Points for Prekindergarten through Grade 8 Mathematics: A Quest for Coherence*. Reston, Va.: NCTM, 2006.

National Education Association (NEA). *Report of the Committee of Ten on Secondary School Studies*. New York: American Book Co., 1894.

National Institute of Education (NIE). *The NIE Conference on Basic Mathematical Skills and Learning: Volume II: Reports from the Working Groups*. Washington, D.C.: NIE, 1975.

Payne, Joseph N. "The New Math and Its Aftermath, Grades K–8." In *A History of School Mathematics*, edited by George M. A. Stanic and Jeremy Kilpatrick, pp. 559–98. Reston, Va.: NCTM, 2003.

5

Reflections on Five Decades of Curriculum Controversies

Stephen Willoughby

MANY controversies in mathematics education that make news today have existed for centuries. Some seem to be continuously discussed, whereas others come and go, often in different forms and with different labels. Because of the importance of education, particular perspectives and those advocating those perspectives have been the subject of criticism. I have witnessed many of the controversies and felt much of the criticism since 1954, when I began teaching[1]. In this article, I reflect on three central, sometimes controversial, issues that impinge on curriculum: differences in philosophical orientations toward learning and teaching mathematics; the influence of textbook publishing, marketing, and selection; and the influence of standards and other state and federal dictums.

The Impact of Differing Views of Teaching and Learning on Curriculum

The Latin word *curriculum* translates to English as *race* or *race track*, reminding us of the teachers and students who believe that "covering the material" as quickly as possible is the goal of schools. Others believe—like Lao-Tse, the founder of Taoism—that reaching the goal is not as significant as appreciating

---

1. The author has been a grades K–12 teacher, college professor, textbook editor, and textbook author. He served as president of NCTM from 1982 to 1983. During his career, he was an observer and an active advocate in many of the controversies.

textbooks until good ones that are available are adopted. Publishers are inclined to follow the model of the currently popular textbook series so teachers will choose them and feel comfortable using them.

Careful evaluation, preferably including piloting any new program, would help evaluators decide whether it really is an improvement (see National Council of Teachers of Mathematics [NCTM] 1984). The primary person here is the teacher. If teachers continue learning throughout their lives, from professional meetings, from trying new procedures, from in-service and summer institutes, and so on, they will be better prepared to use new and better materials. Government agencies could help, without interfering in local autonomy, by supporting many more summer and academic-year programs for continuing teachers' education.

Recommendations of major education organizations have historically had more influence on marketing by commercial publishers than on the published textbooks themselves. In 1959, I worked as an editor for a major publisher. A new edition of its first-year algebra book had recently been published. The College Entrance Examination Board (CEEB) Commission on Mathematics (1959) was about to issue its influential recommendations three months later than originally promised. Two questions I was asked in my first month with the publisher are pertinent.

First, a customer asked me why the commutative and associative laws of the algebra 1 textbook were on page 16 and the distributive law did not appear until page 112. I asked the principal author. He responded that those were the first two pages from which they could delete material to make sufficient space for CEEB recommendations. The rationale had nothing to do with an intellectual matter. The first two laws were unused in the intervening 96 pages, and none had any significant impact on the rest of the curriculum. The words were needed so that marketing could say, "We satisfy the CEEB Commission's recommendations."

Second, a representative of the CEEB Commission asked me how our ad could claim we satisfied the Commission's recommendations when the report had not yet been published. I, of course, had nothing to do with the ad, and the best I could do was say that on the basis of preliminary reports, the publisher thought we would satisfy them. The publisher had thought the report would be published before the ad. I asked the CEEB representative why the report wasn't published when it was scheduled. There had been a glitch. An editor had decided the term "real number" was used too often and had randomly changed about half the instances to "actual number." Correcting this editorial misconception without computers took time. In fact, the CEEB recommendations were "satisfied" in the algebra 1 textbook in only the most superficial way with the insertion of sanc-tioned words and no modification of pedagogy or mathematics.

At the 2000 NCTM Annual Meeting, where *Principles and Standards for School Mathematics* (NCTM 2000) was first made available, I stopped by the booth of the same publisher and asked the representative why his grades K–6 series of books was good. He responded, "We satisfy all of the recommendations of the new *Principles and Standards*." *Principles and Standards* had been available for only about two hours, although a draft document had been circulated widely for review. In my opinion, commercial publishers of textbooks treated most major educational reports during the twentieth century (and there were many) much the same way. That is, publishers kept the textbooks as familiar as possible to teachers and remarkably similar to previous, financially successful, textbooks while inserting important phrases from the recommendations into sales materials and superficially into the textbooks. Few improvements were made.

This phenomenon is not new. Only fourteen years after Colburn published his very popular textbooks, Roswell O. Smith (1835) published an arithmetic textbook in which he said (p. iii), "The Pestalozzian professes to unite a complete system of Mental with Written Arithmetic. So does this." He continued to explain why his books do everything the "Pestalozzian" (that is, Colburn) does and why they do them better.

Between 1966 and 1972, I was offered a senior authorship of eight different projected elementary school textbook series on the condition that I would not actually write the books or insist on particular innovations I thought would be effective. In 1972, I found a small publisher in rural Illinois who worked with me for thirteen years as I, with my coauthors, wrote and longitudinally field-tested a grades K–8 program, *Real Math* (Willoughby et al. 1973). An independent study (Dilworth and Warren 1980) showed that *Real Math* was highly successful with students. *Real Math* also generated enthusiasm for mathematics among both students and teachers. Some big publishers copied superficial features of the program, claiming they did the same thing, only better.

Some years later, the small publisher sold its two textbook programs to a large school textbook publisher that previously had been unwilling to do anything so innovative. The large publisher promptly began adding "features" and other material to the program that more than doubled the size of the teachers' edition and substantially increased the size of the students' books. Not all the new features were bad, and very little of the excellent material in the old curriculum had been deleted, but so much new material was included that teachers and students were challenged to find and use much of it.

The Influence of State Curriculum Standards

In 1981, as the new president-elect of NCTM, I proposed that the Council develop a set of standards for mathematics education. This suggestion was a reaction to the many "back to basics" textbooks that were common and that failed to teach higher-order-thinking skills or foster a positive attitude toward learning and using mathematics. "Back-to-basics" programs had been a reaction to what many people thought was an overemphasis on the abstract logic and useless formalism of many of the "new math" programs. The proposed standards seemed reasonable because several new and different curriculum programs had been developed by 1981. These programs (e.g., Wirtz 1974; Baratta-Lorton 1976; Willoughby et al. 1973) were showing success in developing higher-order-thinking skills as well as traditional basic skills and were generating positive student attitudes toward mathematics.

In 1981, NCTM had been losing both money and members at a frighteningly increasing rate for several years, and the Board of Directors chose to postpone consideration of the proposed standards until the financial future of the Council was more assured. The Council did, however, support the development of a short, excellent set of standards for the selection and implementation of instructional materials (NCTM 1984). Several years later, NCTM published *Curriculum and Evaluation Standards for School Mathematics* (NCTM 1989), which had a substantial, but not altogether expected or positive, influence on the mathematics curriculum. Some people misinterpreted the standards to mean that students no longer should learn many of the traditional basic skills. A second unexpected development was the move by numerous states to develop their own sets of standards that, in many instances, spelled out the curriculum for every grade in extreme detail. No two states had identical standards, nor were the standards of any state the same as the NCTM *Standards* (Reys 2006).

The importance of traditional basic skills has been reconfirmed by representatives of NCTM in both *Principles and Standards for School Mathematics* (2000) and *Curriculum Focal Points for Prekindergarten through Grade 8 Mathematics* (2006). The variation in state standards that has produced large, incoherent textbooks, however, has not been resolved. Leaders in each state are charged with the task of specifying content and performance standards and generally choose to do this work independently from other states. Although some publishers have begun to customize textbooks for some states, such as California and Texas, I believe that differing expectations across states reduces the likelihood of innovative textbook development. *Curriculum Focal Points* was published in the hope of reducing the diversity of standards, although whether the identified focal points will be adopted by states or whether doing so will contribute to more uniformity across state standards remain unclear.

With pressure to align textbooks to state and national standards, publishers are indeed faced with a difficult challenge—either to customize textbooks or to include many additional topics within a textbook series. Given the cost of customization, the textbooks available to teachers and schools in all but the largest states overburden teachers and students both physically and intellectually without improving education.

Conclusions and Speculations

Teaching has been recognized as one of the most important occupations. It has also been one of the most widely criticized occupations throughout history. Almost everybody believes education is important, and almost everybody thinks they know what is wrong with education and how to improve it.

Curriculum changes have increased the quantity and sophistication of mathematics to be learned at a given age as society has become more quantitative and technologically dependent. Although average citizens are not likely to be involved in the creation of new science and technology, they do make financial, social, and political decisions on the basis of quantitative data. The ability to understand and use such data, no matter how they are presented, is essential to making intelligent decisions.

People are more likely to continue learning and using mathematics if they learn it with understanding and see its beauty and the possibility of applying it to matters that interest them, including games as well as more practical matters. Skill with the traditional basics is important to facilitate creative thinking about complex questions. However, skill alone is unlikely to prepare students for their future.

Even if the traditional basic skills and higher-order-thinking skills are acquired, students who have learned to dislike mathematics while acquiring those skills will likely not use or continue learning them. Those who have learned with understanding are more likely to remember the skills, to apply them efficiently, and to be able to rediscover skills they may forget. They will be able to transfer their knowledge to new problems in the future and figure out mathematics for new situations.

Demand for people who can do jobs that involve thinking, understanding, and creativity will increase for the foreseeable future. Intelligent citizenship requires informed reflection. Surely mathematics education must include both the traditional basic skills and the higher-order-thinking skills of problem recognition, formulation, and solving, as well as the ability to communicate effectively. Many politicians and representatives of the mass media seem to believe the teacher's job is to train and test so that students become very good at doing what a five-dollar calculator can do better. Calls for more-rigorous quantitative research will achieve nothing until we decide what we value (Hiebert 1999).

Curriculum materials and standardized tests that cater to the lowest levels of human thought are easy to write and sell; to teach from such textbooks and prepare for such tests are also relatively easy to do. But to prepare people to function in a global economy and preserve our way of government, I believe that mathematics teaching must place more emphasis on thinking and appreciation for the subject. To accomplish this goal, curriculum materials must become more challenging, more enjoyable, and more closely related to the learner's world.

REFERENCES

Baratta-Lorton, Mary. *Mathematics Their Way.* Menlo Park, Calif.: Addison-Wesley Publishing Co., 1976.

Colburn, Warren. *Intellectual Arithmetic upon the Induction Method of Instruction*, rev. ed. Boston and Cambridge, Mass.: Houghton Mifflin Co. and Riverside Press, 1821.

College Entrance Examination Board. *Report of the Commission on Mathematics of the College Entrance Examination Board: Program for College Preparatory Mathematics.* Princeton, N.J.: Educational Testing Service, 1959.

Dilworth, Robert P., and Leonard M. Warren. *An Independent Investigation of Real Math: The Field-Testing and Learner-Verification Studies.* La Salle, Ill.: Open Court Publishing Co., 1980.

Hiebert, James. "Relationships between Research and the NCTM Standards." *Journal for Research in Mathematics Education* 30, no. 1 (1999): 3–19.

Jowett, Benjamin, trans. *Plato's The Republic, Book VII.* New York: Heritage Press, 1944.

Judd, Charles. "The Relation of Special Training to General Intelligence." *Educational Review* 36 (1908): 28–42.

Kilpatrick, Jeremy, Jane Swafford, and Bradford Findell. *Adding it Up: Helping Children Learn Mathematics.* Washington, D.C.: National Research Council, 2001.

National Council of Teachers of Mathematics (NCTM). *Professional Standards for Selection and Implementation of Instructional Material.* Reston, Va.: NCTM, 1984.

———. *Curriculum and Evaluation Standards for School Mathematics.* Reston, Va.: NCTM, 1989.

———. *Principles and Standards for School Mathematics.* Reston, Va.: National Council of Teachers of Mathematics, 2000.

———. *Curriculum Focal Points for Prekindergarten through Grade 8 Mathematics: A Quest for Coherence.* Reston, Va.: National Council of Teachers of Mathematics, 2006.

Reys, Barbara J., ed. *The Intended Mathematics Curriculum as Represented in State-Level Curriculum Standards: Consensus or Confusion?* Greenwich, Conn.: Information Age Publishing, 2006.

Smith, Roswell O. *Practical and Mental Arithmetic.* New York: Paine and Burgess, 1835.

Stein, Mary Kay, Margaret S. Smith, and Janine Remillard. "How Curriculum Influences Student Learning." In *Second Handbook of Research on Mathematics Teaching and Learning,* edited by Frank K. Lester, pp. 319–70. Greenwich, Conn.: Information Age Publishing, 2007.

Thorndike, Edward L., and Robert S. Woodworth. "The Influence of Improvement in One Mental Function upon the Efficiency of Other Functions, Part 1." *Psychological Review* 8 (1901a): 247–61.

———. "The Influence of Improvement in One Mental Function upon the Efficiency of Other Functions, Part 2: The Estimation of Magnitudes." *Psychological Review* 8 (1901b): 384–95.

———. "The Influence of Improvement in One Mental Function upon the Efficiency of Other Functions, Part 3: Functions Involving Attention, Observation, and Discrimination." *Psychological Review* 8 (1901c): 553–64.

Willoughby, Stephen S., Carl Bereiter, Peter Hilton, and Joseph H. Rubinstein. *Real Math.* LaSalle, Ill.: Open Court Publishing Co., 1973.

Whitehead, Alfred North. *The Aims of Education*, New York: Free Press, 1967.

Wirtz, Robert W. *Mathematics for Everyone*. Washington, D.C.: Curriculum Development Associates, 1974.

ADDITIONAL READING

Jones, Philip S., ed. *A History of Mathematics Education in the United States and Canada*. Thirty-second Yearbook of the National Council of Teachers of Mathematics (NCTM). Washington D.C.: NCTM, 1970.

Young, Jacob William Albert. *The Teaching of Mathematics in the Elementary and Secondary School*. New York: Longmans, Green, & Co., 1906.

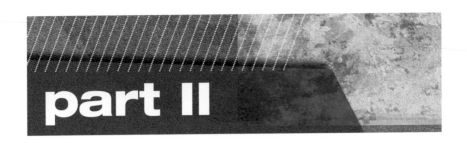

part II

The Intended Curriculum

What We Teach Is What Students Learn: Evidence from National Assessment

Peter Kloosterman
Crystal Walcott

MATHEMATICS curricula in the United States have experienced several shifts in content emphasis over the past one hundred years. Early in the twentieth century, instruction focused on drill and practice, emphasizing rote memorization and procedural understanding. Midway through the century, curricula began to focus on meaningful mathematics, eventually leading students to investigating the underlying structure of the discipline. The back-to-basics movement of the late 1970s and early 1980s pushed curricula back toward procedures and skills until publication of *Curriculum and Evaluation Standards for School Mathematics* (NCTM 1989) moved the pendulum toward problem solving and conceptual understanding (Lambdin and Walcott 2007). The focus of this article is the extent to which these shifts in curricular emphasis, especially shifts resulting from those *Standards,* are connected to what students learn as measured by the National Assessment of Educational Progress (NAEP).

The National Assessment of Educational Progress

Conceptualized in the 1960s as a tool for assessing what students across the United States are learning in school, the first mathematics NAEP took place in

1973, with additional assessments taking place at two- to five-year intervals. In contrast with such assessments as the SAT that are taken only by college-bound students, NAEP results are based on a representative sample of all students regardless of ability or aspiration. NAEP questions are created using a framework developed by the National Assessment Governing Board, and many questions are used for multiple years, making it possible to look at changes in students' performance over time. No Child Left Behind (NCLB) requires that NAEP be used as an independent measure of performance by state, and thus developers of state standards often pay attention to the NAEP framework. In brief, NAEP is the most respected indicator of students' performance in the United States (Kloosterman 2004). The primary message of this article is that NAEP provides strong evidence that changes in curricula, including changes based on the NCTM *Standards* publications, have had a substantial impact on what students learn[1].

Although NAEP was originally conceived as a single assessment, it has evolved into two separate assessment programs in mathematics. The original NAEP program, now referred to as the Long-Term Trend assessment (LTT), assesses students at ages nine, thirteen, and seventeen. For every assessment from 1982 to 2004, LTT NAEP used identical items and procedures and thus documented changes in students' mathematics skills over that period. The major limitation of LTT NAEP is that because it is based on the curriculum of the 1970s, it includes a relatively small number of items that assess the topics that have received increased attention since that time.

NAEP results are reported through scale scores ranging from 0 to 500. The meaning of a score is consistent across grades and from one administration to the next (e.g., a nine-year-old who scored 250 in 1990 would know as much mathematics as a 13-year-old in who scored 250 in 2000). Between the first assessment in 1973 and the LTT assessment in 2004, scores for nine-year-olds increased from 219 to 241 and scores for thirteen-year-olds increased from 266 to 281. As we describe subsequently in this article, these gains are substantial and show that nine- and thirteen-year-old students today know more mathematics than their counterparts in 1973 (Kloosterman, Rutledge, and Kenney 2009a, 2009b; Kloosterman and Walcott 2007).

In contrast with the performance of nine- and thirteen-year-old students, the performance of seventeen-year-old students has remained relatively stable, with scores increasing from 304 in 1973 to 307 in 2004. A six-point drop occurred in the scores of seventeen-year-olds between 1973 and 1982, and although some gain has been made by this age group since 1982, it is still minimal in relation

---

1. Because NAEP is not an experimental research program, NAEP data cannot be used to "prove" a connection between curriculum and students' achievement. Thus, readers should keep in mind that NAEP supports rather than proves a connection between the curriculum studied and students' achievement.

to gains by younger students. One mitigating factor is that LTT test items for seventeen-year-olds are predominantly based on middle school mathematics. In fact, very little on the assessment for seventeen-year-olds goes beyond beginning concepts of algebra and geometry (Rutledge, Kloosterman, and Kenney 2009). Thus, gains in the more advanced skills taught in upper-level high school courses may not be measured by LTT NAEP.

The second NAEP program, which is now the primary NAEP program, began for mathematics in 1990 and is usually referred to as Main NAEP. This program spun off from the original NAEP and differs from the original in three important ways. First, most of the administrations of Main NAEP have included new items to measure content that has been added to the curriculum over time. Second, schools can more easily test intact classes of students rather than only students of certain ages. Main NAEP samples students in grades 4, 8, and 12 rather than at ages nine, thirteen, and seventeen. Third, Main NAEP provides results by state as well as for the nation as whole. From 1992 to 2000 state participation in NAEP was voluntary, but the NCLB legislation required participation of all states in mathematics NAEPs starting in 2003. Although some items in Main NAEP do change over time, the majority of them are used on multiple administrations. Thus, like LTT NAEP, it is a trustworthy indicator of change in students' performance over time.

Main NAEP Results

Overall results on Main NAEP (fig. 6.1) parallel those of LTT NAEP in that substantial gains have been made at grades 4 and 8, but little change has occured at grade 12[2]. Although no grade-level equivalent exists for NAEP results, Kloosterman and Walcott (2007) argue that approximately two grade levels of gain occurred between 1990 and 2003 at grades 4 and 8. These gains, like those on LTT, are substantial and suggest that changes in curriculum and instruction at these levels have had a significant impact on achievement. A modest increase was seen in grade 12 performance between 1990 and 2000, although the average score in 2000 was lower than it had been in 1996. Main NAEP was not administered at grade 12 in 2003; the scaling system for grade 12 was changed with the 2005 administration, making it impossible to compare the 2005 results with those of previous years. Although a larger number of complex grade 12 items are included by Main NAEP than for age seventeen by LTT NAEP, many Main

---

2. Prior to 1996, students with disabilities or limited proficiency in English either took the mathematics NAEP under the same conditions as all other students or did not take NAEP at all. Since 1996, accommodations have been provided for these students. This change in administrative procedures had minimal affect on scores, but readers should be aware that the population of students taking Main NAEP in 1990 and 1992 was slightly different from those taking Main NAEP since 1996 (see Kloosterman and Walcott [2007]).

NAEP items are still based on middle school mathematics. Should a higher percent of grade 12 Main NAEP items reflect high school mathematics in the future, the resulting scores at this level will be interesting to observe.

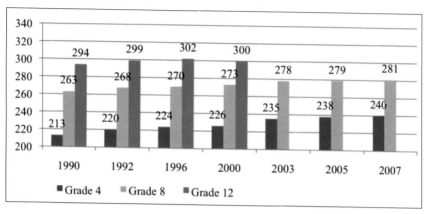

Fig. 6.1. Main NAEP average scale scores, 1990–2007

Changes in Content Emphases in Grades 4 and 8

In addition to collecting achievement data, the NAEP provides demographic data obtained from student, teacher, and school background questionnaires. As part of the 1996, 2000, and 2003 mathematics assessments, fourth- and eighth-grade teachers were asked to report the curricular emphasis given to each of the five Main NAEP content strands (number and operations, measurement, geometry, data analysis, and algebra) in their respective classrooms[3]. The possible responses were "heavy," "moderate," and "little/no." The percent of students who had teachers answering in each category is given in table 6.1.

These data shed light on classroom teachers' perceptions of changes in their instruction. Even though number and operations content continues to receive the highest percent of "heavy emphasis" in the fourth- and eighth-grade classrooms, the percent of fourth-grade students whose teachers claim giving "heavy emphasis" and "moderate emphasis" to geometry, data analysis, and algebra content has grown over the years surveyed. Likewise in grade 8, well over half the teachers surveyed claimed to give heavy emphasis to algebra content.

The evidence implies that changes in curricula recommended in the NCTM *Standards* (1989, 2000) are affecting classroom teaching. Just as suggested by NCTM, the overwhelming majority of teachers surveyed by NAEP report heavy

---

3. In 2003, the eighth-grade assessment did not include this questionnaire item.

Table 6.1
Percentage of 4ᵗʰ and 8ᵗʰ grade students whose teachers report heavy, moderate, or little/no curricular emphasis in the content of the five strands assessed by NAEP

	Heavy Emphasis		Moderate Emphasis		Little/No Emphasis	
Number and Operations	4th	8th	4th	8th	4th	8th
1996	91	83	7	9	<1	2
2000	83	64	13	22	<1	3
2003	84	n.a.	11	n.a.	<1	n.a.
Measurement						
1996	20	16	62	56	16	22
2000	24	17	68	56	3	16
2003	23	n.a.	66	n.a.	5	n.a.
Geometry						
1996	10	22	53	49	33	21
2000	20	23	67	55	7	10
2003	22	n.a.	66	n.a.	6	n.a.
Data Analysis						
1996	8	14	39	44	41	30
2000	18	19	58	56	19	14
2003	23	n.a.	60	n.a.	12	n.a.
Algebra						
1996	7	55	30	29	40	9
2000	16	58	53	29	26	3
2003	25	n.a.	54	n.a.	15	n.a.

emphasis on number and operations content. In addition, fourth-grade teachers' perception of the curricular emphasis placed on algebra content has grown over the three years surveyed and remains consistently high in grade 8. By 2000, only 14 percent of the eighth-grade teachers reported "little/no" emphasis on data analysis content.

Changes by Content Area: Grade 4

Figure 6.2 shows performance in each of the five NAEP content areas for students in grade 4. Scale scores for content areas do not depict strength in one content area as compared with another, which means, for example, that analysts cannot appropriately say that students were best in measurement (score of 218) in 1990 or best in algebra and functions (score of 243) in 2005. The scale scores, however, are reasonable indicators of change in performance over time. As figure 6.2 shows, the greatest gain from the period 1990 to 2007 for grade 4 students was in the area of algebra and functions. At grade 4, algebra and functions items involve patterns and other types of algebraic thinking rather than traditional eighth- or ninth-grade algebra topics (e.g., equation solving). Prior to the publication of *Curriculum and Evaluation Standards* (NCTM 1989), little if any coverage of algebraic thinking was included in the elementary school curriculum; thus, we can reasonably assume that the increased emphasis on problem solving and algebraic thinking in the 1990s had substantial impact on the large achievement gains in the algebra and functions content strand.

Figure 6.3 provides an example of one of the algebraic thinking problems used on Main NAEP from 1990 to 2003. As with about one-third of the algebra strand items used at grade 4 in 2003, this item involves a pattern. In 1990, 34 percent of students correctly solved this problem[4]. This increased to 40 percent in 1992, 47 percent in 1996, and 55 percent in 2000 but then dropped to 52 percent in 2003. This item was also given at grade 8, where the percent correct increased from 50 percent in 1990 to 65 percent in 2003. Although these increases may not seem that great, they are substantially more than the increases on most other items. The fact that more fourth-grade students correctly answered the question in 2003 than eighth-grade students in 1990 is evidence of both the significance of the increase over time and of the fact that not a lot of emphasis was placed on patterns at the middle school level in 1990.

The second highest area of gain in grade 4 was number sense, properties, and operations[5], increasing 28 points from 1990 to 2007. The items in this content strand focus on understanding of, and computation with, whole numbers, fractions, and decimals and by the upper grades include integers and real numbers. Ratios, percents, and estimation are also assessed. Figure 6.4 gives an example of an item that assessed understanding of decimal values on a number line. In 1992, 39 percent of grade 4 students correctly answered the problem. That rose to 41 percent in 1996, 51 percent in 2000, and 56 percent in 2005. NCTM's *Curriculum and Evaluation Standards* (1989) argued for introduction of decimal concepts in grades K–4, and the dramatic increase in performance on this item is likely connected to this call for early study of decimals.

---

4. To assess students' performance on a broad range of mathematics topics, Main NAEP used 181 grade 4 items and 197 grade 8 items in 2003. Each student completed only 15 to 30 of those items, and thus percent correct on an item is based on those students who were asked to complete that item.

5. Not enough items were included in the data analysis, statistics, and probability strand in 1990 to calculate a scale score. As figure 6.2 shows, more gain was made in this area than in number and operations between 1992 and 2007.

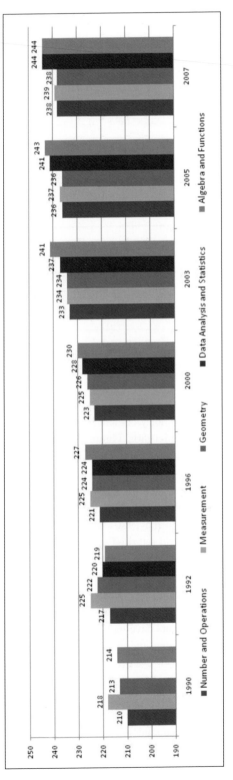

Fig. 6.2. Grade 4 average scale score by content strand

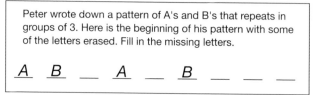

Fig. 6.3. Pattern problem used for grade 4 and grade 8

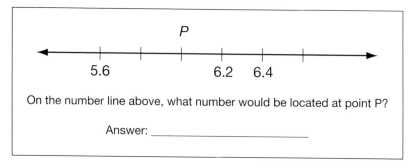

Figure 6.4. Number sense, properties, and operations item
used for grade 4 and grade 8

Those who have been teaching at the elementary school level for a number of years may recall that very little geometry content beyond shape recognition was included at that level prior to the mid-1980s. Figure 6.5 is an example of a Long-Term Trend NAEP geometry problem given to nine-year olds from 1982 to 2004. Twenty-five percent of students correctly found the perimeter of the rectangle in 1982, and that dropped to 19 percent in 1986. Because this was a multiple-choice item, 25 percent of students should have responded correctly just by guessing; thus it appears very few students in the 1980s were experienced in computing perimeters. By 1990, the percent had returned to 25 percent; it increased to 29 percent in 1994, 35 percent in 1999, and 51 percent in 2004. The growth on this item indicates that many nine-year-old students are now experienced in finding perimeters. As an aside, it is interesting to note that the most common incorrect response, selected by 29 percent of students in 2004, was option A (13 meters). In most instances, nine-year-old students have had little if any classroom exposure to problems involving area calculations, and this is evident in the fact that only 14 percent selected option C (40 meters). The growth pattern on this item is similar to the growth pattern for geometry on Main NAEP (fig. 6.2). The results for this item, therefore, as for the geometry strand in general, give evidence that changes in curriculum, including those advocated in the NCTM *Standards* documents (1989, 2000), are closely tied to what students learn.

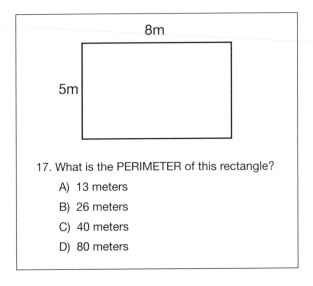

17. What is the PERIMETER of this rectangle?

    A) 13 meters

    B) 26 meters

    C) 40 meters

    D) 80 meters

Fig. 6.5. LTT perimeter item administered to nine-year-olds

Changes by Content Area: Grade 8

Figure 6.6 shows changes in scale score by content area for students in grade 8. As can be seen in figure 6.6, the largest gain between 1990 and 2007 for any content area was the same as that for grade 4, algebra and functions. The scale score for this area increased from 261 to 285. Figure 6.7 contains an algebra and functions item that was used from 1990 to 2003 at grades 4, 8, and 12. Like many items in the algebra and functions strand at grade 8, this item assesses what would often be considered a prealgebra rather than a true algebra skill. Performance on the item rose more on this item than most grade 8 items, with 56 percent of students answering the item correctly in 1990 and 63 percent of students answering it correctly in 2003. The item was clearly very difficult for fourth graders. Although one would expect 25 percent to answer the item correctly by just guessing, performance ranged from 17 percent correct in 1990 to 24 percent correct in 2003. Grade 12 students had little problem with the item, with 78 percent to 80 percent responding correctly each time it was administered.

The area with the next highest gain for grade 8 students, 22 points from 1990 to 2007, was data analysis, statistics, and probability. Figure 6.8 shows a Main NAEP item that was used at grades 8 and 12 from 1990 to 2003. This item had one of the most dramatic gains of any on the NAEP, with 20 percent of eighth graders answering the item correctly in 1990, 23 percent in 1992, 32 percent in 1996, 46 percent in 2000, and 57 percent in 2003. Although finding a mean has been common in textbooks for a number of years, few middle school

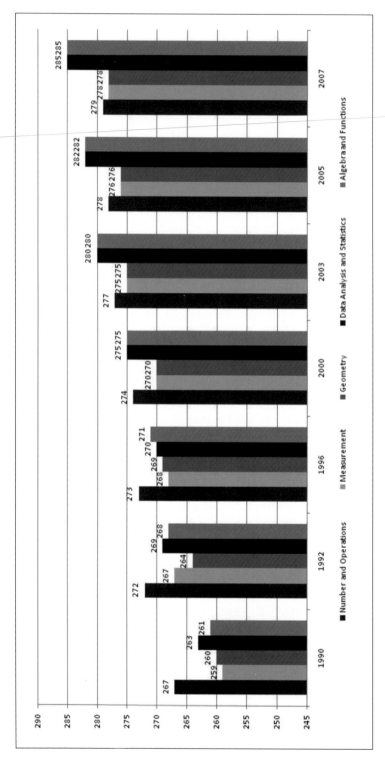

Fig. 6.6. Grade 8 average scale score by content strand

What are all the whole numbers that make 8 – ☐ > 3 true?

A) 0, 1, 2, 3, 4, 5

B) 0, 1, 2, 3, 4

C) 0, 1, 2

D) 5

Fig. 6.7. Algebra and functions item used at grades 4, 8, and 12

textbooks emphasized medians prior to the publication of the *Standards* (NCTM 1989). Median is now a standard topic at the middle school level; thus the results from this item provide strong evidence that when a topic is covered, students will learn it.

4, 8, 3, 2, 5, 8, 12
What is the median of the numbers above?

A) 4

B) 5

C) 6

D) 7

E) 8

Fig. 6.8. Item involving median used at grades 8 and 12

Whereas the grade 8 results on the median item in figure 6.8 are heartening, the grade 12 results are of some concern. In 1990, 22 percent of twelfth graders correctly answered the median question, with the percent correct increasing to 23 percent in 1992, 33 percent in 1996, and 41 percent in 2000, the last year the item was used at grade 12. These percents are almost identical to the grade 8 per-cents—except for 2000, when twelfth graders were 5 percent points *below* eighth graders. The likely reason for the poor performance of twelfth-grade students on this item is that medians are a middle school topic and are not generally covered in high school classes. Students are apt to forget the difference between median and mode, as evidenced by the fact that the most common incorrect response to the item in figure 6.8 was E, which is the mode. In other words, the poor perfor-mance of grade 12 students on the median problem is likely connected to the fact that they have not seen the term in several years rather than the fact that they do not understand the difference between median and mode.

Changes by Content Area: Grade 12

Keeping in mind the change in grade 12 scaling, and thus the lack of comparable grade 12 scores after 2000, the gains by content area in grade 12 mirrored the minimal change between 1990 and 2000 in overall results at this level (fig. 6.1). Specifically, small but statistically significant gains were made in each content area between 1990 and 1992. Those gains were maintained in all content areas except number sense, properties, and operations, in which performance in 2000 dropped back to near the performance level in 1990 (Kehle et al. 2004). One hypothesis that could explain the drop in this content area is that students are taking more advanced courses that do not repeat numbers and operations material, and thus students have forgotten more about those concepts than concepts in the other areas that have more coverage in high school. The items in figures 6.7 and 6.8 are clearly examples of such material.

Unfortunately, of the grade 12 items that have been used for more than several years, a relatively small number have been released to the public, and thus looking at trends on individual items is difficult. On a few grade-12 problems used over a period of time, significant gains were made, and on others, significant deterioration in performance occurred. However, for the majority of items the percent of students correctly answering specific problems was relatively stable. This could reflect the fact that high school curricula have changed less in the past twenty years than curricula at the elementary and middle school levels.

What Do NAEP Results Say about Curriculum?

In addition to mathematics, National Assessment assesses precollege students' performance in art, civics, geography, U.S. history, reading, science, and writing. Reading is the only area that has been assessed as many times as mathematics, but the good news for mathematics teachers is that gains in mathematics achievement over time for grades 4 and 8 have been far greater than gains in any other subject area (Kloosterman and Walcott 2007). The achievement gains in mathematics at grade 12, although modest, are also higher than gains at grade 12 in other subject areas. On the basis of this fact alone, one can argue that focused changes in curriculum across the country, particularly improvements recommended by NCTM (1989, 2000), had a positive impact on students' learning. The gains by content area—and the performance patterns on the items discussed in this article—offer further evidence that the curriculum studied does make a difference. The greatest gains at grade 4 are in algebra and functions, the content strand for which no clear recommendations had been made before the 1989 NCTM *Standards*. The greatest gains at grade 8 were also in algebra and functions, followed closely by data analysis, statistics, and probability, another strand highlighted by the *Standards*. With respect to the latter, curriculum has shifted from emphasis on simple sampling and finding means to much more robust coverage of the fundamental ideas of probability and their application to a variety of problems. The poor performance of twelfth graders on the median problem in figure 6.8 is explainable if we assume that students forget such skills as finding a median and the meaning of terminology that they do not practice. Performance on items for which students can arrive at an answer without having to remember a specialized definition tends to be higher across periods when students are not exposed to such items. In short, data from NAEP give evidence of a positive relationship between what is taught and what is learned.

REFERENCES

Kehle, Paul, Diana Wearne, W. Gary Martin, Marilyn E. Strutchens, and Janet Warfield. "What Do Twelfth-Grade Students Know about Mathematics?" In *Results and Interpretations of the 1990–2000 Mathematics Assessments of the National Assessment of Educational Progress*, edited by Peter Kloosterman and Frank K. Lester, Jr., pp. 145–74. Reston, Va.: National Council of Teachers of Mathematics, 2004.

Kloosterman, Peter. "Interpreting the 2000 NAEP Mathematics Data: Issues and Monograph Overview." In *Results and Interpretations of the 1990–2000 Mathematics Assessments of the National Assessment of Educational Progress,* edited by Peter Kloosterman and Frank K. Lester, Jr., pp. 3–32. Reston, Va.: National Council of Teachers of Mathematics, 2004.

Kloosterman, Peter, and Crystal Walcott. "The 2003 Mathematics Assessment: Overall Results." In *Results and Interpretations of the 2003 Mathematics Assessment of the National Assessment of Educational Progress,* edited by Peter Kloosterman and Frank K. Lester, Jr., pp. 23–42. Reston, Va.: National Council of Teachers of Mathematics, 2007.

Kloosterman, Peter, Zachary Rutledge, and Patricia A. Kenney. "Research, Reflection, Practice: A Generation of Progress: Learning from NAEP." *Teaching Children Mathematics* 15 (February 2009a): 363–39.

———. "Exploring Results of the NAEP: 1980s to the Present." *Mathematics Teaching in the Middle School* 14 (February 2009b): 357–65.

Lambdin, Diana V., and Crystal Walcott. "Changes through the Years: Connections between Psychological Learning Theories and the School Mathematics Curriculum." In *The Learning of Mathematics,* Sixty-ninth Yearbook of the National Council of Teachers of Mathematics (NCTM), edited by W. Gary Martin and Marilyn E. Strutchens, pp. 3– 25. Reston, Va.: NCTM, 2007.

National Council of Teachers of Mathematics (NCTM). *Curriculum and Evaluation Standards for School Mathematics.* Reston, Va.: NCTM, 1989.

_____. *Principles and Standards for School Mathematics,* Reston, Va.: NCTM, 2000.

Rutledge, Zachary, Peter Kloosterman, and Patricia A. Kenney. "Mathematics Skills and NAEP Results over a Generation." *Mathematics Teacher* 102 (February 2009): 445–51.

7

Curriculum Alignment in an Era of Standards and High-Stakes Testing

Shannon W. Dingman

W HAT MATHEMATICS should be the focus of the grades K–12 mathematics curriculum? How should the mathematics be sequenced and developed across grade levels? At what grade level(s) should specific mathematical content be emphasized? These questions have been a rich source of discussion and debate in the United States for more than a century. Recommendations from national committees and organizations from as far back as the *Committee of Ten* report (National Education Association 1894) and present-day efforts of the National Council of Teachers of Mathematics (NCTM) in *Curriculum Focal Points for Prekindergarten through Grade 8 Mathematics* (2006) and the National Mathematics Advisory Panel's *Foundations for Success* (2008) have provided input and guidance to debaters of these questions. However, given the long history of local control of public education in the United States, curriculum decisions have historically resided at the local (i.e., district or state) level. Indeed, curricular emphasis often reflects the needs and goals of those that comprise the local educational establishment—teachers, parents, administrators, and local citizens (Reys 2006). Textbook developers have also played a prominent role in determining and sequencing the content and focus of the school mathematics curriculum.

Over the past thirty years, we have seen a gradual movement away from local control of curricular decisions in the direction of increased involvement of state and federal entities in developing educational policies and establishing curricular standards (Long 2003). This movement was spurred, in part, by comparatively low performance of U.S. students on international assessments, and it resulted in calls for improvement, such as those described in *A Nation at Risk* (National Commission on Excellence in Education 1983). In response, many states acted to increase schools' accountability for students' learning by passing legislation aimed at improving public education. These measures included the development of curriculum frameworks (standards) that specified what students should learn and be able to do at particular grade levels or grade bands in specific subjects such as mathematics. States also moved to create mandatory annual examinations that measured students' performance with respect to the prescribed state standards. During the 1980s alone, forty states created or refined their school accountability practices, and by 1992, forty-six states were administering state-mandated assessments to measure students' achievement (Bauer 2000).

By 2001, the movement to hold schools accountable for students' learning reached the national level with the passage of the No Child Left Behind Act (NCLB) (U.S. Department of Education 2001). Among the many provisions of the legislation, states were required to develop academic content standards—commonly referred to as grade-level learning expectations (GLEs)—and yearly assessments in both reading and mathematics for grades 3–8 (Linn, Baker, and Betebenner 2002). The enactment of NCLB initiated a massive effort in many states to develop and implement grade-specific mathematics content standards (Reys et al. 2005). In fact, between 2002 and 2006, thirty-seven states as well as the District of Columbia and the Department of Defense Education Activity produced new or updated standards that outlined learning expectations for mathematics at specific grade levels (Reys 2006).

Since the passage of NCLB, state-level content standards have taken on increased importance by defining what mathematics is to be taught at each grade level. Although teachers have typically relied heavily on the district-adopted mathematics textbook as an outline for the sequencing of mathematics topics, they are increasingly turning to state standards as their primary guide for identifying what mathematics should be taught and learned by students (Tarr et al. 2008).

The increased stature of state standards in determining the curriculum that is enacted in the classroom raises several questions. To what extent is there consensus across states about the mathematics that should be emphasized, how it should be sequenced, and at what grades particular topics should be emphasized? What is the impact of variation in state standards on the development of grades K–8 textbook materials? Do textbooks emphasize and develop the mathematical content that students are expected to learn (and teachers are expected to teach) in each state?

Given the centrality of mathematics textbooks to the work of teachers and the increased importance of state standards in influencing curricular decisions, some have called for the development of a common set of content standards (national standards) for the study of mathematics (Schmidt 2004; Borst and Rorvig 2006). Some proponents of common standards argue that setting uniform standards across the United States for the study of mathematics could improve the quality and focus of mathematics textbooks. That is, textbook publishers could work from the common standards to design curricular materials rather than customize textbooks to satisfy the needs of particular states (e.g., California and Texas), or repeat content across multiple grade levels or combine standards across multiple states to produce a "national" textbook (Reys 2006). Others argue that curricular innovation would be stifled with uniform descriptions of specified mathematical content, and that countries that have adopted common curricular standards contribute less to curriculum development than countries without common standards (Usiskin 2007).

Although the debate continues about the value of common standards, little has been documented about the extent to which textbook series are "aligned" with particular state standards. The purpose of this article is twofold: to summarize the extent of consensus of standards related to one mathematical topic across various states, and to describe the alignment of state standards involving this topic with mathematics textbooks. This analysis will provide a glimpse of the dilemmas facing textbook publishers as well as district leaders and classroom teachers.

Curricular Consensus across State Standards for Mathematics

NCLB legislation prompted many states to create new, more detailed, standards for mathematics. Across the United States, state teams of educators, often working independently, used a range of approaches (e.g., representative committees, panel of experts) and resources (e.g., *Principles and Standards for School Mathematics* [NCTM 2000] and the *MAP Foundations for Success* [Achieve 2002]) in developing or refining state standards (Reys et al. 2005). The variety of methods used to create state standards and the diversity of opinions about the importance of various mathematical topics contributed to considerable variance in the grade placement of mathematical content in grades K–8.

In their analysis of forty-two state-level standards documents, Reys and her colleagues (2006) compared the grade level at which states expect instructional emphasis on particular topics. For example, as depicted in figure 7.1, state standards vary greatly concerning when the topic of addition and subtraction of fractions is introduced (denoted as the initial learning expectation), over what grades the topic is developed (intermediate learning expectations), and at what grade level students' proficiency in adding and subtracting fractions is expected (culminating learning expectation).

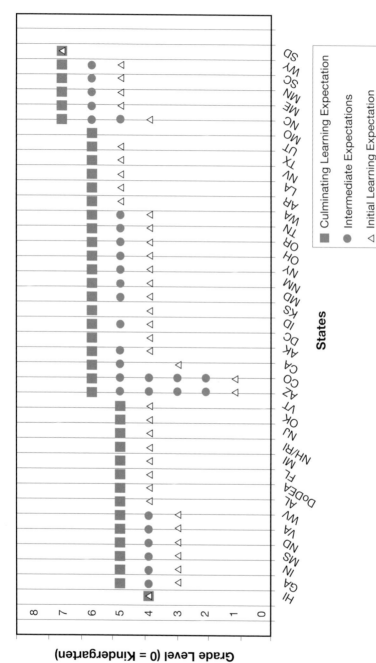

Add and Subtract Fractions

Fig. 7.1. Progression of initial to culminating learning expectations for the addition and subtraction of fractions, by state (Reys et al. 2006)

As illustrated, in some states (Arizona and Colorado) the topic is introduced at an early grade and developed over a period of years before proficiency is expected. Other states (Missouri and South Dakota) specify learning expectations for this topic at only one grade level in their standards. One would expect that the curriculum materials (e.g., textbooks) needed to support the goals specified by these state standards would be quite different in developmental trajectory and emphasis on fraction computation. Yet few of the states are large enough to warrant "state specific" editions of textbook materials.

The analysis by Reys and her colleagues concluded that although the set of learning goals specified for the entire grade K–8 spectrum is similar across states, the grade level at which emphasis on particular mathematics topics is specified varies considerably and is likely to lead to difficulties in constructing a focused and coherent set of national textbooks to guide instruction. The next section presents a closer examination of the alignment of a set of state standards with textbook series that are widely used in the United States.

Alignment between State Standards and Mathematics Textbooks

The differences in grade-level emphasis of particular mathematics topics specified in state standards undoubtedly creates a dilemma for textbook publishers, who must take into account the expectations of different states in developing a national product. In designing a mathematics textbook series that aligns with multiple state standards, the results are generally a textbook series that does not align perfectly with any one set of state standards.

As a follow-up to the state standards analysis described earlier (Reys et al. 2006), I conducted a study (Dingman 2007) to describe the extent to which widely used elementary and middle grades mathematics textbooks give instructional attention to the standards related to fraction concepts and computation in several states. For this analysis, the standards from a sample of states that employ a system of state-level textbook adoption (Texas, Florida, North Carolina, Georgia) and a sample of states that have open adoption policies (New York, Ohio, Michigan, Washington) comprised the data set. These highly populated states were chosen to examine possible differences in curricular alignment between textbook-adoption states and nonadoption states.

Market share data from the 2004–05 school year (Education Market Research 2005) were used to identify the two most popular elementary and middle grades textbook series. The results were as follows:

Grades K–6
  Everyday Mathematics (Bell et al. 2002, 2004a, 2004b, 2004c)
  Scott Foresman–Addison Wesley Mathematics (Charles et al. 2004, 2005)

Grades 6–8

Glencoe's *Mathematics: Applications and Concepts* (Bailey et al. 2004)

Connected Mathematics Project (CMP) (Lappan et al. 2002)

In both groupings, the textbook selection included a publisher-generated curriculum (*Scott Foresman–Addison Wesley Mathematics* and *Mathematics: Applications and Concepts*) and an NSF-funded curriculum (*Everyday Mathematics* and *CMP*), which allowed for further comparisons of alignment across different types of curricular materials.

Instructional segments (e.g., lessons, activities, games, and problem-solving sections) across grades K–8 whose primary focus concerned fraction concepts and computation were compiled from each of the four textbook series. In addition, a set of generalized learning expectations related to fractions was developed on the basis of a review of many state standards and research on students' learning of fractions. The set of generalized learning expectations provided a shared language and a common level of specificity to analyze and compare the grade-level expectations (GLEs) and textbook instructional segments. Each state GLE pertaining to fractions, along with each textbook instructional segment, was coded to this set of generalized learning expectations. The coded data sets were then compared to identify the level of alignment concerning attention to fractions across state standards and textbooks.

The results of the study indicate that the level of alignment of any particular state's GLEs with the instructional segments found in the corresponding grade-level textbook is generally greater than the alignment of the instructional segments with the GLEs. In other words, although many, if not most, state standards are covered in textbooks, these textbooks generally include additional instructional segments that are not specified at the particular grade level in the state standards.

The differences in alignment for a subset of states can be seen in table 7.1. For example, 90 percent (27/30) of Texas's K–6 GLEs involving fractions are given instructional emphasis in the corresponding *Scott Foresman–Addison Wesley Mathematics* grade-level textbook (i.e., a grade 4 GLE was given instructional attention in the grade 4 textbook). However, of the 147 instructional segments pertaining to fractions identified in the Scott Foresman series across grades K–6, only 45 (31%) related directly back to Texas' GLEs at the same grade level. In other words, 31 percent of the instructional attention devoted to fractions in the Scott Foresman series provided attention to 90 percent of Texas' fraction GLEs across grades K–6. The remaining 69 percent of the instructional segments devoted to fractions in the Scott Foresman series did not provide instructional attention to a Texas GLE at the same grade level. As seen in the table, these remaining instructional segments provided coverage to Texas GLEs specified at earlier grade levels (16%) (i.e., an instructional segment in the grade 3 textbook that aligned with a Texas GLE found at grade 2 or earlier), GLEs designated at later grade levels (50%) (i.e., an instructional segment in the grade 4 textbook that aligned with a Texas GLE found at grade 5 or later), or with no Texas GLE (28%). As seen in table 7.1, the differences in curricular alignment between the Scott Foresman series and state GLEs were prevalent across multiple states; in fact, varying degrees of alignment between state GLEs and textbooks were evident for all four textbook series.

Table 7.1
Breakdown of Curricular Alignment between the State GLEs of Texas, Ohio, North Carolina, and Washington and the Grade-Level Textbook Instructional Segments in the Scott Foresman–Addison Wesley Mathematics Series[1]

	Proportion of State GLEs Aligned with Instructional Segments	Proportion of Instructional Segments Aligned with State GLEs	Proportion of Instructional Segments Devoted to State GLEs Found at Earlier Grade Levels*	Proportion of Instructional Segments Devoted to State GLEs Found at Later Grade Levels	Proportion of Instructional Segments Not Devoted to Any State GLE
TX	27/30 (90%)	45/147 (31%)	22/141 (16%)	73/147 (50%)	41/147 (28%)
OH	27/33 (82%)	57/147 (39%)	37/141 (26%)	59/147 (40%)	43/147 (29%)
NC	20/37 (54%)	57/147 (39%)	21/141 (15%)	44/147 (30%)	39/147 (27%)
WA	29/52 (56%)	44/147 (30%)	14/141 (10%)	91/147 (62%)	31/147 (21%)

* The six instructional segments found in the kindergarten textbook were not included here, as they could not be devoted to earlier GLEs.

The relationship between state standards and mathematics textbooks is further highlighted when the alignment for particular topics related to fractions is examined. Figure 7.2 illustrates the grade placement of GLEs and textbook instructional segments for adding and subtracting fractions across the elementary

---

1. Because of the repetition of GLEs across grade levels, an instructional segment may give coverage to GLEs at the same grade level as well as to GLEs at an earlier or later grade level. Therefore, the percents of instructional segments devoted to GLEs at earlier grade levels, the same grade level, or later grade levels, or to no GLE at all, do not sum to 100 percent.

grade levels (K–6). As illustrated, a general connection can be seen between the grade placement of state GLEs and the grade placement of instructional segments offering attention to the topic. Each state analyzed in this study initiates the topic of adding and subtracting fractions with like denominators in grade 3, 4, or 5. Accordingly, the Scott Foresman series provides instructional coverage for this topic at each grade level. For example, the grade 3 Scott Foresman textbook gives instructional coverage to adding and subtracting fractions with like denominators, which aligns with the grade 3 learning expectations described in Michigan and Georgia. However, the instructional coverage provided in the Scott Foresman grade 3 textbook does not align with any grade 3 GLEs for this topic in the remaining six states. These states specify introduction to this topic at grade 4 or 5. Likewise, Michigan and Florida initiate the topic of adding and subtracting fractions with unlike denominators in grade 4, which corresponds to the first instructional segment giving attention to this topic in both the Scott Foresman series and the Everyday Mathematics series. The variance in grade placement of learning expectations pertaining to addition and subtraction of fractions leads to repetitive coverage of this topic in the textbook series as the publisher works to meet the demands of the various states.

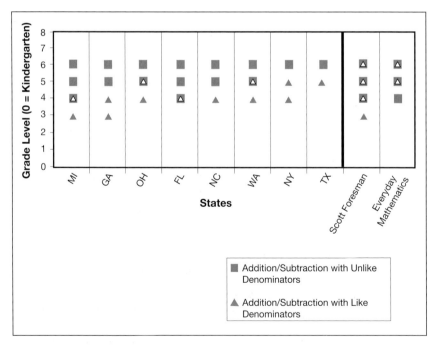

Fig. 7.2. Grade placement of GLEs and elementary textbook instructional segments concerning addition and subtraction of fractions with like and with unlike denominators across grades K–6

These findings suggest that although a strong relationship exists between the curriculum as outlined in state GLEs and the content found in mathematics textbooks, this relationship varies by state and by textbook series. "Perfect" alignment, in which every GLE prescribed by the state is accounted for in the corresponding grade-level textbook while every instructional segment in each grade-level textbook gives attention to state GLEs at the same grade level with no additional coverage of other topics, does not exist in this sample. The fact that alignment between a particular state's GLEs and any given mathematics textbook series is not "perfect" complicates both the job of textbook adoption committees at the state and local levels as well as the job of the classroom teacher. The alignment of standards and textbooks is therefore vital in ensuring clear visions about what mathematics should be the emphasis of instruction and at what grade level(s) particular content is to be taught.

Summary

The passage of the No Child Left Behind Act elevated the importance of state-level curriculum standards in the realm of public education. Historically, the mathematics textbook has guided much of the instructional decision making that occurs in the classroom. With the increased importance of adhering to state standards, teachers now must work to integrate the sometimes-conflicting messages sent by GLEs and mathematics textbooks to make instructional decisions and enact the mathematics curriculum in their classrooms.

The increased movement toward state and federal involvement in setting curriculum policy, along with the lack of consensus of learning expectations across states as well as between GLEs and mathematics textbooks, has prompted debates regarding the need to identify common standards for the learning of mathematics. By adopting common standards, proponents argue that all students, regardless of the state in which they reside, will be given equitable learning opportunities and be held to the same expectations for learning mathematics (Schmidt 2004). Common standards might also provide clear and coherent messages to all stakeholders—teachers, administrators, policymakers, textbook publishers, and so on—regarding the mathematics that should be the focus of instruction at particular grade levels. Opponents of common standards point to the fact that among numerous national organizations, including NCTM, the College Board, and the American Statistical Association, no agreement is found about what mathematics should comprise the U.S. mathematics curriculum and when it should be taught. Such disagreement would therefore disenfranchise those who do not agree with the final set of standards (Usiskin 2007). Opponents also note that common standards would stifle reform efforts in schools and diminish the voices of local officials who serve different student populations.

Although compelling arguments can be made for and against a common set of standards (Borst and Rorvig 2006), state and federal policies are likely to continue to exert influence on the educational system in attempts to find ways to better support students' learning. These policies necessitate an earnest debate about the need for common standards as a means of increasing curricular coherence and focus and strengthening textbook-development processes in the United States.

REFERENCES

Bailey, Rhonda, Roger Day, Patricia Frey, Arthur C. Howard, Deborah Hutchens, Kay McClain, et al. *Mathematics: Applications and Concepts (Course 1, 2, and 3—Student and Teacher's Editions)*. Columbus, Ohio: McGraw Hill-Glencoe, 2004.

Bauer, Scott C. "Should Achievement Tests Be Used to Judge School Quality?" *Educational Policy Analysis Archives* 8, no. 46 (September 2000). epaa.asu.edu/epaa/v8n46.html, August 3, 2009.

Bell, Max, Jean Bell, John Bretzlauf, Amy Dillard, Robert Hartfield, Andy Isaacs, et al. *Everyday Mathematics (Second Edition, Grades 1, 2, and 3—Student and Teacher's Edition)*. Chicago: McGraw Hill-Wright Group, 2004a.

Bell, Max, Jean Bell, Dorothy Freedman, Nancy Goodsell, Nancy Hanvey, and Kate Morrison. *Everyday Mathematics (Second Edition, Kindergarten—Student and Teacher's Edition)*. Chicago: McGraw Hill-Wright Group, 2004b.

Bell, Max, John Bretzlauf, Amy Dillard, Robert Hartfield, Andy Isaacs, James McBride, et al. *Everyday Mathematics (Second Edition, Grades 4 and 5—Student and Teacher's Edition)*. Chicago: McGraw Hill-Wright Group, 2002.

———. *Everyday Mathematics (Second Edition, Grade 6—Student and Teacher's Edition)*. Chicago: McGraw Hill-Wright Group, 2004c.

Borst, Robert W., and Vickie Rorvig. "A National Mathematics Curriculum for the United States: Two Perspectives." *Mathematics Teaching in the Middle School* 12 (September 2006): 70–72.

Charles, Randall I., Warren Crown, Francis Fennell, Janet H. Caldwell, Mary Cavanagh, Dianah Chancellor, et al. *Scott Foresman–Addison Wesley Mathematics (Grades 1, 2, 3, 4, 5 and 6—Student and Teacher's Editions)*. Glenview, Ill.: Pearson-Scott Foresman, 2004.

———. *Scott Foresman–Addison Wesley Mathematics (Kindergarten—Student and Teacher's Editions)*. Glenview, Ill.: Pearson-Scott Foresman, 2005.

Dingman, Shannon W. "Mathematics Textbooks and State Curriculum Standards: An Analysis of the Alignment between the Written and Intended Curricula." Ph.D. diss., University of Missouri—Columbia, 2007.

Education Market Research. *Mathematics Market, Grades K–12: Teaching Methods, Textbooks/Materials Used and Needed, and Market Size*. Rockaway Park, N.Y.: Education Market Research, 2005.

Lappan, Glenda, James T. Fey, William M. Fitzgerald, Susan N. Friel, and Elizabeth D. Phillips. *Connected Mathematics Project (Individual Units—Student and Teacher's Edition)*. Palo Alto, Calif.: Dale Seymour Publications, 2002.

Linn, Robert L., Eva L. Baker, and Damian W. Betebenner. "Accountability Systems: Ramifications of the *No Child Left Behind Act of 2001*." Education Commission of the States, 2002. http://ww.ecs.org/clearinghouse/35/65/3565.htm, August 2, 2009.

Long, Vena M. "The Role of State Government in the Custody Battle over Mathematics Education." In *A History of School Mathematics*, edited by George M. A. Stanic and Jeremy Kilpatrick, pp. 931–54. Reston, Va.: NCTM, 2003.

Mathematics Achievement Partnership. *Foundations for Success: Mathematics Expectations for the Middle Grades, Consultation Draft*. Washington, D.C.: Achieve, 2002.

National Commission on Excellence in Education. *A Nation at Risk: The Imperative for Educational Reform*. Washington, D.C.: U.S. Government Printing Office, 1983.

National Council of Teachers of Mathematics (NCTM). *Principles and Standards for School Mathematics*. Reston, Va.: NCTM, 2000.

———. *Curriculum Focal Points for Prekindergarten through Grade 8 Mathematics: A Quest for Coherence*. Reston, Va.: NCTM, 2006.

National Education Association. *Report of the Committee of Ten on Secondary School Studies with the Reports of the Conferences Arranged by the Committee*. New York: American Book Co., 1894.

National Mathematics Advisory Panel. *Foundations for Success: Reports of the Task Groups and Subcommittees*. Washington, D.C.: U.S. Department of Education, 2008.

Reys, Barbara J. "State-Level Curriculum Standards: Growth in Authority and Specificity." In *The Intended Mathematics Curriculum as Represented in State-Level Curriculum Standards: Consensus or Confusion?* edited by Barbara J. Reys, pp. 1–14. Greenwich, Conn.: Information Age Publishing, 2006.

Reys, Barbara J., Shannon Dingman, Angela Sutter, and Dawn Teuscher. "Development of State-Level Mathematics Curriculum Documents: Report of a Survey." Columbia, Mo.: Center for the Study of Mathematics Curriculum, 2005. http://www.mathcurriculumcenter.org/ASSM_report.pdf, August 3, 2009.

Reys, Barbara J., Shannon Dingman, Travis A. Olson, Angela Sutter, Dawn Teuscher, and Kathryn Chval. "Analysis of Number and Operation Grade-Level Learning Expectations in State Standards Documents." In *The Intended Mathematics Curriculum as Represented in State-Level Curriculum Standards: Consensus or Confusion?* edited by Barbara J. Reys, pp. 15-57. Greenwich, Conn.: Information Age Publishing, 2006.

Schmidt, William H. "A Vision for Mathematics." *Educational Leadership* 61 (February 2004): 6–11.

Tarr, James E., Robert E. Reys, Barbara J. Reys, Oscar Chavez, Jeffrey Shih, and Steven J. Osterlind. "The Impact of Middle-Grades Mathematics Curricula and the Classroom Learning Environment on Student Achievement." *Journal for Research in Mathematics Education* 39 (May 2008): 247–80.

United States Department of Education. "No Child Left Behind Act." Public Law no. 107-110, 2001. http://www.ed.gov/policy/elsec/leg/esea02/index.html, August 9, 2009.

Usiskin, Zalman. "Do We Need National Standards with Teeth?" *Educational Leadership* 65 (November 2007): 38–42.

Preschool Mathematics Curricula

Julie Sarama
Douglas H. Clements

WHY WORRY about mathematics in the preschool? Shouldn't "kids be allowed to be kids"? Specific instructional attention to mathematics in preschool is crucial for at least three reasons.

Why Mathematics in the Preschool?

First, the common worry—that mathematics in preschool is a developmentally inappropriate "pressure"—has no historical basis. Frederick Froebel, the inventor of kindergarten and preschool, was a crystallographer who believed that geometry and other mathematics stood at the core of the universe. Almost every aspect of his kindergarten crystallized into beautiful mathematical forms. As an

This paper was supported in part by the National Science Foundation (NSF) under grant no. ESI-9730804, "Building Blocks—Foundations for Mathematical Thinking, Prekindergarten to Grade 2: Research-Based Materials Development" and grant no. REC-0228440 (Interagency Educational Research Initiative, a collaboration of NSF, U.S. Department of Education, and National Institutes of Health), "Scaling Up the Implementation of a Prekindergarten Mathematics Curricula: Teaching for Understanding with Trajectories and Technologies"; and by the U.S. Department of Education's Institute of Education Sciences (IES), grant no. R305K05157, "Scaling Up TRIAD: Teaching Early Mathematics for Understanding with Trajectories and Technologies." Any opinions, findings, and conclusions or recommendations expressed in this publication are those of the authors and do not necessarily reflect the views of the NSF or IES.

illustration, Froebel used "gifts," such as cubes, cylinders, and other blocks, to teach children the geometric language of the universe. The cubes that children had made into play chairs and stoves later would be made into geometric designs, guided by the square grids etched into the top of their table. Later, these cubes would be laid into two rows of four each and expressed as "4 + 4." In this way, connections were paramount: The "chair" became an aesthetic geometric design, which became a number sentence. Mathematical structure was everywhere.

However, during certain phases of history, Froebel's mathematics was largely forgotten or diluted (Balfanz 1999). As one striking example, early in the twentieth century Edward Thorndike emphasized health by replacing the first gift—small spheres representing points—with a toothbrush and replacing the first mathematical occupation with "sleep" (Brosterman 1997). Today, we realize that most strong early childhood programs, such as Froebel's and Montessori's, include attention to mathematics. In fact, children naturally engage in mathematics in their play and in their everyday lives and enjoy doing so.

A second reason that mathematics should play a crucial role is that *early* knowledge of mathematics is important to children's later success in school. Children with underdeveloped mathematical ideas and skills at entry into school remain relatively low achievers throughout their education. A knowledge of mathematics in *preschool* correlates with *tenth-grade* achievement in mathematics (Stevenson and Newman 1986). Indeed, early knowledge of reading predicts subsequent success in reading. However, early knowledge of mathematics is a *stronger* predictor of subsequent success in mathematics.

Third, early knowledge of mathematics predicts not only subsequent success in mathematics but also subsequent success in reading (Clements and Sarama 2009). Early attention to mathematics is especially important for children most at risk for school failure. A large gap is evident between children growing up in higher- and lower-resource communities in their exposure to, and thus knowledge of, mathematics. Attention in preschool to mathematics can contribute to closing that gap.

What Mathematics in the Preschool?

NCTM's *Curriculum Focal Points for Prekindergarten through Grade 8: A Quest for Coherence* (NCTM 2006) identifies a few essential mathematical topics at each age level. The preschool Focal Points are based on research and the wisdom of expert practice, including the results of a national conference on early mathematics standards (Clements, Sarama, and DiBiase 2004).

In preschool, the focus is on number, geometry, and spatial sense. For example, "[d]eveloping an understanding of whole number, including concepts of correspondence, counting, cardinality, and comparison" (NCTM 2006, p. 11) focuses on quantification, or assigning a number to a set of objects—the first, and most basic, mathematical algorithm. It also signals a *developmental sequence*. That is, children begin counting by learning number words in order—verbal counting. Next they learn to use one-to-one correspondence in counting objects. Then they develop an understanding of the *cardinal principle*—the idea that the last number word in counting tells you "how many" in the set of all objects counted. Later, preschoolers learn to use this knowledge to compare the number in two sets.

Recognizing the number in very small sets without counting is most children's *first* method of quantification. Such number recognition is called *subitizing* (Clements 1999). When children count, subitizing the number in the set encourages and reinforces understanding of the cardinal principle. Subitizing also follows a developmental sequence.

Turning to geometry and spatial sense, children learn about shapes in the environment. Children identify and name shapes but also discuss their attributes. They describe the relative positions of objects by using important vocabulary, such as *above* and *next to*. Such language learning supports children's development of general cognition and literacy.

The third Focal Point for prekindergarten involves foundations for measurement. Children identify measurable attributes and compare objects directly using those attributes. For example, children identify objects as "longer" or "shorter" and learn to differentiate whether "bigger" refers to length, area, weight, or some other attribute.

NCTM's *Curriculum Focal Points* also identifies connections for each grade, supporting breadth and depth in the mathematics curriculum. For example, preschool children should *apply* the knowledge identified in the Focal Points in solving problems. In addition, preschool children should describe, sort, and compare physical and mathematical objects' attributes, such as size, quantity, or shape.

How Should We Teach Mathematics in the Preschool?

How Much Mathematics Is Going On in Most Preschools?

Most preschoolers experience too little mathematics. Observations of a full day of three-year-olds' lives revealed that 60 percent of the children had *no structured* mathematics experience, and few instances of mathematics teaching were recorded (Tudge and Doucet 2004). Preschool teachers said they believed that mathematics was important and that they engaged in mathematical discussions. Apparently, the teachers believed that selecting such materials as puzzles, blocks, games, songs, and finger plays was sufficient (Graham, Nash, and Paul 1997).

The National Center for Early Development and Learning (NCEDL) studies report that children are not engaged in learning or constructive activities during a large proportion of the prekindergarten day (e.g., Winton et al. 2005). In fact, the students spent the largest part of their day, up to 44 percent, in routine, maintenance activities, such as standing in line and in eating. An average of only 6 to 8 percent of the day involved mathematics activities in any form. On average, less than 3 percent of the time were the children engaged in learning experiences, and fewer than half the children experienced these at all (Winton et al. 2005). Finally, even in one of the highest-quality programs, the Abbott programs, the quality of mathematics materials and teaching was rated as very low. In other literacy-based programs, the situation can be just as bad. A literacy-oriented (Bright Beginnings) program and a developmentally focused (Creative Curriculum) program included no more mathematics instruction than other programs (Aydogan et al. 2006).

Another study (Farran et al. 2007) showed that a literacy-based curriculum might be inadequate. In a study of the Opening the World of Learning (OWL) program, which includes mathematics in its all-day, prescribed program, out of a 360-minute day, only 58 seconds were devoted to mathematics. The program allowed for little instruction, few opportunities for children to engage with mathematics materials, and few opportunities for children to talk about mathematics. The study found that none of the children gained mathematics skills through the program, and those beginning with higher scores lost mathematics skills over the year. They did gain in literacy skills, but only modestly.

Thus, present pedagogical practice is inadequate. What type of curricular activities might provide children with better mathematics experiences?

Mathematics in Play and throughout the Day

Most educators believe that children should learn throughout the day, especially in their play. Such learning is meaningful and motivating and promotes a view of mathematics as a positive, self-directed, problem-solving activity. Preschoolers naturally engage in a kind of premathematical thinking in their play, even when teachers have not designed the activity to include mathematics. For example, the children showed at least one sign of such thinking during 43 percent of the minutes during which they were observed. They classified (2%), compared (13%; "This isn't big enough to cover the table"), counted (12%), explored dynamics (5%; e.g., motions such as flipping), created patterns and shapes (21%), and explored spatial relations (4%) (Seo and Ginsburg 2004).

Materials such as sand, play dough, and blocks offer many rich opportunities for mathematical thinking and reasoning. Teachers can provide suggestive materials, engage in parallel play with children, and raise comments or questions regarding shapes and the quantity of things. For example, they might furnish play dough and cookie cutters, and discuss shapes and congruence as children use the cookie cutters to make multiple "cookies" having identical shape; or they might discuss transforming play dough shapes into one another. One teacher told two students that she was "going to hide the ball" made of play dough. She covered it with a flat object, and pressed down. The students said the ball was still there, but when the teacher lifted the flat object, the ball was "gone." This outcome delighted the students, and they copied her actions and discussed that the ball was "in" the "circle" (Forman and Hill 1984, pp. 31–32).

Similarly, sociodramatic play can be naturally mathematical in the right setting. In one classroom's dramatic play area, teachers and children created a shop in which the shopkeeper fills orders and asks the customer for money (e.g., $1 for each dinosaur toy). Gabi was playing the shopkeeper. Tamika handed her a 5 card (5 dots and the numeral "5") as her order. Gabi counted out five toy dinosaurs.

Teacher: (just entering the area) How many did you buy?

Tamika: Five.

Teacher: How do you know?

Tamika: Because Gabi counted.

Tamika was still working on her counting skills, and trusted Gabi's counting more than her own knowledge of five. The play context allowed her to develop her knowledge.

Janelle: I'm getting a big number. (She handed Gabi a 2 and a 5 card.)

Gabi: I don't have that many.

Teacher: You could give Janelle two of one kind and five of another.

Gabi counted out the two separate piles and put them in a basket, and Janelle counted out dollars. She miscounted and gave Gabi $6.

Gabi: You need $7.

The sociodramatic play setting, with the teacher's help, was beneficial for children at various levels of understanding and development.

This example illustrates an essential point. The "mathematics" observed in play is in the mind of the observer but not necessarily in the mind of the child. It forms a premathematical foundation, but it is not fully mathematical until the teacher guides the children themselves to mathematize it. Mathematizing involves reinventing, redescribing, reorganizing, quantifying, structuring, abstracting, and generalizing that which is first understood on an intuitive and informal level in the context of everyday activity (Sarama and Clements 2009). The teacher in the foregoing example intentionally created mathematical situations. Further, her interactions with the children made their play more reflective and more mathematical.

Similarly, when a child turns or flips puzzle pieces in free play, that free play is good physical foundational activity. But when the teacher asks them to *describe* what they are doing—when they use mathematical tools on the computer to slide, flip, and turn shapes, or when they tell their friend "flip it over, it will fit perfectly"—then they are building mathematical understandings of geometric motions.

Thus, the teacher can employ many ways to make play and other everyday early childhood activities more mathematical. Such *enriched* everyday activities can help raise mathematics knowledge in Head Start classrooms (Arnold et al. 2002). However, research indicates that such enriched activities are often not sufficient to promote strong learning of mathematics, especially for children who come to school without a history of opportunities to learn mathematics. However, organized learning of mathematics (and literacy) actually *helps children play*. Children in classrooms that engaged in mathematics were more likely to engage at high-quality level during free play time (Aydogan et al. 2006). Focused instruction is needed to close the gaps in young children's mathematics knowledge. Such instruction also promotes high-quality play.

Focused Activities

Focused activities can be whole-group, small-group, or individual. They can help organize and sequence the development of mathematics skills and ideas. Whole-group activities are efficient ways of demonstrating activities and using books to introduce mathematical ideas. Done well, they engage children in discussing mathematics. Effective strategies go beyond teachers' presentations. Effective teachers ask children to turn to their neighbors to answer questions or share their ideas and strategies. In other activities, children might respond chorally or engage in movement games in which they must listen carefully and respond physically and verbally (e.g., talking to themselves as they perform the movement).

Small-group activities can also help children transfer what they have learned to tasks that have not been explicitly taught (Clements 1984). In effective small-group activities, children work in pairs, switching roles. The teacher observes them carefully to learn what level of thinking they are capable of and to individualize tasks to help each child develop the next level of thinking.

Individual children can interact with teachers or with high-quality technology. Few preschool teachers use technology presently, even though educational technology can make a unique contribution to learning and teaching (Clements and Sarama 2003). As an example, computer tools can complement and expand what can be done with other media. Children might "break apart" computer-based manipulatives, or make them larger or smaller, actions that are difficult or impossible with physical manipulatives. Computer tools can also track children's progress and help individualize tasks so that children continually advance toward the next level of thinking.

Combining Approaches

An example that integrates several of these ideas began with preschoolers playing with a specially designed foam shape set from the Building Blocks project (Clements and Sarama 2007a, 2007b), as illustrated in figure 8.1. They felt, stacked, and generally explored the shapes. The teacher observed whether they matched the shapes and by what method—for example, by side length or superimposition (laying one on top of the other to find shapes that match exactly, i.e., *congruent* shapes). Did children spontaneously begin to make pictures and designs? If so, how did they represent objects? Did they incorporate symmetry?

Fig. 8.1. A foam shape set from the Building Blocks project (Clements and Sarama 2007a)

Later, the teacher led a whole-group discussion regarding puzzles familiar to children. The children talked to their neighbors and then shared some ideas with the whole group. Later, in small groups, the teacher worked with small groups of children who solved puzzles together, observing them and figuring out where they were in the "shape composing learning trajectory" (see fig. 8.2, from the Building Blocks project [Clements and Sarama 2007a]) and gradually introduced new puzzles to help each child progress.

Working with the software offered unique advantages. When using the computer, the children solved puzzles at their level, receiving feedback and assistance as needed. For example, sometimes children covered too much, putting a shape over a puzzle section but also outside the puzzle area. When using physical manipulatives, they often do not notice this problem. The computer program alerted them to the problem and made the shape they placed semitransparent, so they saw through it to the puzzle pattern "underneath." This feature helped them correct their work. When using the computer, the children also had to think about the actions they needed to take, such as turning or flipping a shape, to choose the right tool. That is, they had to think explicitly about geometric motions.

Finally, computer technologies made a special contribution because the management system assessed whether each child was successfully operating at any given level of the learning trajectory. If not, the child was gently and automatically routed to activities at a lower level. Likewise, successful children are directed to more challenging tasks.

Over the course of several days, the children began to play not just with the shapes but also with mathematical ideas. For example, two children tried to complete a puzzle in as many different ways as they could. One of them attempted to make a hexagon with every possible combination of shapes. The teacher encouraged all the children to make their own puzzles for others to solve using the Shape Puzzle—Free Explore tool in the software. The children created many arrangements with shapes, then pressed a button that converted them to outline puzzles. This activity led to a discussion of what made a "good puzzle."

These examples illustrate combinations of whole-group, small-group, everyday, and computer activities (Clements and Sarama 2004, 2007a). These approaches have proved to be successful in helping young children learn mathematics. The teachers played an essential role in making the experience successful.

Summary

Mathematics has a long history in preschool. Building on that history is important because mathematical knowledge is an important part of a firm foundation for students' success in school. Children engage in intuitive mathematics naturally and enjoy learning basic ideas related to number, geometry, spatial

Level	Examples (above, free-form pictures; below, puzzles)	Instructional Task
Precomposer. Children manipulate shapes as individuals, but are unable to combine them to compose a larger shape. In free-form—"make a picture"—tasks, shapes often do not touch (upper picture in middle column). In puzzle tasks, shapes do not match simple outlines (lower picture in middle column). The instructional task (illustrated on the computer in the last column; similar tasks are presented with manipulatives and paper outlines or wooden form puzzles) uses outlines in which children can simply match shapes without turn or flip motions.		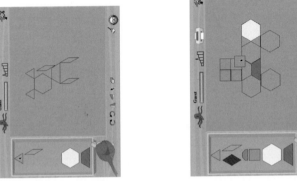
Piece Assembler. Children can place shapes touching each other to form pictures. In free-form tasks, each shape used represents a unique role or function in the picture (e.g., one shape for one leg). Children can fill only simple frames, in which shape is outlined, although their use of turns and flips is limited.	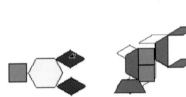	

(Continued)

Fig. 8.2. Examples of puzzle tasks from the Building Blocks project (Clements and Sarama 2007a)

Level	Examples *(above, free-form pictures; below, puzzles)*	Instructional Task
Picture Maker. In free-form tasks, children can concatenate shapes to form pictures in which several shapes combine to play a role (e.g., a leg), but use trial and error. For puzzle tasks, children can match by a side length and use trial and error (a "pick and discard" strategy). Instructional tasks have "open" areas in which shape selection is ambiguous.		
Shape Composer. Children combine shapes to make new shapes or fill puzzles, with growing intentionality and anticipation. Shapes are chosen using angles as well as side lengths. Instructional tasks (here, solving similar problems multiple ways) encourage higher levels in the hierarchy not described here, involving substitutions (three higher levels are described in Clements, Sarama, and Wilson 2001).		

Fig. 8.2. Examples of puzzle tasks from the Building Blocks project (Clements and Sarama 2007a)—*Continued*

sense, and measurements. These ideas can be taught effectively using a combination of teachable moments, informal but planned activities, and sequenced activities. A good preschool mathematics curriculum should integrate all these strategies.

REFERENCES

Arnold, David H., Paige H. Fisher, Greta L. Doctoroff, and Jennifer Dobbs. "Accelerating Math Development in Head Start Classrooms: Outcomes and Gender Differences. " *Journal of Educational Psychology* 94 (2002): 762–70.

Aydogan, Canan, Christy Plummer, Shin Ji Kang, Carol Bilbrey, Dale C. Farran, and Mark W. Lipsey. "An Investigation of Prekindergarten Curricula: Influences on Classroom Characteristics and Child Engagement." Paper presented at the Institute of Education Sciences Research Conference, Washington, D.C., June 2006.

Balfanz, Robert. "Why Do We Teach Young Children So Little Mathematics? Some Historical Considerations." In *Mathematics in the Early Years,* edited by Juanita V. Copley. Reston, Va.: National Council of Teachers of Mathematics, 1999.

Brosterman, Norman. *Inventing Kindergarten.* New York: Harry N. Abrams, 1997.

Clements, Douglas H. "Training Effects on the Development and Generalization of Piagetian Logical Operations and Knowledge of Number." *Journal of Educational Psychology* 76 (1984): 766–76.

———. "Subitizing: What Is It? Why Teach It?" *Teaching Children Mathematics* 5 (March 1999): 400–405.

Clements, Douglas H., and Julie Sarama. "Strip Mining for Gold: Research and Policy in Educational Technology—a Response to 'Fool's Gold.'" *Educational Technology Review* 11, no. 1 (2003): 7–69.

———. *"Building Blocks* for Early Childhood Mathematics." *Early Childhood Research Quarterly* 19 (2004): 181–89.

———. *Building Blocks—SRA Real Math PreK.* Columbus, Ohio: SRA/McGraw-Hill, 2007a.

———."Effects of a Preschool Mathematics Curriculum: Summative Research on the *Building Blocks* Project." *Journal for Research in Mathematics Education* 38 (2007b): 136–63.

———. *Learning and Teaching Early Math: The Learning Trajectories Approach.* New York: Routledge, 2009.

Clements, Douglas H., Julie Sarama, and Ann-Marie DiBiase. *Engaging Young Children in Mathematics: Standards for Early Childhood Mathematics Education.* Mahwah, N.J.: Lawrence Erlbaum Associates, 2004.

Clements, Douglas H., Julie Sarama, and David C. Wilson. "Composition of Geometric Figures." In *Proceedings of the Twenty-fifth Conference of the International Group for the Psychology of Mathematics Education,* edited by M. v. d. Heuvel-Panhuizen. Utrecht, Netherlands: Freudenthal Institute, 2001.

Farran, Dale C., Mark W. Lipsey, Betsy Watson, and Sean Hurley. "Balance of Content Emphasis and Child Content Engagement in an Early Reading First Program." Paper presented at the American Educational Research Association Annual Meeting, Chicago, April 2007.

Forman, George E., and Fleet Hill. *Constructive Play: Applying Piaget in the Preschool.* Rev. ed. Menlo Park, Calif.: Addison Wesley Publishing Co., 1984.

Graham, Theresa A., Cindy Nash, and Kim Paul. "Young Children's Exposure to Mathematics: The Child Care Context." *Early Childhood Education Journal* 25 (Fall 1997): 31–38.

National Council of Teachers of Mathematics (NCTM). *Curriculum Focal Points for Prekindergarten through Grade 8 Mathematics: A Quest for Coherence.* Reston, Va.: NCTM, 2006.

Sarama, Julie, and Douglas H. Clements. *Early Childhood Mathematics Education Research: Learning Trajectories for Young Children.* New York: Routledge, 2009.

Seo, Kyoung-Hye, and Herbert P. Ginsburg. "What Is Developmentally Appropriate in Early Childhood Mathematics Education?" In *Engaging Young Children in Mathematics: Standards for Early Childhood Mathematics Education,* edited by Douglas H. Clements, Julie Sarama, and Anne-Marie DiBiase. Mahwah, N.J.: Lawrence Erlbaum Associates, 2004.

Stevenson, Harold W., and Richard S. Newman. "Long-Term Prediction of Achievement and Attitudes in Mathematics and Reading." *Child Development* 57 (1986): 646–59.

Tudge, Jonathan R. H., and Fabienne Doucet. "Early Mathematical Experiences: Observing Young Black and White Children's Everyday Activities." *Early Childhood Research Quarterly* 19 (2004): 21–39.

Winton, Pam, Virginia Buysse, Donna Bryant, Dick Clifford, Diane Early, and Loyd Little. "NCEDL Prekindergarten Study." *Early Developments* 9, no.1 (Spring 2005).

part III

The Written Curriculum

- Curriculum Development

- Selection of Textbooks

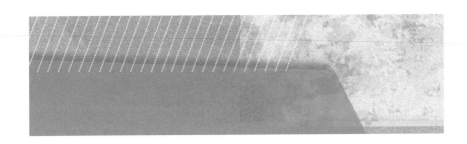

The Written Curriculum

- **Curriculum Development**

- Selection of Textbooks

Supporting Focused and Cohesive Curricula through Visual Representations: An Example from Japanese Textbooks

Tad Watanabe
Akihiko Takahashi
Makoto Yoshida

PRINCIPLES *and Standards for School Mathematics* (NCTM 2000) argues that "[i]n a coherent curriculum, mathematical ideas are linked to and build on one another so that students' understanding and knowledge deepens and their ability to apply mathematics expands" (p. 14). Although both curricular focus and coherence are primarily concerned with specific mathematics content, visual representations used in mathematics curricula may play an important role in both teaching and learning with such focused and coherent curricula. This chapter examines how Japanese elementary school mathematics textbooks use pictorial representations across grade levels (Kroll and Yabe 1987). This analysis, in turn, generates ideas about how visual representations can be used to support a focused and coherent curriculum.

Gradual and Intentional Development of a Representation System

Watanabe (2006) analyzed the use of pictorial representations in the two most widely used Japanese textbook series. He noted that these series used three types of pictorial representations of quantities. The first type is the most concrete and involves pictures of actual objects. Thus, if a problem is about three dogs and two dogs coming together, the student sees a picture of dogs. Moreover, the picture represents the exact quantities—not just to set the context of the problem but also to serve as a visual tool that the students can use to solve the problem.

The second type of pictorial representation of quantities used in these textbooks is pictures of common manipulatives. These items are more abstract than the actual objects. For example, the opening problem in the unit on multidigit addition in grade 2 involves finding the number of origami papers. Again, the exact quantities are represented by counting blocks, similar to base-ten blocks.

The last type of pictorial representation is mathematical diagrams, such as number lines and tape diagrams (see fig. 9.1 for an example). These representations are the most abstract of the three types.

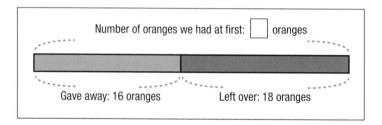

Fig. 9.1. A tape diagram representing the problem "We had some oranges. We gave away 16 of them. We now have 18 oranges. How many oranges did we have at first?" (Hironaka and Sugiyama 2006, 2B, p. 51)

The graphs in figure 9.2 show the relative frequencies of these types of representations across grade levels. The percents shown are based on the total number of pages with these types of representations. Since some pages include more than one type of representation, the percents in a grade level do not add up to 100 percent.

These graphs show a gradual shift toward more abstract representations as the grade level increases. Concrete and manipulative representations are much more common in lower grades. However, both series use more abstract representations in upper grades. These series make the shift from concrete to more abstract representations gradually by paying close attention to possible difficulties children might encounter.

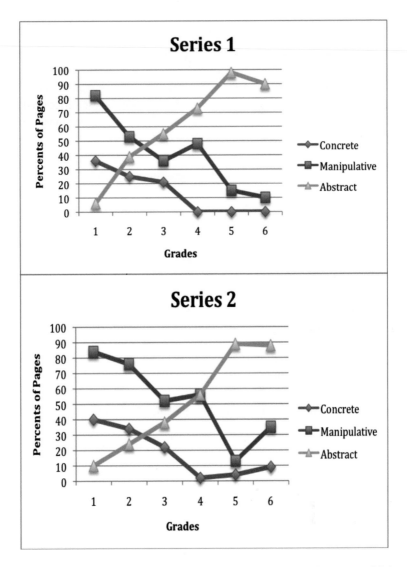

Fig. 9.2. Types of pictorial representations used in two of the most widely used Japanese elementary school mathematics textbook series

To provide a more concrete illustration of how Japanese textbooks use pictorial representations, examples from a recently translated series by Hironaka and Sugiyama (2006)—a newer edition of Series 1 than shown in figure 9.2—are shown. In the grade 1 textbook, as discussed previously, the series often uses more concrete representations, such as pictures of actual objects or familiar manipulatives. For example, one of the first problems in the unit on addition involves soccer balls (see fig. 9.3). Two ideas are worth noting.

Fig. 9.3. An addition problem is represented pictorially with the actual objects and a familiar manipulative in grade 1 (Hironaka and Sugiyama 2006, 1, p. 27).

First, the series includes both the actual objects (i.e., soccer balls) and familiar manipulatives (i.e., counting blocks that are included in children's manipulative kits). The students' manipulative kits are typically provided to all first graders and contain such items as counting blocks, flash cards, model clocks, and plastic tiles (typically squares and isosceles right triangles). In the beginning of grade 1, which is the first year of schooling in Japan, the textbook generally includes pictures of both concrete objects and manipulatives to help children understand that manipulatives may be substituted in place of actual objects to explore numerical relationships.

A second important feature of figure 9.3 is how the items are arranged. There is no logical necessity for the three soccer balls or the three counting blocks to be arranged in a straight line. However, the textbook series authors chose to do so as subtle groundwork for making the transition to a more abstract linear model that students will encounter later.

The transition to tape diagrams begins in grade 2 (see fig. 9.4), when students see fourteen dark-colored counters and twenty-three light-colored counters that are lined up in a straight line. Moreover, the counters are enclosed in a "tape" that is divided into two segments. This particular diagram is used as the first step in the transition because a tape or a segment diagram represents quantities through a continuous quantity—length—whereas counting blocks and other manipulatives used by primary school students are discrete quantities. This shift is not a trivial matter for young children. Thus, the textbook series bridges the gap through a representation like this one, which juxtaposes both types of quantities.

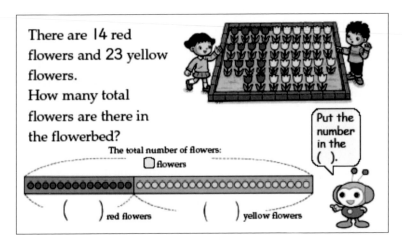

Fig. 9.4. The first step in transition from counters to a tape diagram in grade 2 (Hironaka and Sugiyama 2006, 2A, p. 12)

Later in the grade 2 textbook, in a missing-addend problem, an unknown quantity is represented by a blank segment of a tape as shown in figure 9.5. This problem is the first time a continuous quantity—that is, a tape segment—is used to represent an unknown discrete quantity; however, the known discrete quantity is still represented by individual counters drawn inside the segment of the tape.

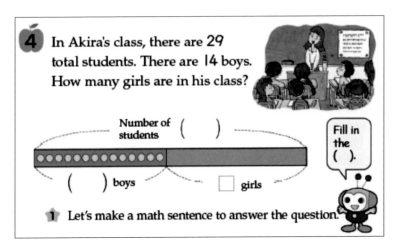

Fig. 9.5. The empty segment of tape is representing an unknown number in grade 2 (Hironaka and Sugiyama 2006, 2A, p. 20).

Finally, at the end of grade 2, the textbook includes a unit focused on developing the tape-diagram representation. In this unit, students no longer use counters inside the tape segments. Instead, they simply label segments with numbers, or a blank box if the quantity is unknown, as shown in figure 9.1.

At the intermediate and upper elementary grade levels, students learn about multiplication and division operations in which two different quantities are involved. These operations are typically introduced in equal-set situations. For example, the grade 3 unit on the division algorithm opens with the following problem:

> There are 72 pieces of origami paper. When you divide them equally among 3 children, how many pieces will each child get?

This problem involves two quantities: the number of origami papers and the number of children. Thus, the textbook introduces the combination of a tape and a number line (fig. 9.6) to represent the problem situation.

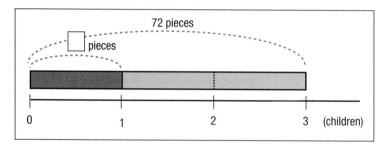

Fig. 9.6. Combination of a tape and a number line to illustrate a division problem in grade 3 (Hironaka and Sugiyama 2006, 3B, p. 13)

This form of representation (integrating tape and number-line models) continues to be used as students investigate multiplication and division of decimal numbers by whole numbers in grade 4. In grade 5, the series introduces a double-number-line representation in the discussion of multiplication and division by decimal numbers (fig. 9.7).

As shown in figure 9.8, the double number lines continue to be used as students explore other multiplicative concepts.

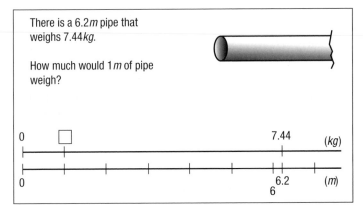

Fig. 9.7. Double number line representing a division of decimal numbers in grade 5 (Hironaka and Sugiyama 2006, 5A, p. 41)

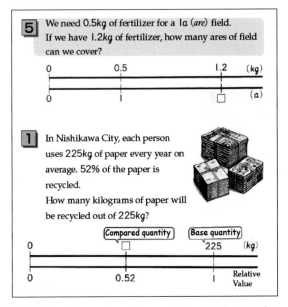

Fig. 9.8. Double number lines continue to be used to explore different multiplicative ideas in grades 5 and 6 (Hironaka and Sugiyama 2006, 5B, pp. 28, 65).

Mathematical Significance of Representations

In the textbook series by Hironaka and Sugiyama (2006), such linear representations as the tape diagram, number line, and double number line play a central role in supporting students' mathematics learning. In this section, we discuss why these representations are mathematically significant.

Helping students become better problem solvers is a major focus of mathematics teaching in Japan. For problems involving computation, at least two important factors should be considered. One is the ability to determine correctly what operation(s) must be used, and the other is having the skills necessary to carry out the selected operation(s). Clearly, both are important, but perhaps the former has become more crucial in recent years because one cannot complete this process with such tools as calculators and computers. Linear representations may serve as useful thinking tools for students to determine what operation(s) are to be done.

For example, primary school teachers know that missing-addend problems like the one represented as a tape diagram in figure 9.1 are difficult for students. A common error is to subtract 16 from 18 because 16 oranges were "given away." However, if students can represent the problem in a tape diagram, it might help them realize that the missing quantity is a combination of the other two quantities; in other words, those two quantities must be added.

Consider the following problem adapted from a grade 5 textbook (Hironaka and Sugiyama 2006, 5A, p. 43):

> The white ribbon costs 240 yen for 1.2 m, and the blue ribbon costs 240 yen for 0.8 m. Which ribbon costs more for 1 m?

Many students can intuitively tell that the price for 1 meter of the blue ribbon is more than 240 yen. Some students also believe that multiplication makes numbers bigger; therefore, they may think that the cost per meter will be obtained by the calculation of 240×0.8. However, a double-number-line representation (fig. 9.9) may clarify the way quantities are related in this problem. In a multiplication problem, we are given the amount corresponding to 1 unit, that is, the *multiplicand.* However, in this problem, both situations involve determining the amount corresponding to 1.

With whole numbers, the operation necessary to determine how many in each group is fair-sharing division as shown in figure 9.6. As students explore division of decimal numbers in grade 5, the meaning of fair-sharing division is extended to the operation necessary to determine per-one quantity (fig. 9.7) whether the divisor is a whole number or a decimal number. Therefore, since we are determining the per-one amount in both instances, the same arithmetic operation—division—should be used regardless of the size of the divisor.

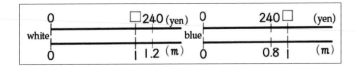

Fig. 9.9. Double-number-line representation clearly illustrates the relationship between the size of divisor and the size of quotient (Hironaka and Sugiyama 2006, 5A, p. 43).

Double number lines are a powerful thinking tool for problems requiring multiplicative reasoning. Multiplying and dividing fractions are arguably the most challenging topics in a grades K–8 mathematics curriculum. We illustrate how double number lines can be used as a thinking tool to solve problems involving division by a fraction in grade 6. Let us consider the following problem (adapted from Hironaka and Sugiyama [2006, 6A, p. 17]):

> With 3/4 dl of paint you can paint 2/5 m² of board. How many m² can you paint with 1 dl of paint?

The textbook includes the picture and double number line shown in figure 9.10.

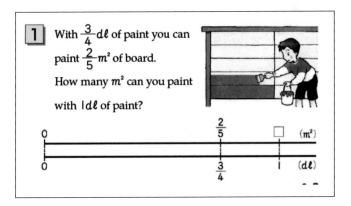

Fig. 9.10. A problem involving the division of fractions is introduced with a picture and a double number line (Hironaka and Sugiyama 2006, 6A, p. 17).

As we saw earlier, students learn in grade 5 that when the per-one amount must be calculated, the necessary operation is division even if the divisor is not a whole number. Furthermore, grade 5 students have also studied that fractions can be written as decimal numbers. Therefore, students are expected to first determine that this problem can be solved by dividing 2/5 by 3/4. Then students are to think about how 2/5 ÷ 3/4 can be calculated using what they have previously

studied. Although this problem can be solved in many ways, the textbook illustrates one possible approach:

> We can determine how much we can paint with 1 dl of paint by multi-
> plying how much we can paint with 1/4 dl by 4. To find how much we
> can paint with 1/4 dl, we need to divide 2/5 (the amount you can paint
> with 3/4 dl) by 3.

This thinking process can be illustrated on a double number line as shown in
figure 9.11.

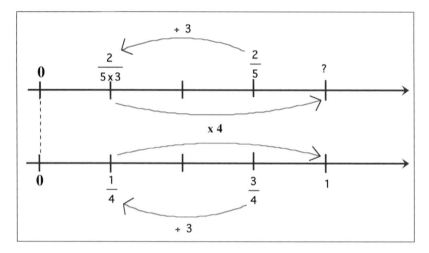

Fig. 9.11. Thinking process illustrated in a double number line

Thus, the quotient of 2/5 ÷ 3/4 can be found by first dividing 2/5 by 3, then
multiplying the result by 4. In other words,

$$\frac{2}{5} \div \frac{3}{4} = \frac{2}{5} \div 3 \times 4.$$

In the Japanese textbook, students have already learned about multiplying and
dividing fractions by whole numbers, so each of the two steps, that is, dividing
by 3 and multiplying by 4, is a part of students' prior knowledge. As a result,
students know that

$$\frac{2}{5} \div 3 = \frac{2}{5 \times 3}, \text{ and } \frac{2}{5 \times 3} \times 4 = \frac{2 \times 4}{5 \times 3}.$$

The textbook then poses the question, What fraction could we have multiplied
2/5 by to get the expression

$$\frac{2 \times 4}{5 \times 3}?$$

Again, from their previous investigation of multiplication of fractions, students can conclude that

$$\frac{2 \times 4}{5 \times 3} = \frac{2}{5} \times \frac{4}{3}.$$

Therefore, they see that

$$\frac{2}{5} \div \frac{3}{4} = \frac{2}{5} \times \frac{4}{3}.$$

Or, in general,

$$\frac{a}{b} \div \frac{c}{d} = \frac{a}{b} \times \frac{d}{c}.$$

The double-number-line representation is a powerful thinking tool for students and also for preservice teachers. For example, after preservice elementary school teachers have investigated fraction and decimal multiplication and division using double-number-line representations, they were posed a problem like the following:

> If a car can travel 90 miles on 4 gallons of gasoline, how far can it travel with 10 gallons of gasoline?

The teachers were able to easily represent this problem on a double number line (fig. 9.12).

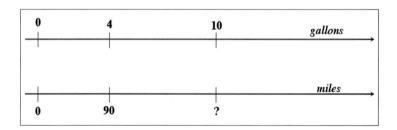

Fig. 9.12. Preservice elementary school teachers represented a missing-value proportion problem using a double number line.

After examining this double number line, some of the preservice teachers noted that it was different from others they had seen previously. The difference was that there was no "1" in this double number line. However, they realized that once a "1" is placed on one of the number lines, the corresponding number can be determined by division. Once they determined the corresponding amount for

1, though, the missing quantity in the original problem could be determined by multiplication. Their thinking process is illustrated in figure 9.13. Thus, by using double number lines as their thinking tool, these preservice elementary school teachers figured out how to solve missing-value proportion problems.

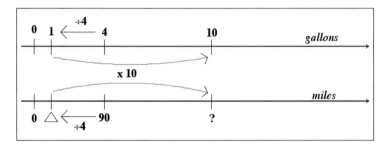

Fig. 9.13. Preservice elementary school teachers used the double number line to solve the missing-value proportion problem meaningfully.

The double number line is also known as a "proportional number line" by Japanese mathematics teachers because it visually represents the underlying proportional relationships between the two quantities involved in both multiplication and division problems. Therefore, for Japanese mathematics teachers, it is an important tool to bridge arithmetic to algebra in the sense of generalized arithmetic.

Concluding Thoughts

In this article, we examined how visual representations are used to support a focused and coherent mathematics curriculum in a Japanese elementary mathematics textbook series. The three primary roles of visual representations are to (1) help students determine the necessary operation to solve a problem, (2) help students think about the process of calculation, and (3) serve as a thinking tool as they engage in challenging tasks. Moreover, visual representations can be a useful tool to bridge between elementary and secondary school mathematics.

The Japanese textbook series shows how visual representations can be used to support mathematical thinking. How these (and other) visual representations are actually developed in classrooms, using textbooks as support, is beyond the scope of this article. Nevertheless, we hope this brief analysis of the ways visual representations are used in Japanese textbooks raises some crucial issues to be considered in our quest for a focused and coherent curriculum in the United States.

REFERENCES

Hironaka, Heisuke, and Yoshishige Sugiyama. *Mathematics for Elementary School.* Tokyo: Tokyo Shoseki, 2006.

Kroll, Diana Lambdin, and Toshiaki Yabe. "A Japanese Educator's Perspective on Teaching Mathematics in Elementary School." *Arithmetic Teacher* 35 (1987): 36–43.

National Council of Teachers of Mathematics (NCTM). *Principles and Standards for School Mathematics.* Reston, Va.: NCTM 2000.

Watanabe, Tad. "Pictorial Presentation of Quantities: Tool for Developing Procedures with Conceptual Understanding." Paper presented at the Annual Meeting of the National Council of Teachers of Mathematics, St. Louis, Mo., April 2006.

10

Cross-National Curriculum Collaboration: Examples Based on Realistic Mathematics Education

Margaret R. Meyer
Truus Dekker
Frank Eade

IN THE early 1990s, the National Science Foundation funded thirteen different mathematics curriculum development projects (Reys 2008). Of the five projects at the middle-grades level, Mathematics in Context (MiC) (National Center for Research in Mathematical Sciences Education and Freudenthal Institute 1997–98) was unique because of its cross-national development team involving mathematics educators at the University of Wisconsin—Madison and curriculum developers at the Freudenthal Institute (FI) at the University of Utrecht in the Netherlands. More than sixteen years later, after contributing to a major revision of MiC, FI was again involved in a collaboration to develop Making Sense of Mathematics (MSM) for use in secondary schools in Manchester, England (Manchester Metropolitan University and Freudenthal Institute, in press). Oceans, cultures, and language separate these countries, and yet successful curriculum collaborations have been possible. What are some lessons learned from these cross-national curriculum collaborations, and how might these lessons inform curriculum consumers?

This article is a conversational reflection among the three authors—Meg from the United States, Truus from the Netherlands, and Frank from England—on what we have learned about curriculum development as a result of our involvement in cross-national curriculum collaborations. Following an overview of the curriculum projects, we offer our perspectives on important lessons learned.

The Development of Mathematics in Context

For six years, mathematics educators from the University of Wisconsin—Madison (Tom Romberg, project director) collaborated with curriculum designers from the Freudenthal Institute at the University of Utrecht in the Netherlands to develop Mathematics in Context, a comprehensive curriculum for grades 5–8. The curriculum work of FI, grounded in the principles of Realistic Mathematics Education (RME) (Webb and Meyer 2007), provided a model for developing mathematics curriculum for the United States. As part of a feasibility study, Romberg invited the FI director, Jan de Lange, to develop and test a data-exploration unit (de Lange et al. 1993, pp. 91–142) in suburban Milwaukee. The success of that collaboration paved the way for FI's involvement in the development of Mathematics in Context.

Although most of the people involved in the development of MiC at the University of Wisconsin had little experience developing instructional materials, they did know school mathematics and United States (U.S.) schools and teachers. This knowledge provided a balance for the people at FI who had many years of mathematics curriculum development experience but limited knowledge of U.S. schools and teachers. (For more information about curriculum reform in the Netherlands, see Case [2005]).

The development process included sending drafts of units back and forth between FI designers and the Wisconsin development team, preparing both the units and teachers for pilot testing, observing the units in pilot classrooms, revising the units, preparing the units and teachers for field testing, analyzing field-test data and revising the units, and finally the publisher's preparing the units for marketing, sales, and distribution. This seemingly linear sequence masks the complexity of the development process, a process made even more complex by the cross-national nature of the MiC project. Because first drafts of all forty units were written in the Netherlands and then "Americanized" at the University of Wisconsin, each team addressed new questions and learned new things. The team from the Freudenthal Institute wondered what prior knowledge could be assumed for students entering U.S. middle schools, what contexts U.S. students would understand and relate to, what an appropriate amount of focus on number skills would be, and how much information U.S. teachers would need to be able to teach with these materials.

On the other side of the ocean, the team from the University of Wisconsin wondered what a "realistic" approach to teaching mathematics meant, how students could engage in complex problem situations without extensive scaffolding, how individual units would fit into the entire curriculum, how the mathematics of a single unit would fit into the grade-level sequence and into the en'⁻° curriculum, and what would be the best way to support the development ber sense and computational fluency while maintaining a balance across ᴜ. content strands. These issues and others were the basis for planning meetings and countless e-mail messages, telephone calls, and overnight courier deliveries (MiC began in the days before electronic document delivery was possible) to negotiate the form and substance of the curriculum materials.

Fast forward to when MiC was complete and commercially available for use in schools. A team of mathematics educators at Manchester Metropolitan University in Manchester, England, introduced MiC into some local schools as part of a research project. On the basis of the success of that project, they began the development of Making Sense of Mathematics to teach "functional skills" to students aged 15–16 in their secondary schools.

The Development of Making Sense of Mathematics

A review of mathematics achievement in England (Smith 2004) identified the need to improve the ability of students to apply mathematics in the workplace on completion of school. In response, the government set up a number of initiatives including an overhaul of the assessment of functional skills at age 16, the age at which English students may opt to leave school. A major concern of a number of mathematics educators in England was understanding how to support students in developing their ability to apply mathematics. The experience with MiC suggested that if the goal is for students to use mathematics, then realistic contexts are needed as a source of the mathematics and as a support for learning the mathematics. A proposal was written to develop materials based on the principles of Realistic Mathematics Education (RME) for use with low- to middle-attaining fourteen- to sixteen-year-old students. The materials were to be similar to MiC in style but would take into account the particular needs of the identified student population in England.

Although MSM dealt with a different age group and a relatively narrow ability range, the principles that sustained MiC were also used to develop MSM. One important difference was the fact that the teacher professional developers and teachers involved in the project had substantial experience with RME. The first challenge for the Freudenthal designers was to appreciate the range of achievement of the students, their previous experience with learning mathematics, and the social issues related to such students. The project built in visits to Manchester for FI developers so that the developers could observe students and classrooms firsthand.

The Manchester development team had its own set of questions and issues to resolve when first using MiC and later when developing MSM. The team members wondered how English students and teachers would relate to a curriculum developed for United States students, whether adaptations would be necessary for the MiC contexts to be meaningful to English students, whether students would ever reach procedural fluency with the RME approach, and whether reaching this procedural fluency should even be the goal of the curriculum.

A Conversation about RME and Lessons Learned

We each learned many things through the process of developing Mathematics in Context and Making Sense of Mathematics. Our conversations about these lessons often centered on three important ideas from Realistic Mathematics Education: context, number models, and progressive formalization. What follows is an attempt to capture the content, if not the spirit, of these conversations. It might help to imagine the three of us talking over cups of tea. We invite the reader to pull up a chair and join us.

Context

Meg: Before working on MiC, I had only experienced two uses of context in math curriculum materials: to promote the study of new mathematics and as a site to apply that mathematics. It never occurred to me that context could also be the source of the mathematics to be studied as well as an anchor for student understanding as it is in MiC (Meyer, Dekker, and Querelle 2001). I am still surprised at how often I hear students identify a strategy or concept by naming the context in which they first encountered it. For example, the following problem (fig. 10.1) from the unit *Comparing Quantities* (Kindt et al. 2006) leads to several solution strategies and representations. Students who use MiC often refer to the "caps and umbrellas" problem when recalling the exchange strategy in which one quantity is exchanged for another.

Truus: What you don't know is how hard it can be for the curriculum designer to find the right context. First of all, you need a context to support the mathematics that you want students to learn. Second, you want a context that students will understand. This does not mean that they always have to have firsthand experience with the context. For example, in MiC we make use of changing

Fig. 10.1. Caps and umbrellas problem

water levels due to the tides to introduce periodic graphs. Even if students have not lived by oceans, they have heard of tides and can make sense of the situation. In another context, we talk about cell division to illustrate the concept of exponential growth. For the sake of the mathematics, we simplify the science aspects of the context. The resulting context is no longer *real* in a strict sense, but it is *realistic,* and the student can begin to use it to make sense of the mathematics. Finally, it is a bonus if students are interested in the context.

Meg: While we are talking about context, we should mention that one cannot take for granted that a context that works in one country will necessarily work in another. For example, in one MiC unit we used ship locks to develop ideas about negative and positive numbers. With all the waterways in the Netherlands, your students are probably very familiar with how locks work to move a ship from one water level to another, but the same is not true in the U.S. I remember preparing a group of teachers to teach that unit and, despite my best efforts, they were hopelessly confused by the context. They could not keep straight which set of doors was open and which set was closed and whether the water level was going up or going down. After working through twelve difficult pages of this context, I finally recommended that they move on to the next section, which presented a context that was more familiar to them. The locks context might have worked if they had more time to develop it, but as it was, instead of supporting the mathematics, it got in the way.

Frank: Some of our teachers using MiC in England worried their students would have trouble doing problems involving American dollars instead of British pounds. In fact, it took the students very little time to adjust, although they sometimes wrote the pound sign with the answer instead of the dollar sign. The context was not the important thing; it was the mathematics that the context supported. When context works well, it supports the learning of the mathematics without getting in the way of that learning.

Number Models

Meg: The use of number models to support understanding of number relationships and operations is another area where I had a lot to learn during the development of MiC. Bar models, ratio tables, and number lines are some of the models I first experienced in MiC. When we first encountered number models, the distinction between a *model of* and a *model for* (Streefland 1993; Gravemeijer 1999) was important for the U.S. development team to understand. After many discussions and examples, here is how I think about it. Imagine a context in which children are sharing submarine sandwiches. A rectangular bar can be used as a *model of* a submarine sandwich, and then one can cut the bar into fractional parts. The rectangular bar is a natural abstraction of the original context. After repeated experience using a rectangular bar as a *model of* various situations, students can use that same abstract bar as a *model for* other situations involving fractional parts (e.g., in a classroom of 20 students, 7 students have 2 or more pets) or to compare and compute percents of quantities (e.g., 15% tip on different restaurant totals), even though a rectangular bar might not be a natural representation as it is with a submarine sandwich.

Truus: That is a good explanation for this concept. The rectangular bar can be used to model many situations, and the visual nature of the model supports students' understanding. Of course, the last step in this process is for students to be able to leave behind the use of the models and to solve the problems using formal, short procedures. Another important number model is the ratio table (Middleton and van den Heuvel-Panhuizen 1995), and I remember that this model was entirely new to both the U.S. and U.K. development teams. The ratio table can support multiplication and division of whole numbers and fractions. Figure 10.2 shows one way that a ratio table might be used to solve the problem:

> Notebooks are shipped with 25 notebooks in one package. Jason ordered 575 notebooks. How many packages will arrive?

The ratio table also helps students organize and solve problems involving proportional reasoning, because it is much more intuitive than the usual cross-multiply algorithm. As a visual representation, ratio tables, like the bar model, can help students organize their thinking and ground their understanding of the procedures they support. In Dutch we say, "Een foto is meer dan duizend woorden," which I think you translate as "A picture is worth a thousand words."

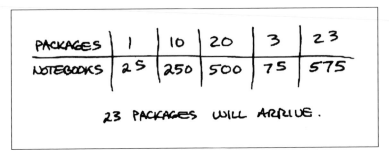

Fig. 10.2. A ratio-table solution

Frank: Exactly! The value of the visual nature of the number models is one of the lessons I learned about MiC when our teachers began to use it. At first, whole-class discussions evaluating the variety of strategies to solve a problem usually took place at only a verbal level: the teacher or students talked and others listened, making little use of visual representations. Now we are much more aware that drawings or models that are visible to all help both short- and long-term shifts in students' understanding. We also see how images can support learners as they move beyond the models into more formal mathematics.

Meg: As I remember, when your teachers began to encourage the use of number models, students and teachers had to make adjustments to an important classroom norm about note taking. Can you talk about how students use notebooks in the U.K. and how teachers had to adjust expectations as a result of using number models?

Frank: Yes, that is a good story that emphasizes the need for professional development. Our students are encouraged to record their class notes and problem-solving attempts in notebooks that are assigned to them at the beginning of each school term. Students are instructed to use the notebooks in an organized and tidy fashion, since the notebooks are technically the property of the school system rather than the individual student. An unexpected consequence of this classroom norm was observed during a MiC lesson involving the use of the bar model to calculate a percent of a number, for example 80 percent of 240. Students were told they should use a percent bar, which is a form of the bar model. There are many different ways to do so with a percent bar. One method (see fig. 10.3) uses reasoning similar to that of a ratio table.

Students find 10 percent (24), then 20 percent by doubling (48 = 2 × 24), and then reason that 80 percent of 240 is the same as 240 less 20 percent (240 − 48 = 192). After a few moments' thought, most students got out their rulers and notebooks and proceeded to draw very precise percent bars in the form of rectangles with carefully measured sides and right-angle corners. Anticipating

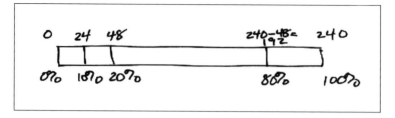

Fig. 10.3. A percent-bar solution

their strategy, some students even measured out the bar so as to accurately be able to find 10 percent and 20 percent. The students were clearly able to represent the problem using the percent bar, but the whole process took significantly more time than was intended. Making the percent bar had become an end in itself rather than a means to an end. There were two likely reasons for this misunderstanding: one was the classroom norm about the use of the notebook, and the other was not thinking of the percent bar as a visual "thinking tool." After this misunderstanding was pointed out, the teacher and his students (and I) were all happy to be able to use the "rough and ready" approach to drawing percent bars and ratio tables. This, however, is still an ongoing issue because government inspection of schools involves looking at the children's books, and neatness is one of the factors used in judging a school's performance.

Truus: I did not realize that Dutch textbooks, assessments, and national exams were very "visual" until my American and English colleagues pointed it out. In developing MiC, we sometimes found it hard to explain that visuals, which include photographs, drawings, and models, are much more than just "something nice" to make a page look more inviting and that by conveying meaning about the context, they support students' thinking. Without the carefully chosen picture, students would not be able to do the problem in the same way. This realization led to heated discussions when the publisher wanted to substitute a carefully chosen picture with one that was perhaps better looking but mathematically different or even meaningless in our eyes.

Meg: The development team didn't always get it right, either. For example, the unit *Comparing Quantities* (Kindt et al. 2006) begins with a story about Paulo, who goes to the market with two sheep and one goat to trade for bags of corn. The solution involves several exchanges. Figure 10.4 shows part of the problem context and accompanying illustrations that appeared in the 1998 and 2006 editions.

Notice that the less detailed 1998 illustration provides a visual representation of that part of the story, whereas the 2006 version conveys no useful information, even though the art is more attractive and color had been added. I am embarrassed to acknowledge that although we saw that a change in art had been made

First he meets Aaron, who says, "I only trade salt for chickens. I will give you one bag of salt for every two chickens."

SALT

1998 illustration   2006 illustration

Fig. 10.4. Old and new problem illustrations

by the publisher, we did not understand the difference this change would make in students' access to the problem until after it was in print. The old black-and-white 1998 version is a much better illustration to further students' understanding.

Progressive Formalization

Truus: As a beginning teacher, I could not understand why many of my students did not seem to "get it" after I did my best to explain a procedure as clearly as I could and after they had practiced with problems of the same kind I showed them. Other times, students seemed to understand what they were doing, but when they encountered a similar problem a few months later, they would say, "We do not know how to do this. We never learned this before." I saw many American and English teachers struggle in the same way. From my work with curriculum development at the Freudenthal Institute, I learned about the idea of *progressive formalization* as a way to structure a learning sequence.

The sequence starts with a real problem, that is, a problem evolving from the world around us that is worth solving. This is the context idea we talked about earlier. At first, students are encouraged to try to solve the problem with *informal* strategies drawing on their understanding and suggested by the problem context itself. The next step in the learning sequence is to present other problems, which at first may seem different to students because the context might differ. However, these problems are based on the same mathematical content and can be solved with *preformal* strategies that become increasingly sophisticated over time. Models, such as the ratio table and bar model, are often used in the informal and preformal stages. Although we want the use of models to be a stage from which most students ultimately move on, students should always be able to go back to them to anchor their understanding. The last step, albeit a difficult one to take, is to leave the context altogether and look only at the mathematical content, to generalize, and be able to reason in a purely mathematical way using *formal* notations and algorithms. Some students may not be able to take this formal step or may take a long time to do so. But at least they have learned some mathematical tools at the informal and preformal levels that they can remember and use with understanding.

Frank: Progressive formalization of students' learning can be illustrated with an iceberg model (Webb, Boswinkel, and Dekker 2008). Figure 10.5 shows an example of the model for the learning of fractions.

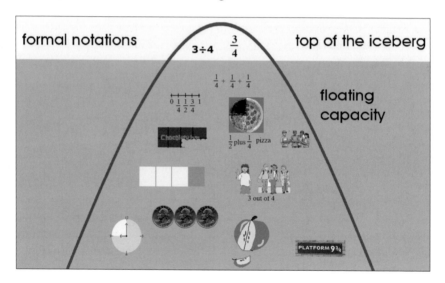

Fig. 10.5. An iceberg model for fractions

The tip of the iceberg model shows formal representations of the learning that we usually hold as a goal for school mathematics. Below the waterline lies the informal and preformal understanding and strategies that are the foundation for the formal mathematics. If we focus only on the tip of the iceberg, we will most likely fail to see how much more students understand. This is especially true if students are not encouraged to reveal their understanding through explanations of their strategies. This model helped us see where contexts—*models of* and *models for*—and formal mathematics fit in with MiC, and most important, it helped me see just how different Realistic Mathematics Education was from the top-level/formal approach that is typically used in England.

Meg: Of all the ideas we have been talking about, the idea of progressive formalization has the most significant implications for teaching and teacher development. With traditional materials, teachers typically introduce concepts or skills and students practice them at a formal level within a relatively short period of time. At the end of the teaching unit, teachers expect a certain degree of mastery. With MiC and MSM, the instructional trajectory often extends beyond a unit, across a grade level, or even across the entire curriculum. As a result, we need to work with teachers so that they do not try to move students to the formal level too fast. Instead, we encourage teachers to value the informal strategies that students come up with and to trust that, over time, the students will move from informal strategies to preformal and finally to formal strategies involving conventional notations. For many teachers, trusting the curriculum materials requires a big leap of faith. This is where professional development is essential. Professional development can allow teachers to experience these ideas as if they themselves were students. We can model for them what it means to expect students to explain how their strategies relate to the problem situation and how they end in a solution to the problem. When we are successful in modeling this outcome, teachers get excited about their own learning and they never want to go back to their old ways of teaching.

Truus: After visiting a large number of schools, both in the U.S. and in the U.K., I realized that teachers and their professional development are a very important factor in the success of a curriculum implementation. It is possible, for example, to use MiC in a very traditional way. In England as well as in U.S. classrooms, I often meet teachers who are afraid to give students control and responsibility of their own learning. Teachers often feel they are the ones solely responsible for the teaching and learning process, instead of the students' gradually taking ownership and being responsible for their own learning, with guidance, of course, from the teacher. We, the designers of MiC, often built in hurdles in the form of difficult problems to challenge the students. The teachers' response to these problems is often, "My students cannot do this," and then they proceed to break the problems down into small, feasible steps or in many cases to show the students how to do the problem. No challenge remains if every problem you try to solve is made easy for you.

Final Thoughts

The process of cross-national curriculum collaboration resulted in significant learning for each of us. Had we not limited ourselves in the paper to important insights, we would certainly have talked about more mundane collaboration issues, such as learning to translate from Dutch to English, interpreting unfamiliar contexts, and the like. Those issues turned out to be much less important than one might have imagined. Instead, what came to the forefront were important features of curricula based on the ideas of Realistic Mathematics Education—such things as context, number models, progressive formalization, and the growth of teachers and the learning of students through the use of well-designed curriculum materials.

REFERENCES

Case, Robert W. "The Dutch Revolution in Secondary School Mathematics." *Mathematics Teacher* 98 (February 2005): 374–84.

de Lange, Jan, Gail Burrill, Thomas A. Romberg, and Martin van Reeuwijk. *Learning and Testing Mathematics in Context: The Case—Data Visualization.* University of Wisconsin—Madison, National Center for Research in Mathematics Education, 1993.

Gravemeijer, Koeno. "How Emergent Models May Foster the Constitution of Formal Mathematics." *Mathematical Thinking and Learning* 1 (1999): 155–77.

Kindt, Martin, Mieke Abels, Margaret R. Meyer, Margaret A. Pligge, and Gail Burrill. "Comparing Quantities." In *Mathematics in Context,* edited by the Wisconsin Center for Education Research and Freudenthal Institute. Chicago: Encyclopaedia Britannica, 2006.

Manchester Metropolitan University and Freudenthal Institute, eds. *Making Sense of Mathematics.* Great Britain: Gatsby Charitable Foundation, in press.

Meyer, Margaret R., Truus Dekker, and Nanda Querelle. "Context in Mathematics Curricula." *Mathematics Teaching in the Middle School* 6 (May 2001): 522–27.

Middleton, James A., and Marja van den Heuvel-Panhuizen. "The Ratio Table." *Mathematics Teaching in the Middle School* 1 (January–March 1995): 282–88.

National Center for Research in Mathematical Sciences Education and Freudenthal Institute, eds. *Mathematics in Context.* Chicago: Encyclopaedia Britannica, 1997–1998.

Reys, Robert. "The Road to Reform." In *A Decade of Middle School Mathematics Curriculum Implementation: Lessons Learned from the Show-Me Project,* edited by Margaret R. Meyer and Cynthia W. Langrall, pp. 3–8. Charlotte, N.C.: Information Age Publishing, 2008.

Smith, Adrian. "Making Mathematics Count: The Report of Professor Adrian Smith's Inquiry into Post-14 Mathematics Education." London: Her Majesty's Stationery Office, 2004.

Streefland, Leen. "The Design of a Mathematical Course: A Theoretical Reflection." *Educational Studies in Mathematics* 25 (July–September 1993): 109–35.

Webb, David C., and Margaret R. Meyer. "The Case of Mathematics in Context." In *Perspectives on the Design and Development of School Mathematics Curricula,* edited by Christian R. Hirsch, pp. 81–94. Reston, Va.: National Council of Teachers of Mathematics, 2007.

Webb, David C., Nina Boswinkel, and Truus Dekker. "Beneath the Tip of the Iceberg: Using Representations to Support Student Understanding." *Mathematics Teaching in the Middle School* 14 (September 2008): 110–13.

11

Three Perspectives on the Central Objects of Study for Grades Pre-K–8 Statistics

Randall E. Groth

OVER THE course of the past two decades, the subject of statistics has gained prominence in grades pre-K–8 mathematics education. Once a subject largely reserved for study at the upper secondary school and university levels, such prominent national groups as the National Council of Teachers of Mathematics (NCTM) and the American Statistical Association (ASA) now recommend that students begin to build knowledge of statistics early on in their school experiences (NCTM 2000; Franklin et al. 2007). These recommendations have contributed to a proliferation of curricular materials designed to support grades pre-K–8 students' learning of statistics as well as inclusion of learning expectations related to statistics in state-level standards. Now the study of statistics is part of students' earliest experiences in mathematics classrooms.

Given the acknowledged importance of statistics, a foundational question remains regarding curriculum development: *What are the fundamental objects of study in grades pre-K–8 statistics?* Chazan (2000) argued that even with a long-standing curricular mainstay such as algebra, debate could ensue over what the fundamental objects of study should be. Algebra can be conceptualized, for example, as the study of generalized arithmetic, the study of equations, or the study of functions. Although all three notions of algebra may enter a curriculum at some point, they exert varying degrees of influence over how the subject is portrayed. Curriculum developers and teachers must make decisions about which points of view should be included, which should be emphasized, and which order of presentation should be used. Such decisions shape the curriculum and unavoidably bring some objects of study to the foreground while moving others to the background.

In grades pre-K–8 statistics, choices must be made about which fundamental objects of study should be moved to the foreground. As with algebra, several competing candidates are found. In this article, I consider three such candidates: (1) mathematical procedures, (2) mathematical concepts, and (3) the process of statistical investigation. I focus on these three approaches because they exert different amounts of influence in prominent curriculum documents that seek to guide grades pre-K–8 statistics instruction: state-level standards, NCTM's *Curriculum Focal Points for Prekindergarten through Grade 8 Mathematics* (NCTM 2006), and the American Statistical Association's *Guidelines for Assessment and Instruction in Statistics Education (GAISE) Report* (Franklin et al. 2007).

A Two-Part Framework for Selecting Objects of Study

One important consideration in selecting objects of study for curriculum development is the level of *cognitive demand* that tasks related to those objects of study may require. Henningsen and Stein (1997) described four prevalent levels of cognitive demand of tasks. They can be summarized, from lowest to highest level, as follows:

- *Memorization*—tasks involving memorization and recitation of facts, rules, or definitions

- *Procedures without connections to concepts or meaning*—tasks using previously learned procedures

- *Procedures with connections to concepts and meaning*—tasks requiring the use of a procedure while prompting students to engage with the procedure's conceptual underpinnings

- *Doing mathematics*—tasks having no prespecified solution method, in which students must draw on conceptual understandings to devise solution strategies

Engaging students in classroom tasks with higher levels of demand is fundamental to the instructional vision outlined in NCTM's *Principles and Standards for School Mathematics.* Therefore, the three candidates for central objects of study in statistics are discussed subsequently relative to their likelihood to support tasks with high levels of cognitive demand.

A second consideration in evaluating candidates for central objects of study is how each one portrays the discipline of statistics. Some statisticians have argued that statistics should be considered a discipline in its own right rather than a branch of mathematics (Cobb and Moore 1997). Although mathematical tools are essential to doing statistics, so are many activities that are primarily non-mathematical, such as constructing survey questions, designing experiments, and understanding the contexts in which data are generated (Groth 2007). Hence, a curriculum that maintains fidelity to the discipline of statistics will include opportunities to develop nonmathematical, as well as mathematical, competencies for doing statistics.

Candidate 1: Mathematical Procedures

Grades pre-K–8 curricula sometimes portray statistics as the study of mathematical procedures. Some learning expectations in state-level curriculum documents for statistics are illustrative:

- Grade 3: "Construct and interpret bar graphs using scale increments of 1, 2, 5, and 10" (Georgia Department of Education 2006, p. 5).

- Grade 5: "Determine the mean of a given data set or data display. Assessment limit: Use no more than 8 pieces of data and whole numbers without remainders (0–1000)" (Maryland State Department of Education 2004, p. 10).

Such curricular statements imply that the instructional end goal should be to prepare students to perform mathematical procedures for producing graphs and summary statistics.

Emphasizing mathematical procedures as central objects of study in statistics has some potential drawbacks. One danger is that tasks with low levels of cognitive demand can begin to dominate the curriculum. Bakker (2004) observed that grades pre-K–8 statistics instruction is often simplified to carrying out procedures for producing graphs and such summary statistics as the arithmetic mean. Students' tasks in such situations are lowered to the cognitive demand level of "procedures without connections" because they can be accomplished simply by using procedures directly from prior instruction.

Not all statistical tasks that emphasize mathematical procedures, however, necessarily fall at low levels of cognitive demand. Some tasks may require students to exhibit flexibility in thinking as well as in executing procedures. Cai (2000) provided an example of such a task related to the procedure for determining the arithmetic mean (fig. 11.1). Sixth-grade students used several different strategies to solve the task. Some found out how many hats should be sold in week 4 by working with a related scenario in which seven hats were sold each week (average as a leveling process). Others represented the situation with an algebraic equation and solved it. Still others used a guess-and-check strategy, trying out different values for the number of hats sold in week 4. The task had a considerable amount of cognitive demand because no prespecified solution path was given for students to follow.

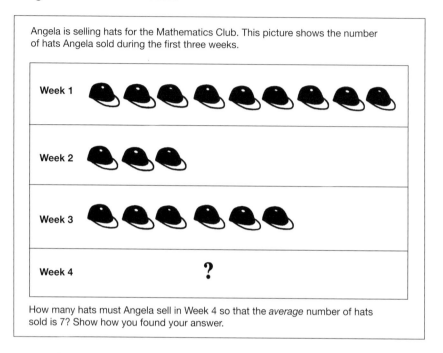

Angela is selling hats for the Mathematics Club. This picture shows the number of hats Angela sold during the first three weeks.

Week 1

Week 2

Week 3

Week 4   ?

How many hats must Angela sell in Week 4 so that the *average* number of hats sold is 7? Show how you found your answer.

Fig. 11.1. Task involving the arithmetic mean (from Cai [2000], reprinted by permission of Taylor & Francis Ltd.)

Even if tasks at high levels of cognitive demand are posed in curricula that emphasize mathematical procedures, care must be taken to maintain fidelity to the discipline of statistics. If mathematical procedures are the central objects of study, then nonmathematical elements of the discipline could be lost. With the arithmetic mean, for example, students need to go beyond just having a deep understanding of the mathematics of the mean. In doing statistics, context must be taken into account in deciding how to deal with a task such as the following (Groth 2006, p. 41):

> Students' grading task: Seven 100-point tests were given during the fall semester. Erika's scores on the tests were 76, 82, 82, 79, 85, 25, and 83. What grade should Erika receive for the semester?

In this situation, the decision of whether to use the mean must be justified on the basis of problem context. Multiple viable decisions based on contextual interpretations are possible. I encourage readers to pose this task to their own students, encouraging them to produce multiple reasonable conclusions by arguing from the problem context.

Candidate 2: Mathematical Concepts

Another way to frame the study of statistics in grades pre-K–8 is to concentrate on the development of mathematics concepts. This approach appears to be embraced by NCTM's *Curriculum Focal Points* (2006). In discussing the treatment of data analysis in the *Focal Points,* Schielack and Seeley (2007) stated that prior to grade 8, "students use data sets as contexts for strengthening their understanding of number, operations, measurement, and geometry" (p. 208). For example, in kindergarten, the examination of data sets is recommended as a context to help develop counting abilities: "they [students] might collect data and use counting to answer such questions as, 'What is our favorite snack?'" (NCTM 2006, p. 12). In this instance, the mathematical concept of counting is foregrounded, rather than such aspects of data collection as conjecturing whether similar results would be obtained if the snack survey were done in a different class.

Emphasis on mathematical concepts as central objects of study continues through grades 3–5 in *Curriculum Focal Points*. Schielack and Seeley characterized statistical data representations as "important problem-solving tools in grades 3–5 that strengthen the development of concepts related to number and operations" (p. 209). Throughout grades 3–5, *Curriculum Focal Points* recommends the study of graphical representations of data because of the opportunities they provide to develop students' conceptions of number and operations:

- Grade 3: "Addition, subtraction, multiplication, and division of whole numbers come into play as students construct and analyze frequency tables, bar graphs, picture graphs, and line plots and use them to solve problems" (p. 15).

- Grade 4: "Students continue to use tools from grade 3, solving problems by making frequency tables, bar graphs, picture graphs, and line plots. They apply their understanding of place value to develop and use stem-and-leaf plots" (p. 16).

- Grade 5: "Students apply their understanding of whole numbers, fractions, and decimals as they construct and analyze double-bar and line graphs and use ordered pairs on coordinate grids" (p. 17).

Emphasizing the study of graphical displays for helping students develop deeper understanding of number and operation can be contrasted with analyzing graphical displays to make inferences about the populations and contexts they represent. Although students may still make such inferences as they study graphs, the foregoing curricular statements characterize the mathematics of graph construction as the central objects of study rather than "reading beyond the data" to make inferences from graphs.

After grades 3 through 5, "*Curriculum Focal Points* for grades 6 through 8 continue with the use of data as a context for problem solving and further development and application of mathematical ideas" (Schielack and Seeley 2007, p. 209). Mathematical ideas developed by using data sets in grades 6 through 8 include attention to proportions and percents. Specifically, in grade 7, "Students use proportions to make estimates relating to a population on the basis of a sample. They apply percentages to make and interpret histograms and circle graphs" (NCTM 2006, p. 19). To illustrate how this curricular statement emphasizes the study of mathematical concepts, it may be helpful to consider a possible reformulation that places nonmathematical elements of statistics as central objects of study: "Students formulate and use techniques to draw trustworthy samples from populations of interest. They choose appropriate mathematical tools, including proportions, to support their investigations." This reformulation emphasizes the study of techniques for drawing trustworthy samples rather than the mathematical concept of proportion. In so doing, it shifts the study of mathematics concepts to the background while placing an essential nonmathematical aspect of statistical practice in the foreground.

Curricula that emphasize mathematical concepts can promote tasks that fall at a variety of levels of cognitive demand. Consider the following two tasks:

> Sample task 1: At Central Middle School, 42% of all students participate in athletics. If you picked a random sample of 50 students from the school, how many would you expect to be athletes?

> Sample task 2: A biologist captured and tagged 40 fish from a lake. A week later, she caught 30 fish, and 12 of them were tagged. On the basis of her data, how many fish do you believe are in the lake?

Sample task 1 requires the straightforward computation of 42 percent of 50, and hence could be considered a low level of cognitive demand for students who have learned how to make this computation and have done similar items in the past. Sample task 2, although incorporating similar mathematics concepts, is not as straightforward. It requires proportional reasoning rather than simple execution of a previously learned procedure. Students must reason that the biologist likely tagged two-fifths of the fish in the lake, and then determine which number has 40 as two-fifths of its value. Although the problems appear to address similar concepts, the complexity of thought needed to solve each one varies.

Candidate 3: The Process of Statistical Investigation

Whereas the NCTM *Curriculum Focal Points* recommend a grades pre-K–8 statistics curriculum that emphasizes the study of mathematical concepts, the

ASA report *Guidelines for Assessment and Instruction in Statistics Education (GAISE)* (Franklin et al. 2007) suggests a curriculum that foregrounds the process of statistical investigation. The GAISE report uses a four-component statistical problem-solving process to frame its curricular recommendations for statistics instruction (fig. 11.2). The four components of the framework are (1) formulate questions, (2) collect data, (3) analyze data, and (4) interpret results. Students are to engage to some extent with each of the four components as they progress through three developmental levels (A, B, and C) related to the study of school statistics. As they move through the levels, they study progressively more sophisticated ideas about such concepts as experimental design, variability, descriptive statistics, and ways in which context should influence the interpretation of data. The three developmental levels are not tied to specific grade levels, although activities recommended for levels A and B bear resemblance to those often done in elementary and middle school.

Some examples from level A of the GAISE report illustrate the experiences that students may have in a statistics curriculum that emphasizes the process of statistical investigation:

- "Example 1: Choosing the Band for the End-of-the-Year Party—Conducting a Survey" (Franklin et al. 2007, p. 24): Students are to conduct a survey to determine the types of music preferred by students at their grade level. The goals of the activity include helping students recognize individual-to-individual variability, begin to understand the mode as a useful measure for summarizing categorical data, and think about if and how the survey results might vary for different populations.

- "Example 2: Growing Beans—a Simple Comparative Experiment" (Franklin et al. 2007, p. 28): Students plant beans in two different locations—one that is well lit and another that is poorly lit. They are to compare the growth in each location. As they graph the data, students are to attend to the shapes of the distributions of heights of the bean plants in the two locations.

In example 1, a curriculum that foregrounds mathematics procedures may include the same type of activity but may emphasize mathematical actions, such as counting, rather than statistical actions, such as understanding variability and thinking about the extent to which the findings can be generalized. Likewise, if the activity described in example 2 were included in a curriculum emphasizing mathematical procedures, proper graph construction might be portrayed as the central activity of value rather than understanding the idea of statistical distribution.

Once students have developed foundational ideas related to statistical investigation at level A, they are to continue to build on them at level B. In the first

Process Component	Level A	Level B	Level C
I. Formulate Question	Beginning awareness of the *statistics question distinction* Teachers pose questions of interest Questions restricted to the classroom	Increased awareness of the *statistics question distinction* Students begin to pose their own questions of interest Questions not restricted to the classroom	Students can make the *statistics question distinction* Students pose their own questions of interest Questions seek generalization
II. Collect Data	Do not yet *design for differences* Census of classroom Simple experiment	Beginning awareness of *design for differences* Sample surveys; begin to use random selection Comparative experiment; begin to use random allocation	Students make *design for differences* Sampling designs with random selection Experimental designs with randomization
III. Analyze Data	Use particular properties of *distributions* in the context of a specific example Display variability within a group Compare individual to individual Compare individual to group Beginning awareness of group to group Observe association between two variables	Learn to use particular properties of distributions as tools of analysis Quantify variability within a group Compare group to group in displays Acknowledge sampling error Some quantification of association; simple models for association	Understand and *use distributions* in analysis as a global concept Measure variability within a group; measure variability between groups
IV. Interpret Results	Students do not look *beyond the data* No generalization beyond the classroom Note difference between two individuals with different conditions Observe association in displays	Students acknowledge that *looking beyond the data is feasible* Acknowledge that a sample may or may not be representative of the larger population Note the differences between two groups with different conditions Aware of distinction between observational study and experiment Note differences in strength of association Basic interpretation of models for association Aware of the distinction between association and cause and effect	Students are able to *look beyond the data* in some contexts Generalize from sample to population Aware of the effect of randomization on the results of experiments Understand the difference between observational studies and experiments Interpret measures of strength of association Interpret models of association Distinguish between conclusions from association studies and experiments
Nature of Variability	Measurement variability Natural variability Induced variability	Sampling variability	Chance variability
Focus on Variability	Variability within a group	Variability within a group and variability between groups Covariability	Variability in model fitting

Fig. 11.2. Summary of the GAISE framework

example ("Choosing the Band for the End-of-the-Year Party"), the GAISE report recommends that students use more sophisticated mathematical and nonmathematical ideas to analyze the situation. The mathematical ideas include using percents and fractions to make comparisons between populations rather than just report raw frequencies. The nonmathematical ideas to be explored include how rephrasing the survey question might be likely to influence the data that are obtained. Mathematical and nonmathematical ideas are to be used in tandem to support the statistical problem-solving process.

Readers should note that the statistical problem-solving process portrayed as a central object of study in the GAISE document differs in at least two subtle, yet important, ways from the mathematical problem-solving process. First, the role played by real-world contexts differs. Cobb and Moore (1997, p. 803) captured this difference by stating,

> *In mathematics, context obscures structure.* Like mathematicians, data analysts also look for patterns, but ultimately, in data analysis, whether the patterns have meaning, and whether they have any value, depends on how the threads of those patterns interweave with the complementary threads of the story line. *In data analysis, context provides meaning.*

Mathematical problem solving ultimately peels back context to uncover underlying mathematical structure, whereas the GAISE statistical problem-solving process emphasizes that context must be considered throughout the process so that interpretations of data are viable. A second major difference between statistical and mathematical problem solving is the certainty with which the results of the problem-solving process should be reported. In mathematics, it is common practice to pose a question with the intent of producing a proof that contains a decisive answer, but in statistics it is common practice to pose a question and then gather evidence to form conditional conclusions. This means that the statistical problem-solving process often yields multiple viable solutions to problems of interest rather than single, decisive answers.

What Value Is Obtained in Identifying Central Objects of Study?

I encourage readers to reflect on the central objects of study in the statistics curriculum they teach: examine the standards documents that drive the curriculum, as well as available instructional activities and assessments. Readers who are teacher educators or policymakers can do the same sort of reflection in regard to the curriculum the teachers they serve are responsible for teaching. Is the curriculum structured around the study of mathematical procedures, mathematical concepts, or the process of statistical investigation? Thinking carefully about the central objects of study can help one avoid pitfalls that occur when implementing the different types of curricula.

Avoiding Pitfalls When Mathematical Procedures or Concepts Are Central Objects of Study

As mentioned previously, mathematical procedures are portrayed as central objects of study in some state-level mathematics standards. Some of the state-level standards are currently under revision in response to the NCTM (2006) *Focal Points* document. Hence, many mathematics teachers are likely to find themselves in the position of being charged with implementing standards for statistics that emphasize either mathematics concepts or procedures. Teachers generally are not at liberty to overhaul state guidelines completely, yet some classroom-level actions can be taken to maintain the quality of statistics instruction in such situations.

First, teachers can attend to the level of cognitive demand in the tasks given to students. Rather than focus on the execution of an algorithm, a teacher can make subtle shifts in questioning to help students dissect the problem. For example, rather than ask students to calculate the mean of a data set, ask them to examine and discuss how removing different values from the set influences the mean. Also, such comparative questions as "How does the mean compare to the median as a measure of center?" prompt students to examine the mathematics behind each procedure and to understand the concept that both can be used to estimate centers in some data sets. Producing data sets to fit a given summary statistic instead of asking students to compute the summary statistics is also useful—students might be given a correlation coefficient and be asked to devise a scatter plot that would produce it. Such tasks help students develop deeper understanding of the mathematics of procedures commonly used in statistics, as well as the meanings and purposes of the procedures, thus helping build conceptual understanding.

Students must also be provided with opportunities to engage in the nonmathematical activities of the process of statistical investigation. These elements can easily be lost in curricula that emphasize mathematics concepts or procedures. Students should, at least occasionally, be asked to design questions of their own to investigate. They need to develop an appreciation of the role that context plays in choosing and interpreting statistics. This outcome can sometimes be accomplished by slight shifts in teachers' questioning, as illustrated in the "grade assigning" task earlier in this chapter. When confronted with this type of novel situation, students may invent their own summary statistics or graphs to make sense of the task, much as statisticians do when they encounter a new type of problem. Student-invented strategies can then be compared with the conventional summary statistics and graphs suggested by the curriculum.

Avoiding Pitfalls When the Process of Statistical Investigation Is the Central Object of Study

When students are allowed to devise their own graphs and summary statistics during statistical investigations, they may not focus on conventional tools of the discipline of statistics. A legitimate concern, then, is that students may not become familiar with tools commonly used by statisticians if the process of statistical investigation is central to the curriculum. If this outcome were to occur, students would have difficulty understanding the statistical claims that infuse everyday discourse. Developing such statistical literacy is a primary motivation for the inclusion of statistics in school curricula. Given this concern, teachers charged with teaching such curricula need to actively seek opportunities that compare student-invented strategies with those used by statisticians. Students can be encouraged to examine how the functions their strategies serve compare with those of conventional statistical tools.

A second possible pitfall associated with curricula that place the process of statistical investigation in the foreground is related to level of cognitive demand. Henningsen and Stein (1997) described two ways that investigation-oriented tasks can break down: (1) When the teacher allows completely unstructured exploration and students disregard the original task, and (2) when the teacher lowers the level of cognitive demand in the task in response to pressures from students for the "right" answer or procedure. Maintaining a middle ground between these two extremes is vital to ensuring that curricula emphasizing statistical investigation are successful. To avoid the first extreme, teachers can reflect on such questions as "Which student ideas should I seize to move the class forward?" and the perhaps more difficult question, "Which student-created strategies will not be fruitful to pursue?" To avoid the second extreme, the question "How can I avoid giving away too much of the problem?" is helpful to consider for each task.

Conclusion

The consequences associated with choosing any of the three candidates for central objects of study for grades pre-K–8 statistics should be weighed carefully. Choosing the first candidate, mathematical procedures, can at times encourage classroom tasks at low levels of cognitive demand. This scenario appears to have played out to an extent in U.S. classrooms (Bakker 2004), alongside the production of state-level standards documents for statistics that emphasize mathematical procedures. Choosing the second candidate, mathematical concepts, can help remedy an overemphasis on mathematical procedures. However, nonmathematical aspects of doing statistics may be underemphasized in such an approach. Choosing the third candidate, the process of statistical investigation, helps ensure study of nonmathematical aspects of statistics alongside mathematical ones.

Under such an approach, teachers must monitor students' work constantly to steer students' statistical investigations in productive directions.

Although teachers are on the "front lines" in terms of implementing curricula, curriculum developers and writers of standards also have important roles to play in offering high-quality experiences to grades pre-K–8 students studying statistics. Curriculum materials and standards documents should not, intentionally or unintentionally, emphasize tasks with low levels of cognitive demand nor deemphasize nonmathematical aspects of doing statistics. Helping students carry out statistical investigations is an important goal that should go hand in hand with learning the mathematics of statistical tools with understanding. In curriculum materials and standards documents that take care to maintain fidelity to the discipline of statistics, learning the mathematics of statistical tools with understanding will support rather than overshadow the goal of helping students become critical consumers and producers of statistical investigations.

REFERENCES

Bakker, Arthur. "Reasoning about Shape as a Pattern in Variability." *Statistics Education Research Journal* 3, no. 2 (November 2004): 64–83. http://www.stat.auckland .ac.nz/~iase/serj/SERJ3(2)_Bakker.pdf, November 6, 2007.

Cai, Jinfa. "Understanding and Representing the Arithmetic Averaging Algorithm: An Analysis and Comparison of U.S. and Chinese Students' Responses." *International Journal of Mathematical Education in Science and Technology* 31 (November 2000): 839–55.

Chazan, Daniel. *Beyond Formulas in Mathematics and Teaching.* New York: Teachers College Press, 2000.

Cobb, George W., and David S. Moore. "Mathematics, Statistics, and Teaching." *American Mathematical Monthly* 104 (November 1997): 801–23.

Franklin, Christine, Gary Kader, Denise Mewborn, Jerry Moreno, Roxy Peck, Mike Perry, and Richard Scheaffer. *Guidelines for Assessment and Instruction in Statistics Education (GAISE) Report: A Pre-K–12 Curriculum Framework.* Alexandria, Va.: American Statistical Association, 2007.

Georgia Department of Education. *Mathematics Georgia Performance Standards.* Atlanta, Ga.: Georgia Department of Education, 2006. http://public.doe.k12 .ga.us/DMGetDocument.aspx/Standards%203-5%20July%202006.pdf?p=6CC679 9F8C1371F6F312729661D7CB3B04B6678D6C100088654A122171035388& Type=D, November 6, 2007.

Groth, Randall E. "Engaging Students in Authentic Data Analysis." In *Thinking and Reasoning with Data and Chance,* Sixty-eighth Yearbook of the National Council of Teachers of Mathematics (NCTM), edited by Gail F. Burrill, pp. 41–48. Reston, Va.: NCTM, 2006.

———. "Toward a Conceptualization of Statistical Knowledge for Teaching." *Journal for Research in Mathematics Education* 38 (November 2007): 427–37.

Henningsen, Marjorie, and Mary Kay Stein. "Mathematical Tasks and Student Cognition: Classroom-Based Factors That Support and Inhibit High-Level Mathematical Thinking and Reasoning." *Journal for Research in Mathematics Education* (November 1997): 524–49.

Maryland State Department of Education. *Voluntary State Curriculum—Mathematics Grades 3–8*. Baltimore: Maryland State Department of Education, 2004. http://mdk12.org/share/vsc/vsc_mathematics_gr38.pdf (accessed November 6, 2007).

National Council of Teachers of Mathematics (NCTM). *Principles and Standards for School Mathematics*. Reston, Va.: NCTM, 2000.

———. *Curriculum Focal Points for Prekindergarten through Grade 8 Mathematics: A Quest for Coherence*. Reston, Va.: NCTM, 2006.

Schielack, Jane F., and Cathy Seeley. "A Look at the Development of Data Representation and Analysis in *Curriculum Focal Points: A Quest for Coherence*." *Mathematics Teaching in the Middle School* 13 (November 2007): 208–10.

12

Designing Curricula to Expand and Extend Mathematical Knowledge

Debra I. Johanning

A COHERENT curriculum develops deep mathematical understanding by focusing on important topics of study. It also extends understanding "with work in later grades building on and deepening what students have learned in the earlier grades, without repetitious and inefficient reteaching" (NCTM 2006, p. 5). Schielack and Seeley (2007) suggest that as a topic is developed across grades, the instructional emphasis should shift from the background to the foreground and then again to the background.

This article presents examples of instructional tasks that illustrate how their placement in a middle-grades curriculum provides both foreground and background emphasis that can lead to a deeper understanding of fractions. What is notable about the tasks is that they are not taken from curriculum units that explicitly focus on fractions. Instead, the tasks are taken from units that follow the explicit study of fractions. The first instructional task, taken from a curriculum unit on decimal operations, places fractions in the foreground, explicitly using fractions to support the development of new content, decimal operations. The second task, taken from a curriculum unit on similarity, places scale factor and area-perimeter relationships in the foreground. Fractions emerge in the background when a fractional scale factor is used. These two examples show ways in which the curriculum can be organized to provide continuing, nonrepetitive experiences for students, leading to a deeper understanding of fractions and a richer, more connected understanding of mathematics.

Designing Curricula That Support Learning to Use Mathematics

For students to *learn to use* mathematical knowledge in meaningful ways, they need planned instructional opportunities that connect the concepts and techniques studied to other areas of mathematics. Consider fractions as a topic of study for middle-grades students. When learning about fractions, instruction typically focuses on developing part-whole reasoning; the role of the numerator and denominator; how the numerator and denominator are related; comparing and ordering fractions; developing meaning for, and connections among, different forms of representations (fractions, decimals, and percents); equivalence; benchmarks and estimation; and operations with fractions. However, research has shown that when new settings are encountered, such as area and perimeter, similarity, and ratio and proportions, students do not readily use what they have previously learned about fractions (Johanning 2008). Once students have learned about fractions, they need to have repeated opportunities *learning how to use* this knowledge in other mathematical contexts.

The perspective argued here is that if a curriculum is cumulative rather than repetitive, it should provide opportunities to use the knowledge gained about a particular topic in subsequent instructional units. For example, understanding how to use fractions is tied to understanding situations in which they can be used and the various ways that fractions and other mathematical content are connected (Thompson 1995). Streefland (1991) refers to this interaction of knowledge as intertwining the learning lines. Rather than single out fractions as a topic of study, one might consider how fractions are situated in other mathematical content and contexts. Designers of curriculum materials should carefully consider what aspects of fractions are appropriate as part of a curriculum unit on fractions and what aspects of fractions are better served by introducing them in curriculum units where they can be used as a context for learning new material and to support connections across content.

One goal of a coherent curriculum is to continually build on and connect the big ideas from one unit or topic to others so that students use previously explored concepts and procedures in new settings. This approach is intended to promote fluency and proficiency in one topic while exploring another (Lappan and Phillips 1998). Learning to use fractions involves taking what students know and understand about fractions (learned in fraction curriculum units in which fractions are in the foreground) and recognizing how and when those ideas and skills can be applied in new settings. This outcome implies more than assigning application homework problems. Instead, fractions should be placed in either the background or foreground of instructional tasks that students explore and discuss when learning new mathematical content. Doing so requires a conceptualization of curriculum that looks across grade levels and across mathematical content. In line with the goals of *Curriculum Focal Points for Prekindergarten through Grade 8 Mathematics* (NCTM 2006), this organization of a curriculum emphasizes connections across mathematical topics.

The tasks presented in this article are taken from instructional units that follow two sixth-grade units focused on learning about fractions and fraction operations. In this curriculum, fractions are foregrounded or explicitly developed in these two sixth-grade units. Fractions are not formally retaught in seventh or eighth grade. However, across the remainder of sixth grade, in seventh grade, and in eighth grade, students revisit fractions in other instructional units, such as area and perimeter, decimal operations, probability, similarity, integers, ratio and proportion, and algebra. Found in these subsequent units are tasks that use fractions. Some of these tasks place fractions in the foreground, and others place them in the background. Examples illustrating each approach are shared in the next section.

Learning to Use Fractions by Foregrounding Fractions with Work on Decimal Operations

One approach to the development of decimal operations is to build the meaning of computational procedures for decimal operations on prior work with fraction operations. Consider the task Adding and Subtracting Decimals (Lappan et al. 2008) in figure 12.1. After students discuss what they know about place value and adding and subtracting in situations with money, they are introduced to a task (fig 12.1) that asks them to use what they know about place value and money, as well as measurement, to solve a set of decimal addition and subtraction problems.

After working on this task, students share their strategies for finding decimal sums and differences. Although an algorithm may emerge, the goal of this discussion is to push students to consider why they need to line up the decimal points. The discussion of this task is used to set up a second task, in which students write their original decimal-number sentences using fraction form with denominators of 10, 100, 1000, and so on. The fraction-number sentences are recorded in the second column of the table in the Adding and Subtracting Decimals task. Drawing from what was learned in an earlier curriculum unit on fraction operations,

ADDING AND SUBTRACTING DECIMALS TASK

Every year, the students at Memorial High School volunteer to clean local highway roadsides. Each club or team at the school is assigned a section of highway to clean. One member of a club measures out each member's part of the section of the highway using a trundle wheel. A trundle wheel can measure distances in thousandths of a mile.

A. Solve each problem. Write a mathematical sentence using decimal notation to show your computation. Record your sentence in a table like the one below.

You will add to your table in the next problem.

Person	Number Sentence (decimal notation)	(Leave this column blank for the next problem.)
Carmela		
Pam		
Jim		
Teri		

1. Carmela signed up to clean 1.5 miles for the cross-country team. It starts to rain after she has cleaned 0.25 of a mile. How much does she have left to clean?

2. Pam cleans 0.25 of a mile for the chorus and cleans another 0.375 of a mile for the math club. How much does she clean altogether?

3. Jim, a member of the chess club, first cleans 0.287 of mile. He later cleans another 0.02 of a mile. How much of a mile does he clean altogether?

4. Teri doesn't notice that she finished her section of highway until she is 0.005 of a mile past her goal of 0.85 of a mile. She claims she cleaned nine-tenths of a mile. Is she correct? Explain.

B. 1. Explain what place value has to do with adding and subtracting decimals.

2. Use your ideas about place value and adding and subtracting decimals to solve the following problems:

a. 27.9 + 103.2   b. 0.45 + 1.2

c. 2.011 + 1.99   d. 34.023 − 1.23

e. 4.32 − 1.746   f. 0.982 − 0.2

Fig. 12.1. Adding and Subtracting Decimals task, adapted with permission from Lappan et al. (2008)

the techer asks the students, "How does the fraction method help explain why you can line up the decimals and add digits with the same place values to find the answer?" (Lappan et al. 2008, p. 11).

This question is posed as the entry point to a discussion in which students make connections between the use of common denominators with fractions and adding values with the same place value. For example, renaming $0.25 + 0.375$ as $25/100 + 375/1000$ leads students to use what they have learned about fraction addition and rewrite the fraction form of the problem using the common denominator of 1000. Renaming in fractional form ($250/1000 + 375/1000$) parallels one strategy for adding decimals, in which a zero is annexed so both addends have the same number of digits after the decimal point. However, the important connection to be made here is that both addends are made out of the same-sized parts of the whole. With either approach, using decimals or using fractions, thousandths are being added to thousandths.

This situation provides an opportunity to discuss why decimal points should be lined up when adding and subtracting decimals. Drawing on the previously developed notion of "adding common denominators" as a case of adding like units, teachers can use fractions to develop an algorithm for adding and subtracting decimals that is based on place value. This algorithm can also be linked with whole-number addition and subtraction operations in which place value is aligned so that the units being combined are the same type or size.

When teachers develop decimal operations by foregrounding fractions, students are positioned to use what they already know about fraction operations to make sense of decimal addition and subtraction. In this example, students have an opportunity to make a connection between fractions and decimals, with fractions being used as a building block to support new learning. By integrating fraction and decimal operations, students expand their conception of place value, place value as an indicator of the size of the unit, the role of the unit, conceptual understanding of the meaning of addition and subtraction, and the written representation of number to yield a rich understanding of number and operation. From a curricular perspective, this trajectory also has implications for algebra, in which like terms are combined when adding and subtracting.

Similarly, fraction multiplication and division algorithms can be used as a building block for decimal multiplication and division. That is, students can be asked to solve decimal multiplication or division problems by converting the problem into fraction form and then reflect on how carrying out the operation in fraction form can be used to help them make sense of decimal form. Placing fractions in the foreground of work with decimal operations can potentially support students' ability to learn to use prior mathematical knowledge as a tool to make sense of new mathematical problems they encounter.

Using Fractions in the Background When Studying Similarity and Scale Factor

A second approach that can be used to integrate and develop topics across the curriculum is to place one topic in the background of work on another. In contrast with the design of the decimal operation task that directly referenced or foregrounded fractions in the task, fractional values can be used as quantities in a task but not be directly referenced. In the example presented here, the foregrounded topic of scale factor and perimeter-area relationships is initially explored using whole-number quantities. However, once basic concepts are established, students begin to explore tasks or situations in which fractional quantities are included. When fractions are placed in the background of the task, students need to address whether concepts that work with whole numbers will also work when fractions are used. The example that follows illustrates the point.

During a seventh-grade unit on similarity, students explore the relationship between scale factor and perimeter and the relationship between scale factor and area. Using whole-number scale factors, students begin with original figures (rectangles) that they scale up using 2, 3, and 4 as respective scale factors. They compare the original and scaled figures to determine the side length, perimeter, and area of each. Students record their findings, indicating how the scaling changed the perimeter and area (see table 12.1).

Table 12.1

Relative Change in Perimeter and Area of Rectangle, Given a Scale Factor

Scale Factor	Perimeter	Area
2	× 2	× 4
3	× 3	× 9
4	× 4	× 16

A discussion leads to the conjecture that when a scale factor of 2 is applied, the area of the scaled rectangle is 4 times the area of the original rectangle. This relationship is signified in the table by writing "× 4" in the area column. By looking at each scale factor and the change recorded in the area column of the table, students establish that the relationship between the area of the original figure and that of the scaled figure was found by squaring the scale factor.

In the task Scale Factors and Similar Shapes (Lappan et al. 2006), students apply a scale factor of 2 1/2 to a 4-by-8 rectangle and then determine both the new area and the new perimeter[1]. Although students were comfortable when each

---

1. The original problem stated the scale factor as 2.5, but throughout the problem, students interchanged 2.5 and 2 1/2.

side length was multiplied by 2 1/2, with the perimeter becoming 2 1/2 times larger, they were struggling to figure out what was happening to the area. Using diagrams of the original 4-by-8 rectangle and the scaled-up 10-by-20 rectangle, a student said that the rectangle was 2 1/2 times larger. The teacher was pushing for an explanation of what that meant. *What* was 2 1/2 times larger? In the following excerpt, the teacher pushes students to realize that the generalizations they established when working with whole-number scale factors are still valid when fractional scale factors are used.

Mrs. Dew: How much bigger is the [large] rectangle compared to the [small] one?

Bryan: It is 6.25 bigger.

Mrs. Dew: Why six and one-fourth?

Bryan: I did the 200 [area of larger scaled rectangle] divided by the 32 [area of original rectangle], and I got 6.25.

Mrs. Dew: What does that have to do with the scale factor?

Another solution offered by a student focused on showing that one can physically place four 4-by-8 rectangles inside of the scaled-up 10-by-20 rectangle. Although the division and physical placement approaches are mathematically reasonable, concern arises that students are not connecting this situation involving a fractional scale factor to their previous work with whole-number scale factors.

Mrs. Dew: So the scale factor will not help me figure out how the area changed?

Ali: If you divide 200 by 32, you get the 6.25, and if you times it by 6.25, that would be what you would get, so that would be your scale factor.

Mrs. Dew: If I take the area of 200 and I divide by 32, which is where Bryan started us a few minutes ago, and when I say I get 6 and 1/4, what does that mean?

Student A: You get 6.25.

Mrs. Dew: What does that mean in terms of this picture?

Ali: That is how many times you multiplied the smaller one.

Student B: The area to get how many you need to make the bigger one.

Mrs. Dew: So 6 1/4 of these [small rectangles] makes this [larger rectangle]?

Class:	Yes.

Students are still struggling to use their earlier generalization that change in area can be found by multiplying the original area by the squared scale factor. The teacher suggests that students look at the table developed in the previous task that used whole-number scale factors.

Mrs. Dew:	Do I have to know the area of this [original rectangle] and the area of this [scaled rectangle] and divide them to find out how many of these fit inside of this? [*pause*]
Janine:	For Problem 3.1[2], when you double it is 4, and when it is 3 it goes to 9, and 4 is 16. So the scale factor is 2.5. So wouldn't you square 2 point 5 or times it by itself to see the area change?
Mrs. Dew:	What is 2.5 times 2.5?
Class:	6.25.
Mrs. Dew:	So, Janine, is the same thing holding true?
Janine:	Yes.
Mrs. Dew:	Just because I went to something that wasn't quite as nice and pretty as a 2, a 3, and a 4, the rule we have had for a week now didn't go away. The way you prove that, like Bryan said, [dividing 200 by 32] just helped me solidify that. Even with an ugly scale factor, I still have the same relationship. The scale factor times itself will tell me how that area will change.
Amy:	So we spent almost a half an hour talking about that when we could have just done that?
Mrs. Dew:	Yeah.

Situating fractions in the background of this similarity task helps extend students' understanding of fractions. For example, the mathematical concept that the area of a two-dimensional figure grows by a factor that is the square of the scale factor is an important idea that applies regardless of whether a whole number or fractional scale factor is used. The last student's comment points to her realization that ideas carry from whole numbers to other forms of number, in this instance, fractions. Extending situations that could be and often are explored with whole numbers to include more complex numbers affords students the opportunity to see that the simplicity or complexity of the number or quantity is irrelevant. Stu-

---

2. "Problem 3.1" is a reference to the previous instructional task whose data were presented in the chart on the board. Problem 3.1 used whole-number scale factors.

dents broaden their understanding of how fractions behave by experiencing them in the context of similarity.

Situating fractions in the background of a curriculum unit on similarity can also create a context for exploring reciprocal relationships and the inverse nature of fraction operations. For example, applying a scale factor of 3 to a 2-by-3 rectangle leads to a new rectangle that is 6 by 9. However, if one wants to scale a 6-by-9 rectangle down to a 2-by-3 rectangle, the scale factor is not "three times smaller" or "divide by 3," as was offered by this class of seventh graders. When students in this class offered the "divide by 3" response, the teacher replied, "If my scale factor has to be something that I multiply by, if you are saying that I am going to divide by 3, but I want to say my scale factor is what I multiply my side lengths by, what would I be multiplying by?" Pushing students to consider the resulting effect of applying a scale factor of 3 and a scale factor of 1/3 led to a conversation about the inverse nature of multiplication and division and the reciprocal nature of fractions.

Summary

Opportunities to use mathematical knowledge need to be included and highlighted in the development of instructional tasks and units. Doing so requires a lens that looks across grades and across content strands. It also calls for careful placement of mathematical skills and concepts in the foreground and background of tasks in instructional units in which a topic such as fractions is not the explicit topic of study.

A review of content previously studied is important. However, the amount of review students need is greatly diminished when a curriculum includes situations in which students repeatedly use prior knowledge in meaningful ways in increasingly complex settings. These examples present a view of curriculum in which one topic, skill, or concept is purposefully situated in the development of another. The examples noted here present mathematics as connected and integrated, emerging through problem solving.

Often we assume that if a student has studied or "learned about" a topic, he or she is able to use that knowledge in subsequent problems. The instructional tasks presented in this article highlight the need to support the "use" of mathematical knowledge. These students did not struggle with the concepts they learned when studying fractions directly. The conversations did not focus on how to multiply fractions or how to find equivalent fractions. Rather, the focus was on using fraction concepts and skills in new settings. Initially, it was not always clear to students that they could use fractions in these new settings.

The examples presented here suggest that the acquisition of useable mathematical knowledge needs to be purposefully developed. Like NCTM's *Curriculum*

Focal Points (2006) or *Principles and Standards for School Mathematics* (2000), these examples offer support for an integrated curriculum in which mathematical concepts and skills are developed across the grades rather than repeated from year to year. By purposefully situating mathematical ideas in the foreground and background of instructional tasks, the teacher can focus instruction on a smaller number of main ideas and at the same time concentrate on developing a deep understanding of mathematics.

REFERENCES

Johanning, Debra I. "Learning to Use Fractions: Examining Middle School Students' Emerging Fraction Literacy." *Journal for Research in Mathematics Education* 39 (May 2008): 281–310.

Lappan, Glenda, and Elizabeth Phillips. "Teaching and Learning in the Connected Mathematics Project." In *Mathematics Teaching in the Middle,* edited by Larry Leutzinger, pp. 83–92. Reston, Va.: National Council of Teachers of Mathematics, 1998.

Lappan, Glenda, James T. Fey, William M. Fitzgerald, Susan N. Friel, and Elizabeth D. Phillips. *Stretching and Shrinking: Similarity.* Boston: Pearson Prentice Hall, 2006.

———. *Bits and Pieces III: Computing with Decimals and Percents.* Boston: Pearson Prentice Hall, 2008.

National Council of Teachers of Mathematics (NCTM). *Principles and Standards for School Mathematics.* Reston, Va.: NCTM, 2000.

———. *Curriculum Focal Points for Prekindergarten through Grade 8 Mathematics: A Quest for Coherence.* Reston, Va.: NCTM, 2006.

Schielack, Jane F., and Cathy Seeley. "Implementation of the NCTM's *Curriculum Focal Points:* Concept versus Content." *Mathematics Teaching in the Middle School* 13 (September 2007): 78–80.

Streefland, Leen. *Fractions in Realistic Mathematics Education: A Paradigm of Developmental Research.* Boston: Kluwer Academic Publishers, 1991.

Thompson, Patrick W. "Notation, Convention, and Quantity in Elementary Mathematics." In *Providing a Foundation for Teaching Mathematics in the Middle Grades,* edited by Judith T. Sowder and Bonnie P. Schappelle, pp. 199–221. Albany: State University of New York Press, 1995.

13

Mathematics Applied to Curriculum Development: Lessons Learned on the Job

Al Cuoco
Jean Benson
Bowen Kerins
Sarah Sword
Kevin Waterman

MATHEMATICS, in addition to being a scientific discipline in its own right, is a basic tool in many professions. Engineers, physicists, carpenters, financial advisors, computer scientists, and a host of other professionals all use mathematics, each in profession-specific ways. Late in the last century, education researchers began talking about the profession-specific uses of mathematics made by mathematics teachers. "Pedagogical content knowledge" (Schulman 1987), "mathematical knowledge for teaching" (Ball, Hill, and Bass 2005; Cuoco 2001), and other constructs became objects of research and subjects of papers on teacher education and professional development. These constructs describe many of the ways that teachers use mathematics in and out of their classrooms. The topic of this paper is connected to one such use: the mathematics that teachers use behind the scenes in their lessons. Making curriculum choices, creating tasks for students, and gauging the appropriateness of problems and activities for students are central components of effective teaching.

High school teachers make curricular decisions every day. Some of these decisions are small and localized: creating a problem set or a quiz, sequencing examples and activities for a class, or trying out an example before class to get a feel for how it might go. Others are quite large: developing a syllabus for a new course, an end-of-year assessment, or a cross-disciplinary unit. These decisions call for profession-specific applications of mathematics.

The development of a published mathematics curriculum involves similar applications of mathematics. At the precollege level, curriculum development is often carried out by teams that include teachers, mathematics educators, and mathematicians, and each of these groups brings its own knowledge of mathematics to the task of producing textbooks that work in modern classrooms and that help students come to understand core ideas in mathematics. Over the past decade, we have been working on such a team, creating the CME Project, a four-year, National Science Foundation–funded high school curriculum (Education Development Center 2009). We have come to see that, in addition to the mathematics that people bring to the job of curriculum development from their mathematical professions, a body of mathematical applications exists that is specific to, and useful in, the profession of curriculum development itself—a body of mathematics that is not the primary focus of teaching or research in either mathematics or education.

The purpose of this article is to describe some of these applications. Through a series of examples, we describe some mathematical ideas and results that, if not completely new to us, led to new and interesting applications in our work on the CME Project and in our efforts to create curricula for professional development and teacher preparation programs. Our examples fall into four categories—

- organizing content around big-picture ideas,
- finding surprising depth in seemingly simple mathematics problems,
- reaching into classical mathematics to design tasks, and
- making use of available technological tools to support students' learning.

This list is in no way exhaustive; our uses of mathematics in the process of curriculum design are as extensive as in any mathematics-related field. Our goal here is to give a few examples that will open a discussion among curriculum developers (at any scale) around this kind of applied mathematics.

Organizing Content around Big-Picture Ideas

Every mathematics curriculum puts forth a stance about what mathematics the authors think is important. So the first use of mathematics that curriculum developers need is a big enough picture of mathematics itself to form such a stance. But a deep understanding of a mathematical area is clearly not sufficient if one wants to convey the central ideas of that area to beginning students.

For example, working though a proof of the central limit theorem or the fundamental theorem of algebra would be out of reach for most high school students. Still, we want students to have an understanding of what these theorems say, and, if possible, to get a glimpse, perhaps through concrete and transparent examples, of the mathematics needed to prove them.

Infusing different "big picture stances" into high school curricula is one of the reasons for the variations we see in innovative curriculum materials. Over the past two decades, we have seen curricula that center on modeling, statistics, discrete mathematics, data analysis, and other organizing principles. In such programs we see an underlying philosophy about what constitutes important mathematics for target audiences of high school students and teachers.

In the CME Project, the big picture centers on the style of work used by mathematicians—the mathematical habits of mind that are indigenous to various branches of mathematics. One of the wonderful things about mathematics is that, although the topics studied at the frontiers of the discipline require years of background building to understand, the habits of mind used by researchers can be developed through activities that are tractable for high school students. The work of developing such activities is a good example of profession-specific mathematics for curriculum development: the task is to take a sophisticated mathematical idea and to find a context or setting that is both faithful to the idea and accessible to high school students. Two examples illustrate this kind of work, one that focuses on reasoning by continuity and the other, on transforming equations.

Reasoning by continuity is a habit of mind that is ubiquitous in mathematical analysis. The knack for imagining continuously changing systems, for finding invariants and extreme cases in these systems, and for approximating solutions to problems involving real numbers is at the heart of analysis. These analytic skills are usually developed in calculus or precalculus courses. In the CME Project, we wanted to expose students to this kind of thinking much earlier, without all the trappings of derivatives and limits. Some time and research were required to come up with a setting, and we eventually chose geometric optimization, a classical circle of ideas that is developed beautifully in Courant and Robbins's classic text (1941) and that is made all the more accessible with dynamic geometry software.

In the CME Project, students experiment with the problem of situating an airport that will serve three cities to minimize the building of new roads. They investigate and prove (except for one technical detail) the isoperimetric theorem that shows that a circle maximizes the area for fixed perimeter. They find a geometric solution to the classic problem of minimizing the trip from a point to a line and then back to another point on the same side of the line. All this is worthy of inclusion in a curriculum for no other reason than the fact that it is beautiful and classical mathematics, but we had a different and more important reason for including it: It provides a locus for developing mathematical habits that will serve students well in analysis, physics, and many other fields.

Transforming expressions to reveal hidden meaning is an algebraic habit of mind that is so ingrained in algebraists' style of work that many are not even conscious of it. In the CME Project, we try to help students find an expression that is equivalent to a given expression but that is better suited for the job at hand. For example, it might seem silly to express the right-hand side of

$$f(x) = 4x^2 - 12x - 4$$

as

$$3(x-1)(x-2) + 4(x-1)(x-5) - 3(x-2)(x-5).$$

But this second expression allows one to easily find $f(x)$ if x is 1, 2, or 5. This idea is at the core of Lagrange interpolation. We decided to include Lagrange interpolation in the CME Project because, in addition to providing students with a general-purpose tool that allows them to find a minimal-degree polynomial that agrees with any table of data, it helps students develop the habit of rewriting expressions for specific purposes. Several of the authors of the program were adamant that we develop Lagrange interpolation in a way that parallels the classic derivation of the Chinese remainder theorem, so that students could make the connection between the following two problems:

- I am thinking of a number. The remainder when I divide it by 3 is 1. The remainder when I divide it by 5 is also 1. The remainder when I divide it by 11 is 4. What could my number be?

- I am thinking of a polynomial. The remainder when I divide it by $x - 1$ is -12. The remainder when I divide it by $x - 2$ is also -12. The remainder when I divide it by $x - 7$ is 108. What could my polynomial be?

One of our goals in the CME Project, and certainly one of the goals for most curriculum development teams, is to situate school mathematics in the larger landscape of mathematics as a scientific discipline. The fact that we have so many strikingly different high school curriculum programs in this country attests to the fact that this discipline can be perceived in many different ways. All these ways require applications of mathematics specific to curriculum development.

Finding Surprising Depth in Seemingly Simple Mathematics Problems

Sometimes curriculum developers and teachers pose an interesting and seemingly simple problem for students only to realize that it can be mined for some deep mathematics. Uncovering the deep mathematics often leads to a refinement of the problem and to further ideas for student investigations.

Here is a problem similar to one in the CME Project second-year algebra course:

There are six numbers in set *D:* {54, 11, 24, 53, 98, 30}.

1. Change one of the numbers in set *D* to make a new set with a smaller standard deviation.

2. Change one of the numbers in set *D* to make a new set with a larger standard deviation.

3. Change one of the numbers in set *D* to make a new set with the same standard deviation.

Before reading further, you might take a moment to think about how to solve all three parts.

Our goal in this problem, and throughout the CME Project, was to integrate statistics into the rest of the program, with special emphasis on how algebra and statistics can work hand in hand: students with a strong understanding of algebra can more easily understand some difficult topics in statistics, and vice versa. In this instance, we wanted students to see the effects on statistical measures brought about by transforming data sets in some regular way.

When we worked out the solutions, we realized that part 3 seemed (to us, anyway) much more difficult than the first two, and the solution involved an application—new to us—of some very nice algebra. Here is how one of us solved part 3:

For any finite set of numbers, let x be the sum of the elements of the set, $\bar{x}$ the mean of the elements of the set, and σ the standard deviation of the set, so that σ^2 is the variance for the set. To solve part 3, we used the following identity, which we prove in *Algebra 2:*

$$\overline{x^2} - \bar{x}^{-2} = \sigma^2.$$

Let's see if we can replace the element 30 by something that maintains the standard deviation. Replace 30 by a and recalculate σ^2:

$$\sum(x^2) = 16926 - 900 + a^2$$
$$= 16026 + a^2$$
$$\sum x = 270 - 30 + a = 240 + a$$
$$\overline{x^2} = \frac{16026 + a^2}{6}$$
$$\overline{x}^{-2} = \left(\frac{240 + a}{6}\right)^2 = \frac{(240 + a)^2}{36}$$

The new variance should equal the old, so we have an equation involving a:

$$\frac{16026 + a^2}{6} - \frac{(240 + a)^2}{36} = \sigma^2, \quad (*)$$

where σ^2 is the variance of the original set D. The only thing needed is that σ^2 is constant; we do not actually need to figure out what it is.

Equation $(*)$ simplifies to

$$5a^2 - 480a + K = 0 \ (**)$$

for some constant K. This is the equation that must be satisfied by any a that makes the variance of $\{54, 11, 24, 53, 98, a\}$ equal 30. One such number is 30, so 30 is a root of $(**)$. And the sum of the roots of this equation is 96. So the other root is 66. The variance (and hence the standard deviation) of $\{54, 11, 24, 53, 98, 66\}$ is the same as that of the original set D.

After working out a few more examples, we saw that if we replace any element n of D by

$$\frac{2(270 - n)}{5} - n,$$

the standard deviation is unchanged. More generally, we have a theorem:

Theorem: If a set of numbers has t elements, replacing one element m by

$$\frac{2\left(\sum x - m\right)}{t - 1} - m$$

preserves the standard deviation.

We found this result very satisfying and a nice application of the algebraic result that relates the roots of a quadratic equation to the equation's coefficients. It also implies that, for any data set D, there is at most one replacement for each element that preserves the standard deviation. We say "at most one" because equation (∗∗) above may have a double root. We wonder (and have not worked out the answer) what conditions on the data would cause this to happen.

From a curriculum-development point of view, the result is useful for another reason: Notice that the roots of equation (∗∗) above are both integers. It could have happened that the root we wanted turned out to be a nonintegral rational number, but we used the theorem to construct our data in a way that ensured that this did not happen.

This is one of the most central applications of mathematics to curriculum development: the use of mathematics in the design of problems, assessments, and more general investigations.

Reaching into Classical Mathematics to Design Tasks

When designing an activity, we often want the launch problems to "come out nicely," which often means finding that numerical examples for the solutions are integers when they could be nonintegral fractions. Or the solutions are rational when they could be irrational. Messy numbers have their place, but we want students' first experience with an idea to be uncluttered and to provide some immediate feedback. The design of such activities often involves mathematics from outside the actual curriculum under development—classical mathematics that is behind the scenes of the curriculum, used by the authors to orchestrate what students see.

Here are some examples, from the CME Project and our professional development curricula, for readers to try; each contains a pleasant surprise:

- *The distance formula.* Find the length of the sides of this triangle:

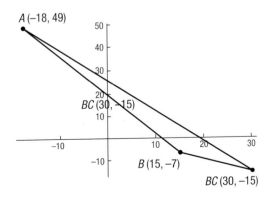

- *The law of cosines.* Find the measure of $\angle Q$:

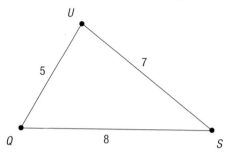

- *Heron's formula.* Find the area of $\triangle ABC$:

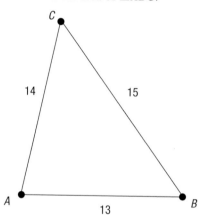

- *Polynomial calculus.* Find the extrema and inflection point for the graph of $y = 140 - 144x + 3x^2 + x^3$:

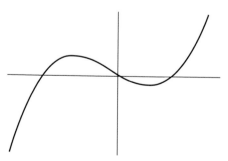

- *Optimization.* Squares are cut out of the corners of a 7×15 rectangle, and the sides are folded up to make a box. Find the size of the cutout that maximizes the volume of the box.

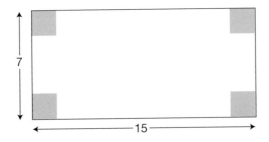

Making up problems like these is the object of a great deal of teacher-room collaboration, and it is an especially relevant skill for curriculum developers. We call these problems "metaproblems"—mathematical problems that spring from making up mathematics problems for students.

One of the oldest metaproblems has to be the generation of Pythagorean triples. Such triples can be found in many ways; one way that we include as a problem sequence in the CME Project is to find points with rational coordinates on the unit circle—that is, on the graph of $x^2 + y^2 = 1$ (see Cuoco [2008] for more details). For example, (3/5, 4/5) is such a point, and it produces the famous (3, 4, 5) triple.

A generalization of this technique—finding rational points on conics—can be used to solve many other metaproblems. For example, consider the problem of finding integer-sided triangles with a 60 degree angle (like the 5-8-7 triangle discussed previously). We want integers *a, b,* and *c* so that the triangle with sides *a, b, c* has a 60 degree angle:

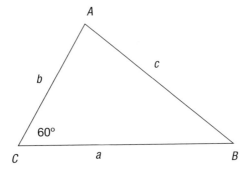

When we call c the "hypotenuse" of the triangle, the law of cosines tells us that

$$c^2 = a^2 + b^2 - 2ab\cos C$$
$$= a^2 + b^2 - 2ab(1/2)$$
$$= a^2 - ab + b^2.$$

So we are looking for triples (a, b, c)—we call them "Eisenstein triples" after Gauss's student George Eisenstein—so that

$$a^2 - ab - b^2 = c^2 \quad (\quad).$$

Dividing both sides by c^2, equation (***) above can be written as

$$\left(\frac{a}{c}\right)^2 - \left(\frac{a}{c}\right)\left(\frac{b}{c}\right) + \left(\frac{b}{c}\right)^2 = 1,$$

so that $(a/c, b/c)$ is a point with rational coordinates on the graph of $x^2 - xy + y^2 = 1$. Conversely, any point with rational coordinates on the graph of this equation produces an Eisenstein triple—put the coordinates over a common denominator; the two numerators and the common denominator will form a triple.

In the CME Project, students show that the graph of $-x^2 - xy + y^2 = 1$ is an ellipse with major axis at a 45 degree angle to the coordinate axes:

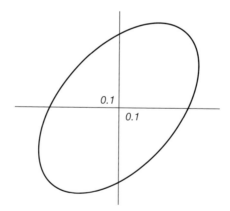

There are four rational points on this graph that produce "trivial" Eisenstein triples:

$$(1, 0), (0, 1), (-1, 0), (0, -1).$$

If we pick one of these points, say, $(0, -1)$ and draw a line through it with rational slope greater than 1, say, 3/2, we get a second intersection point, one that lies in the first quadrant:

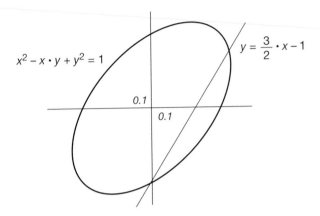

By solving the system

$$\begin{cases} x^2 - xy + y^2 = 1 \\ y = \dfrac{3}{2}x - 1, \end{cases}$$

we find that the second intersection point is (8/7, 5/7). And (8, 5, 7) is an Eisenstein triple—this is the triple we used to generate the law of cosines example earlier:

$$8^2 - (8 \times 5) + 5^2 = 7^2.$$

It is a nice exercise to show that if a line with rational slope contains $(0, -1)$ and intersects the ellipse in two points, the second point will have rational coordinates. So we have a method, which some call the "method of sweeping lines," for generating Eisenstein triples:

> **Theorem:** If $t > 1$ is a rational number, then the graph of $y = tx - 1$
> intersects the graph $x^2 - xy + y^2 = 1$ in a rational point $(a/c, b/c)$ in the
> first quadrant, and (a, b, c) is an Eisenstein triple.

The ability to generate Pythagorean and Eisenstein triples turns out to be the key to solving a host of task-design problems, including all the ones we listed at the start of this section. And the method of sweeping lines gives the curriculum developer a general-purpose tool for creating problems that allow students to get used to ideas without the computational overhead of messy numbers.

Also available is an algebraic general-purpose tool, one that uses complex numbers, for generating Pythagorean, Eisenstein, and more general triples. Details are in Cuoco (2000).

Making Use of Available Technological Tools to Support Students' Learning

The use of technology in a curriculum opens new ways to develop topics, but it can also steer the curriculum toward particular approaches to topics, simply because of the constraints of the software.

One example is the approach that many curricula now use to help precalculus students understand tangent lines to curves without the machinery of calculus. Graphing calculators make it possible to introduce the idea of "local linearity" in precalculus. For example, if one looks at the graph of $y = x^3 - x + 1$ and repeatedly zooms in near $(1, 1)$, the graph begins to look like a line, and the slope of the line is a good approximation to the slope of the curve at $(1, 1)$.

This technique is effective, and we use it in later chapters of the CME Project, but it contains implicit appeal to some rather subtle and delicate mathematics. An older approach to facilitating the idea of tangents to curves involves less subtlety and builds on what students know about tangents from geometry. Going back to the graph of $y = x^3 - x + 1$, imagine a secant to the curve that contains $A = (1, 1)$ and intersects the curve at a second point B:

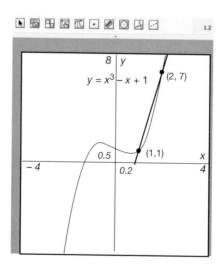

For centuries, teachers have asked students to imagine what happens as B gets closer to A, so that the secant approaches the tangent. Until now, widely available technology handicapped this approach. One could set up an experiment in dynamic geometry software that showed the secant approaching the tangent, but the secant disappeared when B coincided with A, as did the equation of the line through A and B.

The new TI-Nspire handheld devices eliminate this problem, and they allow us (and hence teachers and students) to develop activities that bring this time-honored thought experiment to life.

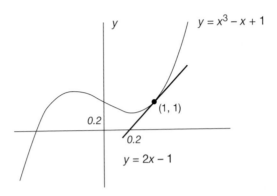

In addition, there is a computer algebra system (CAS) available as part of the TI-Nspire software that communicates with the geometry and graphing environment. This system lets us connect the secant-to-tangent process with the underlying algebra, a connection that uses some classical topics from second-year algebra and that was new to us.

Using the same example as above, let $f(x) = x^3 - x + 1$, and suppose that $f(x)$ is divided by $(x-1)(x-2)$. Standard results from second-year algebra tell us that the remainder $r(x)$ will be linear and that a polynomial $q(x)$ exists such that

$$f(x) = (x-1)(x-2)q(x) + r(x).$$

We can get the remainder from a CAS:

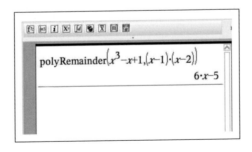

So $r(x) = 6x - 5$. Hence
$$x^3 - x + 1 = (x-1)(x-2)q(x) + 6x - 5.$$
$\quad\uparrow\qquad\qquad\uparrow$
$\quad f(x)\qquad\quad r(x)$

By replacing x by 1 or 2, we see that $r(x)$ agrees with $f(x)$ at 1 and 2. In other words,

$$y = r(x) = 6x - 5$$

is the equation of the secant to the graph of $y = f(x)$ between $x = 1$ (point A) and $x = 2$ (point B).

Now let B slide along the graph toward A. As the x-coordinate, say, a, of B approaches 1, we can divide $f(x)$ by $(x - 1)(x - a)$, and the remainder each time will define the linear function whose graph is the secant that is approaching the tangent:

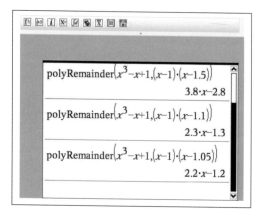

Passing to the limit, the linear function whose graph is the tangent to the curve at $x = 1$ is given by the remainder when $x^3 - x + 1$ is divided by $(x - 1)^2$:

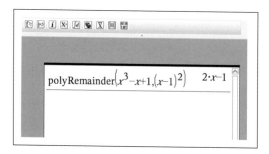

Hence the equation of the tangent to the graph of $y = f(x)$ at $x = 1$ is $y = 2x - 1$.

This became the essence of the development we use for the analysis of polynomial and rational functions in the CME Project. The essential mathematics is summarized in the following theorem:

Theorem:

- If a polynomial $f(x)$ is divided by $(x - a)(x - b)$ and leaves a remainder of $r(x)$, then $y = r(x)$ is the equation of the secant of the graph of $y = f(x)$ between $x = a$ and $x = b$.

- If a polynomial $f(x)$ is divided by $(x - a)^2$ and leaves a remainder of $r(x)$, then $y = r(x)$ is the equation of the tangent of the graph of $y = f(x)$ at $x = a$.

We have shown this result to many users of mathematics, and, although most see the proof almost immediately, few have seen the result beforehand. But it became the organizer for the treatment of the analysis of polynomial and rational functions in the CME Project, allowing us to expose precalculus students to special cases of central ideas in calculus, and showing how a CAS bundled with geometry software can be used to integrate algebra and geometry. In later courses in calculus, students can make the connection between the remainder when $f(x)$ is divided by $(x - 2)^2$ and the first two terms in the Taylor expansion for f around $x = 2$.

Conclusion

Many more examples like this abound. We used mathematics in specialized ways when we developed activities around the tables of arithmetic, the geometry of regression lines, the factorization of polynomials, and the development of area formulas. In most instances, we started from some mathematical and pedagogical experiences, drafted an activity, got "hooked" on a problem that we wrote for students, pushed the problem further for our own curiosity, developed some general results that pertained to the problem, and then applied those results to refine the curriculum materials. This process was iterated repeatedly in the development of the CME Project.

Having lived with this process over the past decade, we are convinced of the existence of a body of mathematics that is applied by curriculum developers to the work of writing for students and teachers. Like all applied mathematics, this body is connected in essential ways to mathematics as a scientific discipline, and, like all applied mathematics, it has its own flavor, its own collection of problems and results, and its own web of habits of mind.

REFERENCES

Ball, Deborah Loewenberg, Heather C. Hill, and Hyman Bass. "Knowing Mathematics for Teaching: Who Knows Mathematics Well Enough to Teach Third Grade, and How Can We Decide?" *American Educator* (Fall 2005): 14–22, 43–46.

Courant, Richard, and Herbert Robbins. *What Is Mathematics?* London: Oxford University Press, 1941.

Cuoco, Al. "Meta-Problems in Mathematics." *College Mathematics Journal* 31 (November 2000): 373–78.

———. "Mathematics for Teaching." *Notices of the American Mathematical Society (AMS)* 48 (February 2001): 168–74.

———. "Introducing Extensible Tools in High School Algebra." *Algebra and Algebraic Thinking in School Mathematics*, Seventieth Yearbook of the National Council of Teachers of Mathematics (NCTM), edited by Carole E. Greenes, pp. 51–62. Reston, Va.: NCTM, 2008.

Education Development Center. *The CME Project.* Boston: Pearson, 2009.

Shulman, Lee S. "Knowledge and Teaching: Foundations of the New Reform." *Harvard Educational Review* 57 (Spring 1987): 1–22.

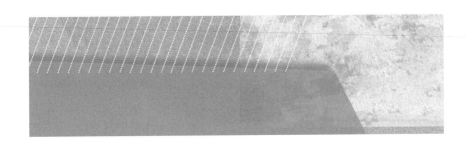

The Written Curriculum

- Curriculum Development

- **Selection of Textbooks**

14

How Do Districts Choose Mathematics Textbooks?

June Mark
Deborah Spencer
Julie Koehler Zeringue
Katherine Schwinden

RESEARCHERS have long agreed that textbooks have a strong effect on the content that students learn in mathematics classrooms (Begle 1979; Porter 1989; Schmidt, Houang, and Cogan 2002). These materials also affect how teachers teach (Ball and Cohen 1996; Reys, Reys, and Chávez 2004). Yet remarkably little is known about how textbook selections in mathematics are made in districts across the country. Who makes these decisions? What role do teachers play in the decision making? What criteria are used for selection? What influences those decisions?

This article reports on a study investigating mathematics textbook selection.[1] To understand the complexities and realities of how districts select curriculum materials, interviews were conducted with more than 150 K–12 mathematics curriculum decision makers from districts in eight states. The states—Colorado, Louisiana, Maine, New York, Ohio, Texas, Washington, and West Virginia—represent a mix of state-adoption and open-territory states across the country. Twenty-one states in the United States are "state-adoption" states,

---

1. The authors are grateful for the National Science Foundation's support of the project (Grant No. ESI-0454022). The opinions expressed are those of the authors and not necessarily those of the Foundation.

which means that the state provides a list of approved textbooks and establishes a timeline for adoption. The remaining twenty-nine are "open-territory" states; the choice of textbooks is unrestricted by the state, and decisions about funding and timing of adoptions are made locally, at the district or school level. The districts selected for interviews in each state reflect a range of characteristics in students' performance level, the percent of students in poverty, geographic region, school and district size, and textbooks currently used.

The curriculum leaders interviewed were typically curriculum coordinators, department chairs, mathematics supervisors, and assistant superintendents. The interviewers sought to understand curriculum-related decision-making processes in various settings, to identify the decisions curriculum leaders make, and to identify the role different sources of information play in those decisions. We were particularly interested in curriculum leaders' use of research, in light of national calls for a broader perspective on the research needed to properly evaluate mathematics textbooks (National Research Council [NRC] 2004). We sought to answer the following questions:

- What processes do school districts use in selecting mathematics textbooks?
- What factors shape those decisions?
- How does textbook selection differ in state-adoption and open-territory states?
- What research do curriculum leaders find most useful in textbook selection?
- What questions about mathematics textbooks do decision makers need answered?

An analysis of our interview data has been supplemented by other sources, including a survey of the members of the Association of State Supervisors of Mathematics, a series of surveys of curriculum leaders nationally conducted by our collaborators at Inverness Research Associates, an investigation of state-level documents and Web sites, and a review of the relevant literature. Subsequently, we discuss our findings in three primary areas—(1) textbook selection in an era of accountability, (2) factors that influence mathematics textbook selection, and (3) typical district selection processes.

Textbook Selection in an Era of Accountability

The selection of mathematics textbooks offers challenges different from those in other disciplines; mathematics teaching at all grades has traditionally relied heavily on the use of textbooks. Choosing good mathematics textbooks is crucial in times of increased accountability. The No Child Left Behind legislation demands greater accountability for students' learning and calls for research-based evidence to support the choice of mathematics textbooks. Most states released new state standards in the early 2000s, many of which were substantially different from past documents and offered greater detail, including grade-level expectations (Reys 2006). With measured outcomes for students in grades 3–10—and consequences for underperformance—aligning mathematics programs with state standards is an increasing concern for districts.

An important finding of our study was that these pressures have resulted in districts' moving toward more centralized decision making about mathematics textbooks. This was most evident in districts that historically allowed schools (or even teachers) to choose mathematics textbooks independently, because these districts now require common materials be used across all schools. The phenomenon was also evident in districts that have always made a centralized decision but have, in the past, allowed teachers to make individual choices about the extent to which they use the selected textbooks. Those districts report introducing mechanisms that hold teachers accountable for using the materials, such as pacing guides and curriculum maps, and common unit and yearly assessments. Roberta Ashton[2], an assistant superintendent from a large district in an open-territory state, talks about her district's move to centralized decision making:

> We have been a district in "academic difficulty" since the designation was created. And part of the reason that we were there was because schools made those decisions locally. Every school had a different reading program. Every school had a different math program. There was no accountability.... Since the district was being accountable for our rating, we needed to be accountable for the programs we were to implement. And so we changed that at the district. Five years ago we said that we would decide on the core programs in reading, math, science, and social studies, what those materials would be. And we would be able to, then, better support the professional development that went along with that. And then we could do our own in-house assessments to see how well students were doing, and then we could make schools accountable for the implementation.

Curriculum leaders across our study reported using the textbook-selection process as an opportunity to create greater consistency in their districts' mathematics programs. A common textbook selection ensures that teachers across a district are using materials closely aligned with state standards and test requirements and enables a district to provide professional development linked closely to those materials.

---

2. The names of all individuals and school districts have been changed.

Factors That Influence Mathematics Textbook Selection

Discussions of the factors affecting textbook selection often focus on such criteria as the content and components of the books. In our interviews, curriculum leaders noted these factors but also reported a broader range of influences on their textbook choices. We identified five factors that appeared to most influence the choice of textbooks: the degree of alignment between the textbook and state standards, committee review of textbook quality, additional sources of data gathered by a curriculum leader or committee, teachers' acceptance of the textbooks under consideration, and advocacy by the curriculum leader.

Alignment with State Standards

Across all eight states in our study, curriculum leaders highlighted the importance of choosing textbooks that aligned with state standards and were consistent with state tests. Mary Wagner, a mathematics curriculum leader in a state-adoption state, described this pressure: "We have a high-stakes math test. We've got to be sure that the students learn those skills first. Because we're accountable to kids who don't graduate from high school as juniors if they don't pass those tests." After receiving sample textbooks, the first thing Mary's selection committee does is look closely at the state mathematics standards and trace them through the books to see how each is addressed.

District leaders in both open-territory and state-adoption states discussed doing this sort of "alignment check" as part of evaluating materials. This check ranged from a cursory look—Does this textbook align with the general direction of our state standards?—to a much more detailed analysis. In state-adoption states, some districts relied solely on the state's approval of materials as evidence of alignment; other districts did their own analysis to look at depth of coverage of a particular topic (e.g., functions) or to examine a concept that was particularly weak for their students (e.g., the division of fractions).

Committee Review of Textbook Quality

An important factor in the choice of textbooks was the outcome of a committee's review of the quality of the materials. This committee evaluation is typically guided by the use of an established set of criteria or a rubric. These rubrics reflect the district's beliefs about mathematics teaching and learning. They keep the process focused on important features of the books and promote a more objective and consistent process. For the districts in our study, alignment to standards was the primary criterion reflected on rubrics. Other crucial factors were the quality of mathematical content, the pedagogical approach, and the organization of the materials.

Reviewing or establishing criteria was an important part of many districts' preparation for the selection process. For example, one curriculum leader described the development of criteria as a crucial step early in the process: "I facilitated them through a process to actually derive or develop or create their own definition of standards-based mathematics and how it applied to instructional materials. And that was tough ... specifically, what is it we were getting at? What really defined standards-based programs? And that became a key for us to use, as an operational definition. Then it becomes useful: does the definition apply to this set of materials?"

Additional Sources of Data

Districts in our study also considered information that went beyond the committee's review of the materials at hand. Curriculum leaders and committee members turn to relevant literature, to knowledgeable and trusted sources of information, to results from piloting, and to advice from similar districts in making their selections. The data gathered from those sources were a significant influence on the choice of textbooks in more than half our interviews.

Relevant literature

Articles and books about mathematics teaching and learning, such as *Adding It Up: Helping Children Learn Mathematics* (NRC 2001) or *Beyond Arithmetic: Changing Mathematics in the Elementary Classroom* (Mokros, Russell, and Economopoulos 1995), were commonly used to orient committee members to best practices and were influential in guiding the development of criteria for selection.

Knowledgeable and trusted sources

In investigating their textbook options, curriculum leaders and committee members were likely to go to trusted sources who were considered knowledgeable to identify "top" mathematics textbooks. These sources included regional and national organizations, state departments of education, and professional networks. Expert reviews, such as the American Association for the Advancement of Science's (2000) Project 2061 textbook evaluations or analyses of textbook alignment to state standards, were used to identify short lists of high-quality mathematics textbooks.

Advice from similar districts

Data from colleagues in other districts were particularly influential in the open-territory states in our study; we believe this is because districts adopt on their own schedules (rather than simultaneously, as they do in state-adoption states). This allows curriculum leaders to make connections to districts that have previously adopted textbooks they are considering. Curriculum leaders contacted other districts to learn which programs they should be seriously considering, organized site visits to see particular textbooks in use, and solicited other users' advice on implementation. Interviewees emphasized the importance of consulting with "districts like us"—districts demographically similar or geographically near them—so credible comparisons could be made.

Results from piloting

A minority of districts in our study piloted materials, but for those that did, the results of those pilots were influential in selection. Piloting provided valuable data about teachers' experience using particular textbooks and fostered insight about the support needed for successful implementation.

Teachers' Acceptance

For curriculum leaders in our study, teachers' acceptance of the selected textbook was crucial and viewed as essential to effective implementation. As one leader put it, "[N]o matter how good the curriculum is, if people don't have ownership … they're not going to utilize it to the fullest extent." Concerns about teachers' buy-in and fidelity of use prompted leaders to design selection processes to include teachers' input through representative committees or a teachers' vote. In some instances, teachers' participation was required by district or board policies. Attention to teachers' experience using the materials was also reflected through the inclusion of "ease of use" elements among the criteria for evaluation, such as whether the materials were teacher-friendly or had additional assessment resources and other desirable ancillaries.

Teachers' comfort with the choices being considered was particularly an issue if any of the options represented a significant change in practice—for example, the NSF-funded curricula were seen by interviewees as requiring a shift in pedagogical approach for many teachers. Many curriculum leaders in our study expressed reluctance to choose textbooks that required significant change in instructional practices, fearing that implementation would suffer from lack of teachers' support. This consideration sometimes meant that curriculum leaders ultimately accepted a textbook choice that was less satisfying for their programmatic needs in exchange for a perceived higher degree of teachers' commitment and use. As one curriculum leader described the phenomenon, "There are times where our needs, and the programs that support them, are just too radical and it's just too much change. And so, when folks have a voice [in the process], they can resist the radical change through that voice. And sometimes, that's probably saved us. And other times, it's actually hindered."

Advocacy by the Curriculum Leader

Curriculum leaders in our study took a range of approaches in how much they revealed their own perspective on the choice of textbooks and whether they influenced a committee to adopt a particular program or approach. Those who took an advocacy approach had a significant influence on the ultimate choice of textbook in two ways—either as an advocate for particular selection criteria or as an advocate for a particular textbook or class of materials (such as the NSF-funded curricula). One curriculum leader described this advocacy role:

> When we've made the [program A] selection this current time, it wasn't because anybody here was pushing for [program A]. What we clearly understood from our student data is that, kids were not math literate. They had no contextual understanding. To put it a different way, they were very algorithms-based, and that's the way we were approaching the math. And we believe that had a significant impact on the learning.... We need a program ... that focuses on mathematical thinking.... That was ... nonnegotiable during the selection process.

These curriculum leaders saw textbook selection as an opportunity to stimulate improvements to their mathematics program and viewed the choice of textbook as pivotal to supporting those improvements.

Although the factors described here were influential in the choice of materials, they also affected the ways in which curriculum leaders designed their districts' selection processes. In the next section, we describe findings about the nature of those processes.

District Selection Processes

We asked curriculum leaders to describe in detail the processes used in choosing mathematics textbooks in their districts, as well as the influences on the design of those processes. We found a set of common elements across state and district contexts. In most districts in our study, a selection committee or similar body had responsibility for the textbook-selection process. In a typical district, that committee would—

- *prepare for the selection process* by reviewing district and state requirements, goals for the process, relevant district data, and recommendations from the field;
- *narrow the options* by creating a "short list" of textbooks for evaluation;
- *evaluate those options* in detail by using established criteria, reading relevant reviews, visiting schools using the textbooks, and/or piloting the materials;

- *decide on a recommendation* by consensus or by official vote; this recommendation almost always requires school board approval.

What varied across districts was the locus of decision making: in some districts, teachers were the primary decision makers; in others, the curriculum leader had the responsibility. Four models or approaches to curriculum selection emerged: committee-guided, teacher-driven, administrator-led, and informal. In the following we describe each in detail.

A Committee-Guided Approach

This was the predominant model identified in our study. In this model, a committee composed largely of teachers serves as the primary decision-making body in the textbook selection process. That committee works closely with a curriculum leader to choose new mathematics materials. Such leaders play a primary role in the committee-guided approach, designing and focusing the selection process.

Franklin Public Schools, a suburban district of 4,000 students in an open-territory state, follows a committee-guided model. Cheryl Hable, the curriculum director in Franklin, works closely with a teacher committee to select textbooks. They begin by establishing a list of textbooks to examine. "When I meet with our teachers, some of them will know programs they want to look at. I'll present programs that I would like them to look at. Everybody gets to look at everything, and then we'll narrow it down to three." They are guided in their analysis by district-created selection criteria. As Cheryl describes, "We'll look at the alignment to the state standards. We'll have the teachers visit classrooms where the programs are being used, so that teachers can talk to teachers. And we'll have parents involved, looking at materials, so they feel they've had a voice." Cheryl guides the committee in reaching consensus on a recommendation to their board for adoption. She believes she plays an important role in keeping the conversation focused on mathematics: "I remember the days when teachers would look at math books, and a sales rep would come in with goodies. But I'm now real conscious of watching how it's done, so that we're looking at the content."

A Teacher-Driven Approach

Some curriculum leaders described an approach that aims to ensure that the process is fair, open, and transparent. This variation on the committee-guided approach protects teachers' participation in the process: the curriculum leader takes a minimal and deliberately neutral role, and the choice of textbooks is left strictly to a committee of teachers. These districts add elements to the process that reduce potential biases: someone other than the responsible administrator may lead the committee, there may be an obligation to hold open and public meetings, there may be a requirement to review all publishers' submissions equally, and there may be procedures for certifying that the process was fair. This teacher-driven approach occurred most frequently in our study in Louisiana and Texas, state-adoption states with strict guidelines for textbook selection.

Fairview City Schools, a large district in a state-adoption state, follows this approach. The process begins when mathematics supervisor Darlene Gray receives the state's list of approved textbooks. She asks principals to recommend teachers to serve on the adoption committee. Once the committee is formed, she provides training focused on what to look for in a mathematics textbook. She works from the state-adopted list to order each text for the committee to review. The district offers a textbook "caravan," in which publishers present their textbooks. The teachers then divide into grade-level groups to review the materials and discuss their relative merits. Those discussions are guided by a district-established set of criteria. The teachers then cast a secret ballot. Darlene tallies the vote and forwards their recommendation to the school board. When asked about her preferences for the outcome, Darlene said, "I have no particular direction I am hoping things will go. I tell them, tell me what you want. They were ultimately the decision makers. They had some debates within the group, but I stayed out of them." She sees her role in the process as ensuring that the committees are composed of productive contributors and preparing them to begin the process.

An Administrator-Led Process

A minority of districts, almost all in open-territory states, reported moving from a committee-guided textbook selection to an administrator-led approach. In this model, the responsible administrator acts as the primary decision maker, and the emphasis is on selecting textbooks that will support needed improvements to the district's mathematics program. The process may still include a committee of teachers, but their choices may be limited to only those options already approved or recommended by the curriculum leader. We found a range of such approaches, from districts in which the committee's choice was restricted to a particular class of materials (e.g., NSF-funded curricula) to districts in which an administrator chooses a single textbook. In our data, this approach appeared more frequently in elementary school selection processes than in middle or high school.

Centerville, a suburban district in an open-territory state, used this approach in two recent mathematics textbook adoptions. Carolyn Spacey, the curriculum supervisor in Centerville, recommends one or two textbooks to a committee of teachers. She believes it is her role to research the options carefully and to inform and educate staff about that research. She wants to ensure that they "don't buy something with a pretty cover and a fast-talking salesperson. My style is not the old style—where we bring in seven publishers and they each get twenty minutes to talk to the staff and then we vote. Now I work hours behind the scenes to investigate options, reading what best practices in math are, what programs are successful, where students are achieving well." In this model, the curriculum leader's role is conducting research and contributing professional expertise about the mathematics program and what is needed to improve its quality.

An Informal Approach

Very small districts, or districts that allow schools to make their own textbook choices, took a less-structured, informal approach in which the involved teachers—those teaching the affected grade level, or teaching a particular middle school or high school mathematics course—together reviewed materials and made a textbook selection. In these instances, no official committee was appointed, and in some cases, no specific criteria were established.

Springfield School District has one small high school, and takes an informal approach to choosing mathematics textbooks. High school teacher Tanya Moller reviews choices with her one colleague in the mathematics department, Sue Marsh, and together they decide on the books they will use in each course they teach. Says Tanya, "We kind of made our own criteria, what we liked about the books. We then came to each other with three books that we really liked. And then we'd kind of explain why. In the end, we both sort of nodded our heads, and we thought this one book was the way to go." This model relies on teachers' expertise in choosing materials that will work best for them and their students.

Goals across the Four Models

Across the approaches described in the foregoing, curriculum leaders are paying attention to the following three goals in designing the mathematics textbook selection process.

- The first goal is to *determine which materials are the best fit* for their mathematics program. Districts pursue this goal by checking textbooks' alignment with state standards, by establishing criteria for quality and analyzing textbooks accordingly, by reviewing student data to determine areas of need; and by looking for evidence—through piloting, research, or independent evaluation—of quality.

- The second goal is to *build teachers' commitment* to using the new textbooks. Curriculum leaders argue that if materials are not appealing for teachers to use—or if teachers do not believe that they have input into the choice of materials—implementation will be less effective.

- The third goal is to *ensure that the process is fair and transparent*. Districts protect against bias and corruption by seeking input from a range of stakeholders, considering multiple options, establishing criteria for evaluating textbooks on their merit, and looking for independent data as evidence of quality.

Conclusion and Recommendations

The study reported here paints a portrait of district selection processes for grades K–12 mathematics textbooks—processes not previously well understood or described in the literature. We found that curriculum leaders were trying to answer several important questions about the textbooks under consideration:

- How do these mathematics textbooks align with state standards and tests?

- Do these textbooks support good mathematics teaching and learning?

- What textbooks are similar districts using, and how are their students performing?

- Are these mathematics textbooks a good fit for our students and teachers?

- What support will these textbooks need to be implemented well in our district?

- Can these materials be used as a lever for change?

Our study was primarily descriptive, but it suggests a few recommendations for improving mathematics textbook selection processes and the resources to support them.

Curriculum leaders need improved mechanisms for obtaining crucial information about the quality and effectiveness of textbooks. The districts in our study turned to a variety of sources of information to identify and learn more about their options for mathematics textbooks. This process was time-consuming, and the information available was inadequate. In the instances where expert reviews were consulted, they were influential in decision making, yet few such reviews were available to districts. In open-territory states, districts had greater opportunities to learn from similar districts about the actual use of textbooks they were considering; those opportunities were more limited for districts in state-adoption states. Districts need better resources for learning about the quality and effectiveness of textbooks, in ways that are accessible and useful for district curriculum leaders.

Curriculum leaders should view the selection of textbooks as an opportunity to improve and bring greater coherence to their district's mathematics program. Curriculum leaders reported using the adoption process to create greater consistency and coherence in their district's mathematics program. Adopting a common set of materials and requiring its use across schools allowed districts in our study to ensure that mathematics teaching and learning was closely aligned with state standards and testing requirements. It also allowed those districts to design professional development and assessments to be consistent with the textbook being used.

Curriculum leaders can design the textbook selection process to support attention to quality and effectiveness. The results of the study emphasize the important role that curriculum leaders played in designing the selection process itself. Curriculum leaders make a set of strategic choices in structuring and facilitating the selection process for mathematics textbooks. These choices include—

- how selection committees are prepared to participate in the process,
- what criteria are used for evaluating the quality of mathematics textbooks,
- what role teachers' input plays in the process,
- whether the curriculum leader advocates a particular approach or program,
- which sources of information are introduced in the process,
- how newly selected textbooks are implemented and supported, and
- how schools and teachers are held accountable for implementation.

These choices provide strategic opportunities for curriculum leaders to influence the decision-making process—and maximize the potential contribution that new textbooks can make in improving the mathematics program.

REFERENCES

American Association for the Advancement of Science (AAAS). *Middle Grades Mathematics Textbooks: A Benchmarks-based Evaluation.* Washington, D.C.: AAAS, 2000.

Ball, Deborah L., and David K. Cohen. "Reform by the Book: What Is—or Might Be— the Role of Curriculum Materials in Teacher Learning and Instructional Reform?" *Educational Researcher* 25 (December 1996): 6–8, 14.

Begle, Edward. *Critical Variables in Mathematics Education: Findings from a Survey of the Empirical Literature.* Washington, D.C.: Mathematical Association of America, 1979.

Mokros, Jan, Susan Jo Russell, and Karen Economopoulos. *Beyond Arithmetic: Changing Mathematics in the Elementary Classroom.* White Plains, N.Y.: Dale Seymour Publications, 1995.

National Research Council. *Adding It Up: Helping Children Learn Mathematics.* Washington, D.C.: National Academies Press, 2001.

————. *On Evaluating Curricular Effectiveness: Judging the Quality of K–12 Mathematics Evaluations.* Washington, D.C.: National Academies Press, 2004.

Porter, Andrew. "A Curriculum out of Balance: The Case of Elementary School Mathematics." *Educational Researcher* 18 (June/July 1989): 9–15.

Reys, Barbara J., ed. *The Intended Mathematics Curriculum as Represented in State-Level Curriculum Standards: Consensus or Confusion?* Charlotte, N.C.: Information Age Publishing, 2006.

Reys, Barbara J., Robert E. Reys, and Óscar Chávez. "Why Mathematics Textbooks Matter." *Educational Leadership* 61 (February 2004): 61–66.

Schmidt, William, Richard Houang, and Leland Cogan. "A Coherent Curriculum: The Case of Mathematics." *American Educator* 26, no. 2 (Summer 2002): 1–18.

15

Considerations in the Review and Adoption of Mathematics Textbooks

Rick A. Hudson
Paula Elmer Lahann
Jean S. Lee

Ms. RHODES reads the memo from her principal: "Would you consider chairing the district's mathematics textbook-adoption committee this year?" She sighs. She immediately recalls her previous experience with textbook adoption and her frustration with the process. She remembers the contentious meetings in which teachers adamantly debated which textbooks would be best for the students in the district. All the teachers had their own opinions about what was important in a textbook, yet none had evidence to support their claims. Questions begin to pour through Ms. Rhodes's mind: What are the most important factors to consider when evaluating textbooks? Does research exist that might guide the committee's decisions? Where can reliable information on specific curricula be found? How should the committee do its work?

As former classroom teachers and participants on textbook-adoption committees, we have experienced many of the same concerns as Ms. Rhodes. The introduction of new kinds of textbooks, such as those developed with support

The authors would like to thank Diana Lambdin, Dick Caulfield, Andrea McCloskey, and the Yearbook Editorial Panel for their constructive comments on earlier drafts of this article.

from the National Science Foundation (NSF), has changed the way that mathematics textbooks are designed and made the textbook-adoption process more complex. Prior to the introduction of these textbooks, much less diversity was found in the types of textbooks available for adoption committees to review. For example, previously, a typical publishing company would present a single algebra 1 textbook for adoption. In today's market, that same publisher may promote a variety of curriculum materials for algebra 1, including NSF-funded materials and those developed by the publishing company. Furthermore, at the secondary school level, the organization of textbook series as integrated or single-subject curricula has provided additional options to consider.

Many factors need to be considered when making textbook-adoption decisions. Having had a wide range of classroom teaching experiences with different age levels and in diverse school settings, we understand the complexities involved in the textbook-adoption process. In preparation for this article, we reflected on our own experiences and reviewed textbook-adoption literature and research on curriculum materials, with the hope of guiding educational practitioners like Ms. Rhodes.

Considerations in Textbook Adoption

Mathematics textbooks are a strong determinant of what students have the opportunity to learn and what they do learn through the actions of the teacher. In fact, teachers often use the textbook as their primary resource to make daily mathematics instructional decisions (Weiss et al. 2001). Hence, the mathematics textbook often becomes the mathematics curriculum for many teachers. Because textbooks play a prominent role in students' learning, making informed decisions is crucial when adopting textbooks. In this article, we review the following factors that are important to consider when adopting a mathematics textbook:

- Instructional Design
- Content Emphasis
- Support for Students' Learning
- Support for Teachers' Learning
- School and District Considerations
- Research on the Curricular Outcomes and Effectiveness

Instructional Design

Does the curriculum include cognitively demanding tasks that provide a balance of procedural knowledge and conceptual understanding?

When analyzing the instructional design of a curriculum, a textbook adoption committee should focus on how the content is presented across grades, looking specifically at the learning trajectories that are established and the pedagogical strategies used. The goal of mathematics programs is for students to learn concepts, applications, efficient skill procedures, and problem solving. However, curriculum materials differ in their approach to introducing and developing important mathematical ideas.

High-quality textbook materials should reflect the latest research about how students learn mathematics. For the purpose of this article, we define high-quality textbooks as those that use cognitively demanding tasks in a student-centered environment that encourages learners to solve meaningful problems, build conceptual understanding, and connect mathematical ideas (Stein et al. 2000). Additionally, high-quality textbooks encourage the practices advocated in *Principles and Standards for School Mathematics* (NCTM 2000). In these textbooks, definitions and procedural techniques related to a topic are typically addressed only after a mathematical concept has been explored and discussed by students (Stein, Remillard, and Smith 2007). They often include lessons that build on students' prior knowledge of mathematics and offer opportunities for teachers to engage students in thoughtful discussions about challenging mathematical tasks. These curricula commonly offer students opportunities to justify and communicate their mathematical reasoning and explore multiple representations of important mathematical concepts.

Figure 15.1 shows an example of how conceptual understanding of the Pythagorean theorem might be developed before the standard formula is introduced. In this problem, students are asked to make and test a conjecture on the basis of a pattern. Furthermore, this example affords students an opportunity to connect algebraic and geometric ideas. Like the example shown in figure 15.1, high-quality textbooks encourage students to conjecture and generalize from patterns and draw connections between mathematical ideas.

Historically, commercially developed curriculum materials emphasized teacher-directed instruction as the basis for teaching and learning mathematics. In these types of textbooks, definitions and examples are provided in the materials, and students are expected to apply their knowledge of a mathematical concept after mastering procedural skills. Concepts and skills are often taught in a specific sequence established by the curriculum. We believe there should be a greater balance between conceptual understanding and procedural knowledge of mathematics.

In today's textbook market, a wide spectrum of curricular choices exists that vary in instructional orientation. Some focus more on memorization and practice; others, on inquiry and exploration. Still others, including some publisher-

Problem 3.1 **The Pythagorean Theorem**

A. Copy the table below. For each row of the table:
- Draw a right triangle with the given leg lengths on dot paper.
- Draw a square on each side of the triangle.
- Find the areas of the squares and record the results in the table.

Length of Leg 1 (units)	Length of Leg 2 (units)	Area of Square on Leg 1 (square units)	Area of Square on Leg 2 (square units)	Area of Square on Hypotenuse (square units)
1	1	1	1	2
1	2			
2	2			
1	3			
2	3			
3	3			
3	4			

B. Recall that a **conjecture** is your best guess about a mathematical relationship. It is usually a generalization about a pattern you think might be true, but that you do not yet know for sure is true.

For each triangle, look for a relationship among the areas of the three squares. Make a conjecture about the areas of squares drawn on the sides of any right triangle.

C. Draw a right triangle with side lengths that are different than those given in the table. Use your triangle to test your conjecture from Question B.

Fig. 15.1. An example of high-quality curriculum. (Source: Lappan et al. [2009]. © 2009 by Michigan State University. Published by Pearson Education, Inc. Used by permission. All rights reserved.)

generated textbooks, have responded to the NCTM *Standards* by incorporating lessons that involve investigations, the use of manipulatives, cooperative learning groups, and adaptations for diverse learners.

We believe that many textbooks in today's market are potentially useful as resources for classroom mathematics teachers. However, we also realize that some materials can be difficult to implement, may require considerable professional development, and might conflict with the beliefs or current practices of some teachers in the school or district. Thus, they may not be appropriate for adoption in every school.

Those reviewing curricula for adoption need to decide the types of knowledge and skills that they expect their students to acquire, and use this decision as a lens for critiquing the instructional design of potential curricular materials. Reys, Reys, and Chávez (2004) believe that curricula "should present material coherently, develop ideas in depth, engage students and motivate learning" (p. 65). Additionally, a curriculum should provide tasks that promote problem solving, high expectations of students, and equity in access. The type of activities suggested in the text should challenge students' thinking rather than merely provide procedural practice.

Content Emphasis

Are mathematical topics in the curriculum presented in sufficient depth and aligned with national, state, and district curriculum standards?

The mathematical content of a textbook series is one of most important aspects to evaluate when considering new mathematics textbooks. A mathematics curriculum should "be coherent, focused on important mathematics, and well articulated across the grades" (NCTM 2000, p. 14). Additionally, it is important to consider the expected content needs of the school or district. State standards are often used to determine such content needs, but these needs can also be influenced by teachers' preferences, local curriculum frameworks, and publications of the National Council of Teachers of Mathematics (e.g., *Principles and Standards for School Mathematics* [2000] or *Curriculum Focal Points for Prekindergarten through Grade 8 Mathematics* [2006]). Many textbook companies provide tables or charts of how their curriculum aligns with individual state standards or the NCTM *Standards*. Textbook-adoption committees can choose to complete their own content analyses or to use reviews provided by an outside resource.

A number of studies have evaluated the content and instructional quality of current textbooks. For example, the American Association for the Advancement of Science (AAAS) (Project 2061 2000) and Mathematically Correct (Clopton et al. 1999) commissioned analyses of middle school mathematics textbooks. These two groups began with different viewpoints—AAAS supporting the vision outlined by NCTM and Mathematically Correct advocating a more traditional approach that focused on skill acquisition. The analysis of textbooks reported by each group differed because of the divergent values and orientations of each group. A review of both reports lends interesting insights and therefore can assist textbook-adoption committees in developing their own framework for reviewing textbook content.

The content analyses performed by AAAS and Mathematically Correct are certainly more thorough than many school or district textbook-adoption committees can individually complete. Accordingly, what should local textbook-adoption committees consider when looking at the mathematical content of a textbook series? The two studies cited provide an important dichotomy to consider: breadth and depth of the content of the textbook series.

First, a textbook-adoption committee should compare the breadth of the textbook series' content with its district or state curriculum standards. The committee should consider each standard and verify whether it is addressed at the appropriate grade level in the textbook series. Many curriculum materials are designed to develop content through a spiral treatment over several grades. In their analyses, AAAS reviewed several middle school mathematics series in their entirety (grades 6 through 8), whereas Mathematically Correct evaluators reviewed only grade 7 textbooks. Although Mathematically Correct attempted to consider a broad range of mathematical topics, it did not identify the content addressed across the entire series (grades 6–8). It is crucial to take time to determine whether content missing in a specific grade is addressed elsewhere in the textbook series. For example, a state may require that students be able to solve problems involving decimals and fractions in its seventh-grade academic standards. A committee might look through a seventh-grade textbook and determine that the textbook does not support this standard sufficiently, but on further inspection find that it was developed in earlier grades.

In addition to looking at the breadth of the mathematics covered in a curriculum, an adoption committee should also look at the attention to the depth of content. Looking at the mathematical depth of all curricular standards will likely be too time-consuming for most adoption committees, so committees may want to focus on one or two topics. This was another major difference between the evaluation methods of AAAS and Mathematically Correct. AAAS chose six specific benchmarks, focusing on both concepts and skills. For example, its benchmark for number concepts was "The expression a/b can mean different things: a parts of size $1/b$ each, a divided by b, or a compared to b." By contrast, the eleven general criteria used in the Mathematically Correct study covered a broader range of subject matter but concentrated primarily on procedural knowledge. With this consideration in mind, a middle school textbook-adoption committee might choose a specific topic (e.g., linear functions) and analyze the extent to which this topic is explored in depth across the textbook series. This in-depth analysis might examine such things as the use of different representations of linear functions, emphasis on an understanding of slope as a constant rate of change, attention to applying knowledge to different contexts, and preparation for the study of nonlinear functions.

Although it is important to review the breadth of specific mathematical topics that are addressed in a textbook series, it is equally important to look in depth at whether those topics are presented in a way that builds both procedural and conceptual knowledge of mathematics.

Support for Students' Learning

Does the curriculum provide quality materials to support students' learning?

Materials that promote concept development, skills practice, and problem solving are primary features of the student textbook. Other useful materials, such as differentiated lessons, lessons involving technology, software supporting technology lessons, student assessments, and manipulatives, may be available in ancillary materials supplied with the student and teacher editions. It is easy for teachers to be impressed by the number and diversity of supplementary materials that textbook companies offer to potential users, but the quantity of ancillary materials should not be the main consideration when assessing materials that support students' learning. Adoption committees must also consider the quality of the supplemental materials. High-quality materials should give teachers opportunities to differentiate instruction through remediation and enrichment while providing a framework for learning that is consistent with the instructional design of the core curriculum.

Support for Teachers' Learning

Is sufficient guidance for the teacher provided to implement the curriculum effectively?

Although textbook publishers generally supply materials for helping teachers plan for instruction, they do not all supply the same type or amount of support for teachers. Tarr and others (2006) suggest that the best textbooks offer many different types of support for teachers, not just "a roadmap of what to teach" (p. 53). Textbook materials should furnish pedagogical support to help teachers understand students' common misconceptions. Additionally, they should help teachers make instructional decisions by providing examples of what students might think or say during class discussions.

NCTM's (2000) Teaching Principle states, "Teachers need to understand the big ideas of mathematics and be able to represent mathematics as a coherent and connected enterprise" (p. 17). High-quality mathematics textbooks require teachers to have conceptual understanding of mathematics and knowledge of how to teach it. Thus, curricula should facilitate teachers' learning and understanding of mathematics rather than just guide teachers' actions (Stein, Remillard, and Smith 2007). For example, figure 15.2 illustrates common misconceptions that high school students have about box plots, offering support for teachers to think about what their own students might encounter as they study this content.

Textbook-adoption committees should consider the need for, and costs of, professional development when choosing a new curriculum. Research suggests

In this investigation, students will use their knowledge about quartiles to describe distributions using the five-number summary and to understand the interquartile range (IQR) as a measure of variability. Box plots are used to display the five-number summaries.

Students sometimes have trouble interpreting box plots, confusing the length of a whisker or section of the box with the number of values. For example, students may think that because the lower whisker is longer than the upper whisker, there are more values in the lower whisker. In fact, each whisker contains about 25% of the values.

Students should be aware that some software makes box plots so that they appear vertically, usually with the scale on the left. See the example below from *Data Desk*.

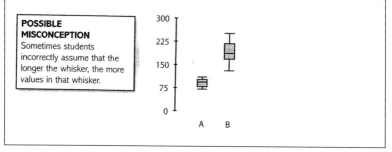

POSSIBLE MISCONCEPTION
Sometimes students incorrectly assume that the longer the whisker, the more values in that whisker.

Fig. 15.2. An example of support for teachers' learning. (Source: Hirsch et al. [2008]. © 2008 by Christian R. Hirsch et al. Published by Glencoe/McGraw-Hill. Used by permission. All rights reserved.)

that professional development is often needed to successfully implement new curriculum materials (Arbaugh et al. 2006). Effective professional development can support curriculum implementation by providing teachers with knowledge of the goals and strategies of the new curriculum, allowing collaborative conversations about upcoming units and providing time for interaction with experienced users of the curriculum (Reys, Reys, and Chávez 2004).

School and District Considerations

Does the curriculum support the local needs and values of the school and district?

Schools and districts have unique attributes that should be considered during the textbook-adoption process. A school's philosophy of learning and teaching of mathematics should be reflected in its choice of textbook. For instance, if the school or district values investigatory or discovery-based learning, the textbooks should reflect this type of pedagogy. During the textbook-adoption process, curriculum articulation between schools throughout the district should also be considered. For example, if a high school has adopted a student-centered curriculum that emphasizes students' investigation and collaboration, an elementary school curriculum that supports the preparation of students for the high school curriculum should be considered. Ideally, a district's grades K–12 mathematics curriculum should reflect a coherent philosophy of teaching and learning so that students who move through the grade levels will not experience major shifts in pedagogical orientation or content emphasis.

The way in which other content areas (i.e. science, language arts) are taught in the school or district is another consideration when adopting mathematics textbooks. Ideally, the mathematics curriculum and pedagogy should be compatible with other content areas. Unfortunately, quite the opposite happens in many secondary schools: students may investigate scientific phenomena in science classes but experience mathematics learning through teacher-centered instruction. This experience can build negative dispositions toward mathematics because students come to view mathematics as a static body of knowledge without any room for creativity (Wilkins and Ma 2003).

The textbook-adoption committee should consider whether a textbook series meets the diverse needs of the students in the district. For example, students not proficient in the English language may have a difficult time understanding mathematical concepts if the textbook relies heavily on verbal description. A good curriculum should provide learning support for these students and their teachers. This support might include suggestions for graphic organizers, bilingual dictionaries, highlighted mathematics vocabulary and main ideas, and concrete examples (Pawan and Sietman 2007). The textbook excerpt in figure 15.3 shows how an

> **Differentiation**
>
> ⓘ **English Language Learners** Make sure that the task is clear by providing two or three concrete examples of the use of fractions, decimals, and percents in everyday life—for example, a set of measuring spoons used for baking, an item with a price tag attached, and an ad announcing a percentage off sale. Some English Language Learners may lack the necessary vocabulary to share their ideas. Have magazines and newspapers available and encourage those students to find pictures of examples they can share. Then provide vocabulary support as needed.

Fig. 15.3. An example of learning support for English language learners. (Source: TERC [2008]. © 2008 by Pearson Education, Inc. Used by permission. All rights reserved.)

elementary school teacher can support nonnative English speakers' learning about rational numbers using concrete, real-world examples. Additionally, a curriculum should offer teachers lesson adaptations for students with learning difficulties and enrichment opportunities for advanced students. For example, figure 15.4 shows an adaptation of a fourth-grade geometry lesson in which students build on their prior knowledge about clocks to learn about angle measurements.

 Adjusting the Activity If students are having difficulty, draw a circle on the board. Mark and label degrees outside the circle and hours inside the circle (*see margin*).

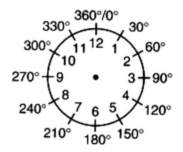

Circle marked with clock numbers
and degree measures

Fig. 15.4. An example of support for differentiated learning.
(Source: Bell et al. [2004]. © 2004 by McGraw-Hill Education.
Used by permission. All rights reserved.)

NCTM (2000) states that technology is essential to mathematics teaching and learning and affects what mathematics is taught. The textbook-adoption committee should carefully evaluate the types of technology that the curriculum advocates and how it is used (e.g., drill and practice, computational efficiency, exploratory learning opportunities, etc.) to determine whether the materials align with the school's learning goals and access to technology. If the current availability of technology is insufficient, schools may need to invest in additional technology or consider different curricula in which the instruction is less dependent on technology.

Research on the Curricular Outcomes and Effectiveness

What does research tell us about the efficacy and implementation of particular curriculum materials?

Can research tell us which textbook series is best for a particular school? Unfortunately, the answer is no (Usiskin 1999). Many factors affect students' learning outcomes, and these factors can be difficult to identify and control (Hiebert 1999). However, research can have an impact on the curricular choices that textbook-adoption committees make. On the basis of a review of the research, adoption committees can learn what obstacles teachers have encountered in the enactment of new curricula and how they overcame such obstacles. Additionally, adoption committees can review evidence on the impact of textbook use on teachers' decisions and students' learning (Stein, Remillard, and Smith 2007).

Research detailing the effectiveness of curricula is available from many sources, as shown in figure 15.5. Senk and Thompson (2003) have compiled an informative book with detailed discussions about twelve standards-based curricula and commentary about these curricula at the elementary, middle, and high school levels. The National Research Council (2004) evaluated the quality of curriculum research studies and compiled a thorough list of research articles related to curricular effectiveness. Professional journals, such as the *Journal for Research in Mathematics Education,* the *Journal for Mathematics Teacher Education,* and *School Science and Mathematics,* feature articles on the effects of written curricula. (Some of these are listed in the reference section of this article.) The Center for the Study of Mathematics Curriculum has created an

---

Sources for Research about Mathematics Curricula

- *Standards-Based Mathematics Curricula: What Are They? What Do Students Learn* edited by Senk and Thompson (2003)
- *On Evaluating Curricular Effectiveness: Judging the Quality of K–12 Mathematics Education* by the National Research Council (2004)
- Professional research journals
  - *Journal for Research in Mathematics Education*
  - *Journal for Mathematics Teacher Education*
  - *School Science and Mathematics*
- Center for the Study of Mathematics Curriculum Web site, http://www.mathcurriculumcenter.org/literature.php
- What Works Clearinghouse Web site, http://ies.ed.gov/ncee/wwc/
- Publishers' and authors' Web sites
- Conferences, workshops, and seminars (e.g., AERA, AMTE, NCTM Research Presessions)
- Pilot studies completed by local schools

Fig. 15.5. Sources for research about mathematics curriculum materials

online database of research literature related to mathematics curricula that can guide adoption committees to available research. The What Works Clearinghouse (WWC) has collected and screened research on the effectiveness of elementary and middle school textbooks; their findings are available on the WWC Web site, http://ies.ed.gov/ncee/wwc/. Additional research and the results of pilot tests of curricula are often available on publishers' or authors' Web sites. A school or district might also consider conducting its own pilot test of a curriculum that it is interested in implementing. Such a pilot allows a school or district to (1) evaluate whether the curriculum meets the specific needs of its students and (2) acquaint some teachers with the details of the curriculum materials.

Summary

We began this article by introducing Ms. Rhodes, a concerned mathematics teacher contemplating the textbook-adoption process. With teachers like Ms. Rhodes in mind, we have developed a rubric for evaluating mathematics curricula (see the Appendix that follows) on the basis of the factors presented in this article. The purpose of the included rubric is to offer a framework to foster informed discussions about textbook review. The rubric was not designed to be exhaustive of factors to be considered. Furthermore, it is not a stand-alone document, but was instead written to be used in conjunction with the context provided by this article. Sample rubrics used by several school districts can be found in Goldsmith, Mark, and Kantrov (2000). In addition, figure 15.6 lists resources that we believe will give teachers like Ms. Rhodes additional insights into the adoption and selection of mathematics textbooks.

Additional Resources for Mathematics Textbook Adoption (see full references in References section)

- "Why Mathematics Textbooks Matter" by Reys, Reys, and Chávez (2004)
- "Selecting High Quality Mathematics Textbooks" by Tarr and others (2006)
- "The Development and Publication of Elementary Mathematics Textbooks: Let the Buyer Beware!" by Reys and Reys (2006)
- *Guiding Curriculum Decisions for Middle-Grades Mathematics* by Goldsmith and Kantrov (2001)
- *Perspectives on the Design and Development of School Mathematics Curricula* edited by Hirsch (2007)
- *Choosing a Standards-Based Mathematics Curriculum* by Goldsmith, Mark, and Kantrov (2000)

Fig. 15.6. Additional resources for mathematics textbook adoption

In this article, we have not advocated the use of any particular curricula or types of curricula, because we believe that curricular choices should be made in the context of the local school. The availability of new types of curriculum materials has changed the textbook-adoption process by giving educators more choices. However, by having more choices, textbook-adoption committees are faced with a more complex task. We encourage textbook-adoption committees to take heed of a variety of considerations when examining curricula, including analyzing the type of instruction and the content, the supports for both students' and teachers' learning, school and district needs, and research related to students' learning outcomes.

Appendix: Considerations for Mathematics Textbook Review and Adoption Form

1) Instructional Design	Strengths/Weaknesses/Comments
How does the pedagogy reflected in the curriculum align with and support the goals of the school or district?	
How often does the curriculum provide multiple opportunities for students to engage in problem solving using cognitively demanding tasks?	
In what ways does the curriculum help students to see the connections between mathematical ideas and their applications?	
Is there evidence that conceptual understanding of mathematical content is emphasized?	
How are students presented with opportunities to develop efficient and appropriate skills?	
In what ways do the tasks in the curriculum require students to justify and communicate their reasoning in various ways?	
How are multiple representations used to introduce and explore mathematical concepts?	

2) Content Emphasis	Strengths/Weaknesses/Comments
Do the mathematical topics in the textbook meet national, state, and district curriculum standards?	
What evidence shows that the content is presented in depth such that students are able to build on mathematical concepts and see the connections between them?	

3) Support for Students' Learning	Strengths/Weaknesses/Comments
What curriculum materials are provided to support student learning?	
Are the supplemental materials consistent with the instructional design of the curriculum?	
In what ways does the curriculum provide teachers with guidance in differentiating instruction?	

Appendix: Considerations for Mathematics Textbook Review and Adoption Form—*Continued*

4) Support for Teachers' Learning	Strengths/Weaknesses/Comments
What types of pedagogical support does the curriculum provide to help teachers understand common student misconceptions?	
How does the curriculum support teachers' learning and understanding of mathematical content?	
What professional development opportunities will be needed to implement the curriculum?	

5) School and District Considerations	Strengths/Weaknesses/Comments
How closely does the curriculum align with the values between and within schools in the district?	
What support structures does the curriculum provide to facilitate the learning of diverse students?	
What will the school or district need to support the technological demands of the curriculum?	

6) Research on Curricular Outcomes and Effectiveness	Strengths/Weaknesses/Comments
What research-based evidence supports the efficacy of the curriculum?	
What are the research-based suggestions for implementing the curriculum?	

REFERENCES

Arbaugh, Fran, John Lannin, Dustin L. Jones, and Meredith Park-Rogers. "Examining Instructional Practices in Core-Plus Lessons: Implications for Professional Development." *Journal of Mathematics Teacher Education* 9 (2006): 517–50.

Bell, Max, John Bretzlauf, Amy Dillard, Robert Hartfield, Andy Isaacs, James McBride, Kathleen Pitvorec, et al. *Fourth Grade Everyday Mathematics Teacher's Lesson Guide, Volume 1.* Chicago: Wright Group/McGraw-Hill, 2004.

Clopton, Paul, Erica McKeown, Michael McKeown, and Jamie Clopton. "Mathematics Program Reviews for Grades 2, 5, and 7." Mathematically Correct, 1999. http://mathematicallycorrect.com/books.htm.

Goldsmith, Lynn T., and Ilene Kantrov. *Guiding Curriculum Decisions for Middle-Grades Mathematics.* Portsmouth, N.H.: Heinemann, 2001.

Goldsmith, Lynn T., June Mark, and Ilene Kantrov. *Choosing a Standards-Based Mathematics Curriculum.* Portsmouth, N.H.: Heinemann, 2000.

Hiebert, James. "Relationships between Research and the NCTM Standards." *Journal for Research in Mathematics Education* 30 (January 1999): 3–19.

Hirsch, Christian R. *Perspectives on the Design and Development of School Mathematics Curricula.* Reston, Va.: National Council of Teachers of Mathematics, 2007.

Hirsch, Christian R., James T. Fey, Eric W. Hart, Harold L. Schoen, and Anne E. Watkins. *Core-Plus Mathematics: Contemporary Mathematics in Context, Course 1, Teacher's Guide, Part A.* Columbus, Ohio: Glencoe/McGraw-Hill, 2008.

Lappan, Glenda, James T. Fey, William M. Fitzgerald, Susan N. Friel, and Elizabeth Difanis Phillips. *Connected Mathematics 2: Looking for Pythagoras.* Upper Saddle River, N.J.: Pearson Prentice Hall, 2009.

National Council of Teachers of Mathematics (NCTM). *Principles and Standards for School Mathematics.* Reston, Va.: NCTM, 2000.

———. *Curriculum Focal Points for Prekindergarten through Grade 8 Mathematics: A Quest for Coherence.* Reston, Va.: NCTM, 2006.

National Research Council of the National Academies. *On Evaluating Curricular Effectiveness.* Washington, D.C.: National Academies Press, 2004.

Pawan, Faridah, and Ginger B. Sietman. *Helping English Language Learners Succeed in Middle and High Schools.* Alexandria, Va.: Teachers of English to Speakers of Other Languages, 2007.

Project 2061. "Middle Grades Mathematics Textbooks: A Benchmarks-Based Evaluation." Project 2061. http://www.project2061.org/publications/textbook/mgmth/report/default.htm.

Reys, Barbara J., and Robert E. Reys. "The Development and Publication of Elementary Mathematics Textbooks: Let the Buyer Beware!" *Phi Delta Kappan* 87 (January 2006): 377–83.

Reys, Barbara J., Robert E. Reys, and Óscar Chávez. "Why Mathematics Textbooks Matter." *Educational Leadership* 61 (February 2004): 61–66.

Senk, Sharon L., and Denisse R. Thompson. *Standards-Based School Mathematics Curricula: What Are They? What Do Students Learn?* Mahwah, N.J.: Lawrence Erlbaum Associates, 2003.

Stein, Mary Kay, Janine Remillard, and Margaret S. Smith. "How Curriculum Influences Student Learning." In *Second Handbook of Research on Mathematics Teaching and Learning*, edited by Frank K. Lester, pp. 310–69. Charlotte, N.C.: Information Age Publishing, 2007.

Stein, Mary Kay, Margaret Schwan Smith, Marjorie A. Henningsen, and Edward A. Silver. *Implementing Standards-Based Mathematics Instruction.* New York: Teachers College Press, 2000.

Tarr, James E., Barbara J. Reys, David D. Barker, and Rick Billstein. "Selecting High Quality Mathematics Textbooks." *Mathematics Teaching in the Middle School* 12 (August 2006): 50–54.

TERC. *Investigations in Number, Data, and Space, Grade 5, Unit 4.* Glenview, Ill.: Pearson Scott Foresman, 2008.

Usiskin, Zalman. "Which Curriculum Is Best?" *UCSMP Newsletter* 24 (Winter 1999): 3–10.

Weiss, Iris, Eric Banilower, Kelly McMahon, and Sean Smith. "Report of the 2000 National Survey of Science and Mathematics Education." 2000survey.horizon-research.com, December 2001. http://2000survey.horizon-research.com/reports/status.php.

Wilkins, Jesse L. M., and Xin Ma. "Modeling Change in Student Attitude toward and Beliefs about Mathematics." *Journal of Educational Research* 97 (September/October 2003): 52–63.

16

Curriculum as a Change Agent: High Schools That Rise to the Challenge and What They Stand to Gain

Kasi Allen-Fuller
Margaret Robinson
Eric Robinson

A PRESERVICE teacher in a local high school arrived for his graduate seminar on teaching mathematics to adolescents and immediately slumped in his seat. "I'm so depressed," he announced to the group, shaking his head. When queried, he shared that much of his day had been spent shadowing a tenth-grade student. In his journal he wrote,

> I don't know how they stand it. I couldn't stand it, and I wasn't even there all day. The lessons are so monotonous it makes you crazy. They just sit there and sort of listen or take notes or respond to the same leading, empty questions. I just thought with the *Standards* and all the new technology and everything that it would be better than when I was in school. But it's not. And yet, it absolutely has to be. *We can't just keep doing the same old thing.*

This observation parallels the conclusions of researchers who have studied

The work reported in this paper was supported, in part, by grants from the National Science Foundation (ESI-9619168, ESI-0001377, and ESI-0137772). The views and conclusions expressed are those of the authors and not necessarily those of the Foundation.

secondary school mathematics classrooms in the United States (Welch 1978; Stigler and Hiebert 1999; Weiss et al. 2003). Such sentiment also reflects common criticisms of United States high school mathematics education articulated in nearly every call for reform since the work of the Committee of Ten in 1893. These criticisms include (1) lack of rigor, (2) irrelevance to life outside of school, (3) a system that perpetuates inequity, and (4) sheer boredom on the part of students, to the point that many leave school altogether (Grubb and Oakes 2007) or abandon the study of mathematics as soon as they have earned the required credits. Despite the repeated calls for reform, little has changed.

Some secondary schools are addressing this issue by initiating major curriculum reform. For the past ten years, we have studied and supported dozens of schools and districts that have succeeded in pursuing a decidedly different path with respect to high school mathematics. These institutions acknowledge the right of all students to learn powerful mathematics and the capacity of all teachers, when given adequate resources and support, to create a learning environment in which every young person can succeed. Consistent with the vision of the National Council of Teachers of Mathematics (NCTM), they maintain that meeting current challenges requires reconceptualizing the classroom experience that has dominated high school mathematics education in the past century, including updating mathematical content, adjusting pedagogy, making use of technology, and attending to issues of access and equity. Leaders in these institutions believe that the choice of curriculum materials makes a substantial difference when initiating and supporting real, significant, and needed change in secondary school mathematics classrooms. Consequently, these schools and districts elected to implement one of the multiyear, integrated high school mathematics curriculum programs developed with funding from the National Science Foundation (NSF)[1]—programs reflecting an extended research and design phase aimed at precisely the classroom issues raised here.

The multiyear programs that resulted from the NSF investment in high school mathematics curriculum development share many common attributes. All were designed and field-tested by teams composed of mathematicians and teachers with the goal of producing rigorous new mathematics courses that would also be relevant to teenagers. Each of these programs chose an integrated design in which concepts from multiple mathematics strands are woven throughout each

---

1. The five high school mathematics programs that resulted from the NSF investment are Mathematics: Modeling Our World, Contemporary Mathematics in Context, Interactive Mathematics Program, MATH Connections: A Secondary Mathematics Core Curriculum, and SIMMS Integrated Mathematics: A Modeling Approach Using Technology. In our earlier work, we have referred to this collection as the "COMPASS-affiliated" programs. For the purposes of this article, we refer to them as the NSF-funded high school mathematics curricula. Although curricular distinctions exist across the five NSF-funded high school programs, our focus is on their commonalities.

course, a marked departure from the traditional sequence (algebra 1, geometry, algebra 2, and so on) that has largely defined secondary school course offerings in the United States for more than a century. All these curricula assume the presence of technology, especially graphing calculators or other dynamic graphing software. Finally, these programs encourage a student-centered pedagogical approach that includes cooperative group work; extended, inquiry-based problems; and the communication of ideas through writing and students' presentations. The shifts in both content and pedagogy place new demands on teachers as well as students.

The COMPASS Center[2] was founded under the premise that implementing comprehensive new mathematics programs at the high school level would require much more work on the part of teachers, schools, and districts than is entailed when adopting a traditional high school textbook series. Although many crucial barriers were identified by COMPASS Center staff early on, successful implementation proved to be even more demanding than anticipated in nearly every respect. And we are still learning. What we know without a doubt is this: *when effectively implemented, these coherently designed mathematics curriculum programs can, indeed, drive comprehensive change that results in significant, authentic improvement for schools, teachers, and students.* The implementation process is complex and decidedly long-term. However, for those who rise to the challenge, the benefits can be substantial, wide reaching, and enduring.

Context for Change

> Attaining the vision … will require that all concerned be committed to improving the futures of our children. The task is enormous and essential. All students need an education in mathematics that will prepare them for a future of great and continual change. (NCTM 2000, p. 8)

Adults in America have witnessed frequent and repeated mandates for improving grades K–12 mathematics education in their lifetime. The publication of *A Nation at Risk* (National Commission on Excellence in Education 1983) was a federal call to action that affected educators across the country, particularly in mathematics and science, subjects in which only a minority of students then succeeded at the advanced level both in and beyond high school. A primary concern

---

2. As the development phase for these programs drew to a close, NSF recognized the need to support and study their use in real schools and districts. COMPASS (Curricular Options in Mathematics Programs for All Secondary Students) was created in 1997 to provide a coordinated and collective dissemination effort for the five NSF-funded high school mathematics projects. Initially, COMPASS consisted of a central site and five satellite sites, one for each of the curricula, which enabled the center to communicate a shared vision as well as provide curriculum specific information and assistance.

at the time was the perceived gap between what students were learning in school and what they would need to know to be productive citizens in an increasingly technological society. The recommendations emphasized the need for *all* young people to master relevant mathematics and science content, to solve engaging real-world problems, and to conduct meaningful research.

During the period of *A Nation at Risk*, consensus appeared to be growing among mathematicians as well as educators that grades K–12 mathematics had become a fixed set of procedures to master as opposed to a dynamic discipline capable of powerfully shaping the modern world. NCTM created a set of recommendations to help move the field ahead in this regard. *Curriculum and Evaluation Standards for School Mathematics* (NCTM 1989) offered a bold vision for what grades K–12 mathematics education might be—a vision strikingly different from what most United States adults had experienced themselves as students.

Given the nature of the changes proposed, any attempt to enact the NCTM (1989) *Standards* document was sure to be daunting, nowhere more so than at the high school level. Teachers and administrators could see the value of the *Standards,* but envisioning what curriculum and instruction might entail, especially given existing course offerings and materials, proved difficult. At this point, the NSF stepped in and provided funding (1992–97) for the development of curriculum programs that would enable schools and districts to implement the *Standards* document's vision, taking into account the latest research on learning and teaching mathematics as well as up-to-date content and technology.[3] The developers reconsidered all assumptions about secondary school mathematics education, so as to redefine the high school mathematics teaching and learning experience.

The five resulting comprehensive programs each had its own individual character. Still, they strongly resembled a family of curricula: they all chose to integrate topics in a coherent fashion and emphasize higher-order thinking, often through mathematical modeling and appropriate use of technology. Most notably, they were all highly ambitious programs that involved much more than incremental change in current course offerings.[4] Full implementation necessitated replacing the familiar algebra 1–geometry–algebra 2 sequence with a rigorous program of integrated courses that were cumulative as well as comprehensive (Hirsch 2007; Robinson et al. 2000).

For more than a decade, the COMPASS Center has worked to inform the field about these materials and to support those who choose to implement them. The need remains for creating awareness, articulating the *Standards'* vision, and assisting schools that engage in curriculum-led improvement of their mathemat-

---

3. We acknowledge that the five NSF-funded high school programs and their counterparts at the middle and elementary school levels are not the only mathematics curricula that claim to embody the NCTM Standards.

4. The first editions of these five curricula became available for purchase in 1997.

ics programs. In an effort to provide structured, ongoing support, COMPASS has organized a network of experienced implementer high schools, the intention being that member schools would support and learn from one another as they face similar issues.

> This meeting has been an eye-opening experience. It's given me my breath back knowing that our school is not only not alone, but also traveling down the right path. It was so refreshing hearing people speak honestly about these programs. They're not perfect, but they are definitely firmly rooted in the best intentions for our students.
>
> *—High school mathematics department chair*

Building a network of teams from multiple implementation sites has proved to be a powerful strategy for supporting ongoing secondary school mathematics improvement in schools and districts as well as across the nation.

Who Dares?

> Only those who dare to fail greatly can ever achieve greatly.
> *—Robert F. Kennedy*

Comprehensive mathematics programs, such as those developed with National Science Foundation funding, go beyond the scope of an average textbook. Schools that adopt these integrated materials and the teachers who undertake their implementation distinguish themselves in multiple ways from their peers. For example, in prior studies of curricular decision-making, researchers have explored school and district readiness to use innovative programs like the NSF-funded curricula (St. John et al. 2000, 2005; Fuller et al. 2003). The findings suggest that most schools and districts in the United States are relatively satisfied with their secondary school mathematics programs. Among those who do express dissatisfaction and a desire to change, the majority would not choose to do so by completely reworking their course offerings; instead, they envision more of an incremental strategy, infusing new activities into the existing curriculum or choosing a new textbook for a specific course. Thus, the desire to fundamentally change the curricular approach sets implementers of the NSF-funded programs apart from their counterparts at the outset. As a group, the schools and districts that undertake major curriculum reform want, for many different reasons, to improve mathematics education in a deep and profound fashion.

Of the many factors that distinguish successful curriculum implementation sites from others engaged in improvement initiatives, we focus here on three qualities that we have found to be the most crucial: *motivation* grounded in equity, *connections* to others doing similar work, and *commitment* to staying the course.

Motivation

Although improving students' academic performance often serves as an impetus for considering programmatic change, the *motivation* for putting into place one of the NSF-funded high school programs generally runs deeper than simply improving scores on standardized tests or purchasing textbooks with newer copyright dates. Those who spearhead curriculum-led change efforts aim to make high-quality mathematics teaching and learning accessible to more students— ultimately to *all* students. They view mathematics as intrinsically valuable and believe that success plays a crucial role in determining students' future career options. They express particular concern over the extent to which mathematics serves as a barrier to students' fully realizing their goals and achieving their aspirations. Thus, leaders perceive implementation of these programs as an initiating event, setting in motion a process that will spur the realization of other broader goals.

Connections

Those who succeed with innovative high school mathematics curricula often indicate that *connections* to others engaged in, and dedicated to, similar work piqued their interest in making a change or helped them persist when the work became difficult. Each of the curricula is an instantiation of a much larger vision associated with the professional world of mathematics education. Connections to other improvement efforts[5] and to schools pursuing similar goals have proved instrumental in nourishing implementation efforts. However it occurs, locally or long-distance, establishing relationships with like-minded educators decreases the feeling of isolation that comes with pursuing an alternative path and places the work in a larger context, creating increased leverage and providing a broader base of support for local change.

Commitment

Having companions in this work is particularly crucial owing to the scope and duration that implementation efforts require. The time span of a successful curriculum implementation effort is generally at least five years—nearly the length of many district adoption cycles. It takes at least that much time, with administrative support, to phase in four years of courses, work with counselors, educate parents, help students acclimate to the new program, and quell critics. In

---

5. In particular, sites have benefited from associations with other systemic reform efforts funded by the National Science Foundation over the past fifteen years. These include but are not limited to the Rural Systemic Initiatives, the State Systemic Initiatives, the Local Systemic Change grants, the Urban Systemic Programs, and the Math Science Partnerships.

short, implementing one of these programs is long-term, stay-the-course work—figuratively and literally. To complicate matters, this longitudinal time line does not align particularly well with school adoption cycles or with other essential system processes, such as the revision of district or state standards, teacher turnover, and changes in administration. The bottom line is that every implementation effort proves to be an example of deeply committed educators—an array of teachers, department chairs, principals, and superintendents—daring to push on parameters of what the system traditionally finds acceptable so as to serve all students.

How It Happens

> I almost quit teaching because I couldn't find resources to teach in the ways that I wanted. If we hadn't started this program, I was seriously considering leaving.
>
> *—High school mathematics teacher*

In the best of worlds, there would be a single, effective step-by-step procedure for selecting, initiating, and sustaining comprehensive programmatic change that would apply to any school or district. However, no single prescription for success exists. To give a sense of the differences across implementation sites, we offer descriptions of two contrasting situations.

Suburban Districtwide Implementation

In a wealthy suburb, a widely respected superintendent aims to unify the curriculum by demanding that the district agree on textbooks that can be used across the district. When the elementary and middle level mathematics committees choose NSF programs for their respective grade level bands, there is strong pressure on the high school to do the same. Indeed, district mathematics leaders come close to requiring secondary school mathematics teachers to choose from one of the five NSF-funded high school curricula.

A Single Champion

In a small, isolated, rural district with a single high school, one accomplished and influential mathematics teacher decides that implementing one of the NSF-funded high school curricula would be the perfect way to raise mathematics achievement of the district's lowest-performing students and simultaneously improve the mathematical learning experiences of all students. Leveraging support from a state reform effort, he convinces the rest of the mathematics department to join him with the district's blessing.

An implementation process that succeeds in one district might not work in another; yet, common elements surface repeatedly in schools and districts that have adopted one of the NSF-funded programs. Table 16.1 catalogs these elements. Undervaluing any one of these components can seriously undermine the implementation process.

Table 16.1

Core Elements of the Implementation Process

Element	Elaboration	Effect
Motivation	Involves much more than student achievement	Establishes reason for change and attracts others to the effort
Vision	Incorporates the NCTM *Standards*, including the principle that all students can do mathematics	Clarifies from the outset the goals and comprehensive nature of the improvement effort
Alignment of beliefs	Includes teachers, administrators, counselors, school board members, and parents	Solidifies a base of support for the effort and allows for high-fidelity implementation
Initial leadership	Speaks for, energizes, and shepherds the early work	Rallies support and resources that safeguard the effort
Administrative endorsement	Authorizes programmatic change rather than incremental change and fosters supportive context	Prioritizes program goals and resources; presents public face, allowing teachers to concentrate on classroom improvement
Professional development	Supports learning about the program as well as the mathematics and pedagogy contained therein; involves personnel beyond teachers	Expands content knowledge and pedagogical skill; reinforces shared vision of improvement
Communication with stakeholders	Includes public events (e.g., Family Math Night, school board meetings), newsletters, progress reports, and so on	Helps parents and community members better understand the effort and their potential role in it
Policies and Practices	Supports major change rather than incremental change	Protects the fidelity, viability, and sustainability of the effort
Benchmarks for progress	Incorporate baseline data, authentic student work, and a variety of locally determined measures	Build internal and external confidence in the program; allows for formative feedback
Networking	Fosters collaboration among like-minded educators and institutions	Eliminates debilitating isolation; assists fidelity and sustainability of implementation
Time	Acknowledges that programs can take 5+ years to fully implement, realizing that there is no quick fix	Allows the effort to strengthen and build, leading to accrual of school, teacher, and student benefits

As the table suggests, curriculum implementation involving this type of comprehensive change requires a paradigm shift, and it affects people in all areas of the system—teachers, administrators, students, parents, community members, and so on. Inside the school, the alignment of teachers' beliefs and regular professional development facilitate this shift. Similarly, fostering administrative support and communicating with stakeholders outside the school help create an informed base of community support for the effort. Attending to such factors from the outset places less strain on the system and increases the implementation effort's likelihood of success.

What Happens When Schools Dare?

> Why not go out on a limb? Isn't that where the fruit is?
> —*Frank Scully*

Operating outside the tradition, culture, and practice that have come to define secondary schooling is no easy task, as any implementer of the high school NSF-funded curricula will quickly point out. Although the process of putting such a program in place serves as a constant force of stretch and pull on the system, this work can lead to numerous benefits for schools, teachers, and students.

Benefits to Schools

The benefits to schools begin with the selection process. Simply working together to articulate criteria for a new curriculum and reaching consensus about moving in the direction of a comprehensive program point toward a greater shared vision of mathematics teaching and learning within the building, not to mention a broader, deeper notion of mathematics as a discipline. When the conversation involves administrators, counselors, and teachers in other departments, as is generally true, the process also involves addressing issues of equity and reducing tracking. As the implementation takes hold, the process fosters a culture of raised expectations for all students. In this climate, powerful discussions also take place about the nature of mathematical rigor and how it involves more than what is measured on standardized tests (St. John et al. 2005).

Benefits to Teachers

The NSF-funded curricula are often referred to as "educative" because of the professional learning implicit in their use. High-fidelity implementation efforts include professional supports that go well beyond mathematics content knowledge. Institutions that commit to one of these programs also dedicate themselves to providing a sustained, cumulative set of experiences that ground teachers in the vision underlying the new curricula, providing multiple opportunities over time to internalize the underlying motivation for the change as well as the technical aspects of achieving it. Teachers report increased collaboration within their mathematics departments. They tell stories of learning new mathematics, coming to a deeper understanding of old topics, using more technology, having a new perspective on students in their classrooms, and completely rethinking how they teach (Resek 1999; Schoen et al. 2003).

Benefits to Students

Students notice the difference. They report enjoying mathematics more than they did before, as well as experiencing greater success; these outcomes lead to taking more mathematics courses. Students talk about seeing connections between mathematical ideas and between what they are learning and their lives. They speak about solving challenging problems and modeling real-life situations. And, beyond their meaningful mathematical experiences, they articulate with considerable candor the challenges and benefits of working in groups (Harwell et al. 2007; Huntley et al. 2000; Senk and Thompson 2003).

> I was thinking the other day about what an incredible and important class math is. I was thinking about racism and the separatism we have at our school and how most of our high school is not designed to promote interracial friendships or activities. In math, we work together in a very diverse group solving problems which can apply to everyday life. Every aspect of our math program by itself is amazing and effective, and the combinations of all of them results in an environment where not only learning takes place but as if naturally with it comes interracial relationships and respect.
>
> —*Tenth-grade mathematics student using an NSF-funded program*

When asked, students readily explain how their mathematics class is different from what they have experienced in the past. Table 16.2 lists some of the positive changes along with some of the derived benefits that we observe in classroom visits and have documented in our interviews with students and their teachers.

Building on Success

> This meeting was far more beneficial than I ever thought it would be. The activities were a huge plus because they got us interacting with members of different innovative mathematics communities and they got us thinking about our individual programs and how to make them more stable. I didn't need any input on the benefits of my program, but I did need to know that the problems I face in my school are the same as those in innovative mathematics programs all over the country.
>
> —*Mathematics teacher/COMPASS Points member*

Table 16.2

Changes in the Student Experience

Nature of the Change	Benefit of the Change
Students experience multiple modes of work that include collaborating with their peers and making conjectures.	Rather than sit passively in class, students participate in their own learning; they have the opportunity to articulate mathematical ideas and justify their thinking.
In mathematics lessons, students begin with contexts and build toward concepts, often requiring that they explore and wrestle with unfamiliar problems and situations.	Students become more comfortable with tackling problems. Their mathematical knowledge is less cued to specific problem types. They persist rather than give up when faced with a new challenge.
Classroom activity focuses on students doing the mathematics rather than on a teacher demonstrating how to do the mathematics.	Students view their peers as resources, posing clarifying questions to their classmates as well as to their teacher. The teacher no longer holds all mathematical knowledge. A community of learners ensues.
Students are actively engaged in learning and exploring mathematics.	Students take more responsibility for their learning. They enjoy mathematics rather than endure it.
Students learn that there are multiple methods for solving almost any problem.	Students are open to the ideas of their peers and curious to discover alternative strategies. They begin asking the question, Is there another way?
Students verify and justify their mathematical thinking through written and oral communication.	Students have the opportunity to engage in true mathematical discourse. They learn to defend their ideas and conclusions.
Students experience multiple forms of assessment, including long-term research projects, journals, and portfolios.	Students view mathematics as a tool for research and discovery. They learn to write about mathematics, generate their own questions, and make presentations. Mathematics becomes more than completing daily exercise sets.
Mathematics is presented as a dynamic subject—attainable and necessary for all, ever-changing and largely responsible for most developments associated with the modern age.	Students feel empowered to participate in an increasingly mathematical world. They view mathematics as a tool for social change as well as technological progress.

In our work with implementers of the high school NSF-funded curricula, we interact with schools and districts that have implemented their programs for more than a decade, others that are only beginning the process, and all those in between. Despite their varying years of experience, all understand that they are constantly learning and adjusting accordingly. Even among those who have been implementing the curricula the longest, rather than profess to have all the answers, they recognize that the work of implementation is constant, unyielding, highly dynamic, and context-specific. "You can never let up," as one department chair has told us, and little can be assumed from one year to the next. So they strive to strengthen and safeguard their efforts by building on prior success and proactively responding to implementation challenges and barriers—knowing that the work of implementation never ends. It evolves.

Users of the NSF-funded high school programs often experience a "honeymoon phase" followed by a period of considerable challenge (St. John et al. 2005). Similarly, the work can level off, and implementers find themselves needing to climb beyond their plateau. A number of patterns for continued success beyond the initial implementation are shown in table 16.3. Such information may help schools embarking on a program of comprehensive change, now or in the future. These actions and attitudes are central to the work of schools and districts that have dared to implement one of these innovative curricula and are succeeding in doing so today—unequivocally, readily, and continually.

Concluding Reflections

> These are exciting times in mathematics [education]. Despite the difficulties in designing, testing, and marketing new mathematics curricula, the need for significant improvement in student learning requires us to overcome those difficulties.
>
> —*Robert Reys,*
> *"Curricular Controversy in the Math Wars"*

The implementation efforts highlighted in this article transcend the status quo. *Curriculum*, here, is much more than a list of topics to be covered; *rigor* is more than the ability to perform intricate computation; *improvement* is more than responding to a mandate for change; and *success* is more than increased scores defined by the limited measurement capabilities of high-stakes tests.

The NSF-funded high school mathematics curricula, with the necessary professional resources and supports, provide the impetus for unprecedented change. The development effort that yielded these curricula took years of research and design, with input from university mathematicians, mathematics educators, and teachers. Moreover, these comprehensive programs each went through several

Table 16.3

Central Actions and Attitudes

- *Embrace communication as part of the ongoing work*
  Every year, new students and their parents enter the school community. Turnover among staff and administration is also a constant. Therefore, those shepherding the implementation must see public relations as something they engage in on a regular basis. As the implementation proceeds, this effort will go beyond communicating the vision motivating the improvement effort and will include sharing results, such as test scores, student portfolios, data on course-taking patterns, and so on.

- *Ensure that opportunities for rich professional learning continue*
  The implementation passes through various stages. In each one, the professional development needs are different. As the effort continues, some teachers and administrators (especially newcomers) will still need training on the "nuts and bolts" of the program, while experienced users will benefit from more advanced work, such as exploring in more depth a particular area of mathematics content, relevant technology, or appropriate pedagogy. However it happens, meeting this range of needs is crucial.

- *Empower students and give them a voice*
  Students can be some of the strongest advocates for using NSF-funded curricula. Once they make the transition from a more sequential, topic-based approach, many speak very articulately about how the experience has changed them, particularly their conception of what mathematics is—and what it is not. We have seen students play a powerful role in the communication effort associated with implementation.

- *Cultivate partners in the implementation process at all levels of the system*
  Once the implementation is up and running, it is imperative to determine who truly supports the effort and to foster those relationships—within the building, among members of the larger community, with other schools and districts, and including policymakers. For example: Does the science department value the new mathematics program because of the extensive use of applications? Do the English teachers appreciate the extent to which students are writing in mathematics class now? Can a nearby school share costs for professional development? Can the local college help host a community math night?

- *Foster leadership for mathematics improvement at all levels*
  Teachers cannot be the only spokespeople for an improvement effort grounded in innovative curriculum. Others within the system must understand, participate in, and be prepared to defend the work. This often includes acting on policies and practice seemingly tangential to the work: for example, committing to hiring teachers that are willing to participate in the effort or supporting a schedule that accommodates longer periods for engaging in lablike mathematics activities. Not enough can be said about the role that a thoroughly supportive school context can play in strengthening the implementation.

iterations, guided by extensive field-testing involving real classrooms and students. Make no mistake: the end result is a quality and cohesiveness far beyond that generally encountered with typical textbooks. The curricula are also outside the realm of what a district-based curriculum development project could be expected to create, given the limits of time, resources, and expertise. The successful publication of these innovative curricula as a family of programs stands as an existence proof that comprehensive curriculum materials can be developed that embody the vision of the NCTM *Standards* and address the needs of the modern era.

Despite their research-driven design and alignment with NCTM *Standards,* these curriculum programs are found in a smaller percent of U.S. schools and districts than their commercial counterparts. Instead, they tend to be adopted by a small niche market of schools and districts that possess the necessary qualities and contextual elements to support implementation. This outcome may be because, in many respects, the greatest benefits associated with these curricula—for example, the inclusion of modern mathematical content—can also pose the greatest challenges to implementation. Therefore, the schools and districts that elect to put such programs in place are consciously making improvement in what mathematics students learn and how they learn it their top priority.

Linda Darling-Hammond argues that, as a nation, we need to shift from educational structures that "design controls" to those that "develop capacity" for improvement (Darling-Hammond 1993). This is, in fact, what those who dare actually do. Where there is complexity in the system, those who dare provide *clarity of vision and purpose.* Where there is resistance, those who dare help foster *support* among the teachers, administrators, and school boards, developing *deeper professional identity* and *leadership* qualities that extend beyond the boundaries of their own classrooms. Where culture breeds inertia, those who dare reach out to explain and *involve others* in taking action. Where there is the common phenomenon of teachers' isolation, those who dare work to build *collaborative opportunities.*

A lingering question is, why dare? Why? Because students deserve more—*all* students! Schools that rise to the challenge enable students to reason mathematically; to use content and procedures flexibly and in new situations; to carry their knowledge beyond the classroom and the temporal boundary of end-of-course examinations; and to develop persistence in mathematical problem solving. Schools that dare assist students in developing the ability to invoke a mathematical perspective: to understand what mathematical conclusions and computations are based on; to see the mathematical features in everyday and job-related situations; and to make decisions involving mathematical information. These skills are fundamental to supporting the next generation of young people in facing the unique challenges of the twenty-first century—and pursuing their career dreams and aspirations with mathematical confidence and competence.

REFERENCES

Darling-Hammond, Linda. "Reframing the School Reform Agenda: Developing Capacity for School Transformation." *Phi Delta Kappan* 74, no. 10 (June 1993): 753–61.

Fuller, Kasi A., Mark H. St. John, Pamela Tambe, Tamara Evans, and Laurie Lopez. *The K–12 Mathematics Curriculum Center at EDC: Cornerstone Claims.* Inverness, Calif.: Inverness Research, 2003. http://inverness-research.org/reports/ab2003-03_Rpt_EDC_CornerstoneClaims.html.

Grubb, Norton W., and Jeannie Oakes. " 'Restoring Value' to the High School Diploma: The Rhetoric and Practice of Higher Standards." Tempe, Ariz.: Education Public Interest Center, Arizona State University, October 2007. http://epsl.asu.edu/epru/documents/EPSL-0710-242-EPRU.pdf.

Harwell, Michael R., Thomas R. Post, Yukiko Maeda, Jon D. Davis, Arnold L. Cutler, Edwin Andersen, and Jeremy A. Kahan. *"Standards*-Based Mathematics Curricula and Secondary Students' Performance on Standardized Achievement Tests." *Journal for Research in Mathematics Education* 38, no. 1 (January 2007): 71–101.

Hirsch, Christian R., ed. *Perspectives on the Design and Development of School Mathematics Curricula.* Reston, Va.: National Council of Teachers of Mathematics, 2007.

Huntley, Mary Ann, Chris L. Rasmussen, Roberto S. Villarubi, Jaruwan Sangtong, and James T. Fey. "Effects of *Standards*-Based Mathematics Education: A Study of the Core-Plus Mathematics Project Algebra and Functions Strand." *Journal for Research in Mathematics Education* 31, no. 3 (May 2000): 328–61.

National Commission on Excellence in Education. *A Nation at Risk: The Imperative for Educational Reform.* Washington, D.C.: U.S. Government Printing Office, 1983.

National Council of Teachers of Mathematics (NCTM). *Curriculum and Evaluation Standards for School Mathematics.* Reston, Va.: NCTM, 1989.

———. *Principles and Standards for School Mathematics.* Reston, Va.: NCTM, 2000.

Resek, Diane. "Evaluation of the Interactive Mathematics Program." Paper presented at the Annual Meeting of the American Educational Research Association, Montreal, April 1999. http://www.mathimp.org/research/AERA_paper.html.

Reys, Robert E. "Curricular Controversy in the Math Wars: A Battle without Winners." *Phi Delta Kappan* 83, no. 3 (2001): 255–58.

Robinson, Eric E., Margaret F. Robinson, and John C. Maceli. "The Impact of Standards-Based Instructional Materials in the Mathematics Classroom." In *Learning Mathematics for a New Century,* 2000 Yearbook of the National Council of Teachers of Mathematics (NCTM), edited by Maurice Burke, pp. 112–26. Reston, Va.: NCTM, 2000.

Schoen, Harold L., Kristin J. Cebulla, Kelly F. Finn, and Cos Fi. "Teacher Variables That Relate to Student Achievement When Using a Standards-Based Curriculum." *Journal for Research in Mathematics Education* 34, no. 3 (May 2003): 228–59.

Senk, Sharon L., and Denisse R. Thompson, eds. *Standards-Based School Mathematics Curricula: What Are They? What Do Students Learn?* Mahwah, N.J.: Lawrence Erlbaum Associates, 2003.

Stigler, James W., and James Hiebert. *The Teaching Gap.* New York: Free Press, 1999.

St. John, Mark H., Kasi A. Fuller, Nina Houghton, Dawn Huntwork, and Pamela Tambe. *High School Mathematics Curricular Decision-Making: A National Study of How Schools and Districts Select and Implement New Curricula.* Inverness, Calif.: Inverness Research Associates, 2000. http://www.inverness-research.org/reports.html.

St. John, Mark H., Kasi A. Fuller, Nina Houghton, Pamela Tambe, and Tamara Evans. *Challenging the Gridlock: A Study of High Schools Using Research-Based Curricula to Improve Mathematics.* Inverness, Calif.: Inverness Research Associates, 2005. http://www.inverness-research.org/reports.html.

Weiss, Iris R., Joan Pasley, P. Sean Smith, Eric R. Banilower, and Daniel J. Heck. *Looking Inside the Classroom: A Study of K–12 Mathematics and Science Education in the United States.* Chapel Hill, N.C.: Horizon Research, 2003.

Welch, Wayne W. "Science Education in Urbanville: A Case Study." In *Case Studies in Science Education.* Urbana, Ill.: University of Illinois, 1978.

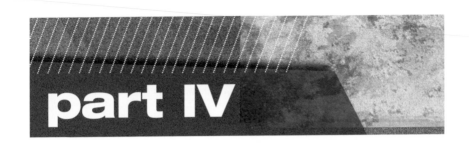

part IV

The Implemented Curriculum

17

Myths about Curriculum Implementation

Denisse R. Thompson
Sharon L. Senk

THINK about a school or school district you know well. Consider the following
statements. Which are true in that school or district? How do you know?

- If a topic is in the mathematics textbook, teachers teach it.
- Teachers who use the same mathematics textbook teach the same
  content.
- Teachers who use the same textbook offer the same opportunities for
  students to continue learning mathematics through homework.
- Teachers of the same mathematics course have the same expectations
  for how their content coverage prepares students for standardized tests.

Curriculum materials have a powerful influence on what students learn and
what they have an opportunity to learn (Begle 1973; Stein, Remillard, and Smith
2007; Valverde et al. 2002). Mathematics teachers have long used textbooks as
a basis for their instruction (Grouws and Smith 2000). With the publication of
Curriculum and Evaluation Standards for School Mathematics (National Council of Teachers of Mathematics [NCTM] 1989) and *Principles and Standards for
School Mathematics* (NCTM 2000), attention focused on the role of textbooks
and curriculum materials to guide instruction, including government support to
fund various curriculum projects with the goal of developing materials aligned
with the *Standards* (Senk and Thompson 2003).

School districts or states often mandate the textbook that teachers are expected to use as the basis for instruction; that is, they determine what is often called the *intended curriculum* for a course (Valverde et al. 2002). However, how that textbook is implemented in a classroom (i.e., the *implemented* or *enacted curriculum*) is a significant determiner of what students are likely to learn. Some districts provide pacing guides in an attempt to ensure that students in all the schools make the same progress through their textbook. Standardized achievement assessments are created on the basis of assumptions about what students will have had or should have had an opportunity to learn at a particular grade or from a particular course (the *assessed curriculum*); results on these tests are then used to determine the *achieved curriculum*. But what evidence exists that the intended curriculum, the implemented or enacted curriculum, and the assessed curriculum (which ultimately determines information about the achieved curriculum) are aligned?

In this article, we focus on the statements from the beginning of this article and provide evidence that all are false. To justify our claims, we draw on data from studies by other researchers and from field studies conducted as part of the development of curriculum materials from the University of Chicago School Mathematics Project (UCSMP). UCSMP is a grades K–12 curriculum development and research project that has been producing mathematics curriculum materials since its inception in 1983. As the secondary school materials are developed and revised, they are field-tested in schools for an entire school year prior to further revision and commercial publication. During the school year, teachers participating in the field studies, whether using the UCSMP or comparison curriculum, complete surveys about various aspects of their use of textbooks and other instructional materials. Data provided by these teachers, as well as data from other researchers about curriculum implementation, give evidence that the four statements that begin this article are myths. We show that far more variability occurs among the intended, implemented, and assessed curriculum than is often imagined by educators and policymakers.

Myth 1: If a Topic Is in the Mathematics Textbook, Teachers Teach It

On the basis of the 2000 *National Survey of Science and Mathematics Education,* Whittington (2002) reported that middle and high school mathematics teachers *estimated* the percent of their textbook that they expected to cover that academic year for a particular class. Table 17.1 summarizes the results of anticipated coverage. The modal response from both middle school and high school teachers indicated they expected to cover between 75 and 90 percent of their textbook. However, considerable variation existed within each group.

Table 17.1

Teachers' Estimated Textbook Coverage for a Particular Target Class

		Percent of Textbook Estimated to Be Covered			
Level	N	0% – 49%	50% – 74%	75% – 90%	More than 90%
Middle school	634	6	30	47	17
High school	1367	7	28	46	19

Note: Based on Whittington (2002).

More recently, Tarr and his colleagues (2006) studied a group of thirty-nine middle school teachers throughout the school year. On average, teachers using NSF-funded curricula taught about 60 percent of the lessons in their textbooks; teachers using publisher-generated curricula taught about 69 percent of the lessons in their textbooks. These results are based on actual records of classroom implementation, not on estimates, and are somewhat lower than the estimates reported by Whittington.

Figure 17.1 summarizes data from chapter-coverage forms completed by UCSMP or comparison teachers collected during field trials conducted between 2005 and 2007 of four courses intended for use in grades 7–10. Thus, these data complement and update those of Whittington (2002) and Tarr and his colleagues (2006). As in the study by Tarr and others, the data indicate actual coverage of the textbook rather than estimated coverage. The graphs represent data from sixty teachers in twenty-eight schools in sixteen states. Although the median textbook coverage across the four course levels differs somewhat, varying from 69 percent at prealgebra and algebra 2 to 76 percent at algebra, the variability within a course is typically quite large, even among the relatively small number of teachers reflected in each box plot.

All these studies document wide variability in the percent of lessons in a textbook that are actually taught by teachers. The vast majority of teachers do not teach all lessons in their textbooks. This finding is not likely to shock some readers, who may struggle to complete all lessons in their own textbooks. Given that a textbook contains lessons that teachers do not teach, in what ways do the choices teachers make vary, and how are their choices of textbook material to cover reflected in their assignments or assessments? These issues are the focus of the next three myths.

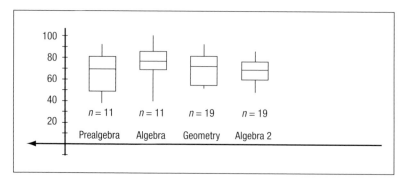

Fig. 17.1. Percent of lessons in textbook taught by teachers using UCSMP
Third Edition or comparison curricula in four courses.
(Note: *n* = number of teachers. Based on all teachers who provided
complete chapter-coverage information.)

Myth 2: Teachers Who Use the Same Mathematics Textbook Teach the Same Content

When teachers are using the same textbook, how much and what content is covered within or across schools? Figure 17.2 reports the percent of lessons taught by sixty-four teachers using the field-trial versions of the third edition of UCSMP secondary school materials across forty-six schools in twenty states. Of these teachers, only one (a teacher in the algebra study) taught 100 percent of the lessons in the textbook. Although the median percent exceeded 60 percent

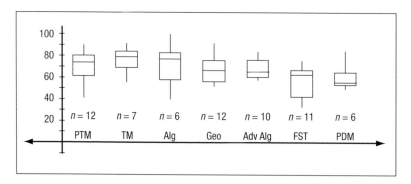

Fig. 17.2. Percent of lessons in textbook taught by teachers using
UCSMP Third Edition curricula in seven courses.
(Note: *n* = number of teachers.)

for six of the seven courses, in four of the courses at least one teacher taught less than 50 percent of the textbook lessons. Even two teachers in the same school did not teach the same content in the Transition Mathematics study; one of the teachers was out for medical reasons quite a bit during the year, and her students covered 1.5 fewer chapters than students in the classes of the other teacher. Thus, even when teachers were using the same textbook, considerable variability was observed in the percent of the lessons taught for each course.

When Tarr and his colleagues (2006) analyzed lessons taught and omitted by a group of middle school teachers using the same textbook, they found that some teachers omitted material that came primarily toward the end of the textbook; others omitted lessons regularly throughout the textbook; still others omitted large portions of the early textbook material. As illustrated by data from the use of the UCSMP *Advanced Algebra*, Third Edition, textbook, we found similar results in our research.

Table 17.2 reports the percent of lessons, other than end-of-chapter review materials, by thirds of the textbook, taught by ten teachers in seven states who were using the field-trial version of UCSMP *Advanced Algebra,* Third Edition. Only 40 percent of these teachers taught at least three-fourths of the lessons in the textbook. Although the mean number of lessons taught in the first two-thirds of the textbook is 89 percent, the mean drops to 36 percent of the lessons taught in the final third. So most students never had an opportunity to learn the content in the final third of the textbook.

Table 17.2

Percent of Lessons Taught in Field-Trial Version of UCSMP Advanced Algebra, Third Edition, by Teacher

Teacher	Chapters 1–4 ($n = 36$)	Chapters 5–8 ($n = 35$)	Chapters 9–13 ($n = 45$)	Chapters 1–13 ($n = 116$)
A	100	86	16	63
B	69	80	31	58
C	97	71	22	60
D	64	83	33	58
E	94	91	53	78
F	81	100	36	69
G	92	94	71	84
H	100	91	42	75
I	97	100	0	60
J	94	89	51	76
mean	89	89	36	68
s.d.	12	9	19	9

Note: n = number of lessons.

Figure 17.3 illustrates the lesson coverage of the *Advanced Algebra* teachers using a display similar to those used by Tarr and his colleagues (2006). Many teachers taught lessons in sequence, so the percent of lessons covered is a matter of pace. However, three of the teachers omitted most of chapter 4 on matrices and transformations with connections to geometry. Some teachers omitted most of this chapter because the content was not part of their district or state guidelines at this level. However, transformations are used in several lessons about functions later in the text. It is not clear how omitting the lessons in chapter 4 affected students' opportunity to understand the lessons involving functions in subsequent chapters. Also, notice that there was not a single chapter in which all ten of these teachers taught all lessons in the chapter.

Thus, even when teachers were teaching from the same intended curriculum, the actual pattern of coverage—that is, the implemented curriculum—was quite different. These data reinforce the following comments made by Kilpatrick (2003, p. 473):

> Two classrooms in which the same curriculum is supposedly being "implemented" may look very different; the activities of teacher and students in each room may be quite dissimilar, with different learning opportunities available, … and different outcomes achieved.

Myth 3: Teachers Who Use the Same Textbook Offer the Same Opportunities for Students to Continue Learning Mathematics through Homework

Teaching a lesson is only one aspect of curriculum implementation. To achieve proficiency with mathematics, students typically need opportunities outside class to engage with the mathematics, individually or in groups. Most mathematics teachers regularly assign homework as a means for students to deepen their understanding of the ideas encountered in lessons. So homework assignments are a crucial aspect of curricular implementation that likely influences students' learning, that is, the achieved curriculum. To illustrate how homework assignments vary, we present data about teachers' use of the UCSMP *Algebra* textbook.

Table 17.3 reports the percent of questions assigned by teachers teaching from the UCSMP *Algebra*, Third Edition, curriculum and is based on just those lessons taught by the given teacher. As described in the UCSMP teachers' editions, sets of homework questions in the UCSMP curriculum are designed so that almost all problems should be assigned to students. Thus, assigning only

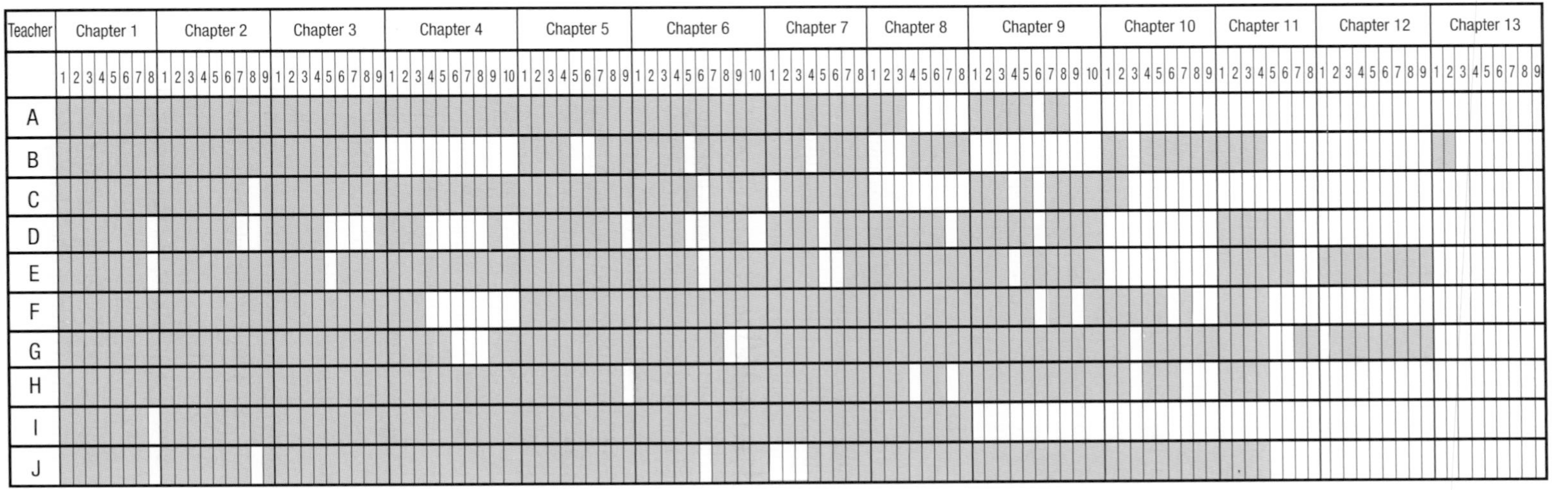

Fig. 17.3. Coverage of lessons taught by teachers A–J using the field-trial version of UCSMP *Advanced Algebra*, Third Edition. (A gray shaded box indicates the lesson was taught.)

even-numbered or odd-numbered problems generally does not offer sufficient opportunities to achieve proficiency.

Table 17.3

Percent of Questions Assigned by Teachers of Field-Trial Version of UCSMP Algebra, *Third Edition, Based Only on Lessons Taught*

Teacher	Number of Questions Assigned	Number of Possible Questions in Lessons Taught	%
A	963	963	100
B	359	431	83
C	795	846	94
D	982	1135	87
E	887	931	95
F	313	656	48

Despite the differences in the percent of lessons taught (see fig. 17.2), five of the six teachers generally assigned most of the problems in those lessons to their students. However, Teacher F assigned considerably fewer problems—fewer than half of those given in the lessons. So, in addition to covering only 58 percent of the lessons in the book, the teacher provided fewer opportunities for students to continue using the concepts and skills than other teachers did using the same textbook. It might be true that this teacher's students were exceptional in some way and did not need the same level of practice as students in other classes. But in a school or district, if significant differences in achievement were noted among students in different classes, a closer look at opportunities to engage with the concepts might be considered.

The results from these algebra teachers can be investigated in a slightly different manner. In only two chapters, 1 and 4, did all the teachers teach all lessons. So an investigation of the questions assigned in lessons taught by all teachers might highlight differences in philosophies or interpretations of the materials.

The questions in each lesson in the UCSMP secondary school materials are grouped into the following four types:

- *Covering the ideas* questions address the core mathematics of the lesson. Students who successfully complete these questions understand the essential ideas of the lesson.

- *Applying the mathematics* questions use the core mathematics in new contexts or in new ways not explicitly demonstrated in the lesson. These questions are intended to deepen students' understanding of the mathematics more than the covering-the-ideas questions.

- *Review* questions give students an opportunity to continue developing their understanding of mathematics presented in earlier lessons or chapters. Such distributed practice is an effective means for students to build proficiency. Although students may have struggled with a concept during the initial lesson, after discussion of homework or seeing connections to related concepts, they can often apply those concepts. Thus using review questions is a crucial component of implementing the UCSMP curriculum.

- *Exploration* questions extend the mathematics concepts in an exploratory manner for students who need an additional challenge. These are the only problems that are not expected to be assigned on a daily basis.

Table 17.4 reports the percent of questions assigned from each of the first three types of questions from a set of lessons in UCSMP *Algebra* taught by all six teachers—the lessons of chapter 4. With the exception of Teacher F, teachers assigned at least 90 percent of the covering-the-ideas questions, thus ensuring that students had an opportunity to engage with the core mathematics of the lesson. Three of the teachers assigned all the applying-the-mathematics questions, and two assigned about three-fourths of them, but Teacher F assigned fewer than a fifth of these problems. Thus, Teacher F's students had far fewer opportunities to apply the concepts of this chapter in new ways. Even more variation occurs in the assignment of review problems. Teacher F assigned none of these problems, so if her students did not master the content on the initial day of the lesson, they had fewer opportunities to engage with the mathematics at another time. Teachers B and D also offered fewer opportunities for review than recommended by the curriculum developers.

Table 17.4

Percent of Covering the Ideas, Applying the Mathematics, and Review Questions Based Only on Lessons Taught in Chapter 4 by All Teachers of Field-Trial Version of UCSMP Algebra, Third Edition

Teacher	Covering the Ideas ($n = 59$)	Applying the Mathematics ($n = 34$)	Review ($n = 61$)
A	100	100	89
B	93	76	62
C	92	100	89
D	98	71	66
E	98	100	95
F	56	18	0

Note: n = number of possible questions.

As the results in tables 17.3 and 17.4 illustrate, teachers who are teaching from the same curriculum materials can have very different expectations for students, even when they teach the same lessons. As Hiebert and Grouws (2007, p. 379) note,

> The emphasis teachers place on different learning goals and different topics, the expectations for learning that they set, the time they allocate for particular topics, the kinds of tasks they pose … all are part of teaching and all influence the opportunities students have to learn.

Myth 4: Teachers of the Same Mathematics Course Have the Same Expectations for How Their Content Coverage Prepares Students for Standardized Tests

Many educators and policymakers support the use of standardized tests because they believe that such tests eliminate bias in the design of the test. However, even when teachers are teaching from the same curriculum materials, differences in teachers' coverage of content may unwittingly create bias for or against their students.

When posttests are administered at the end of a school year as part of UCSMP evaluation studies, teachers are asked to complete an opportunity-to-learn (OTL) form on which they indicate, for each item, whether they taught the content needed for their students to answer the item. For instance, as figure 17.4 indicates, for only sixteen of the thirty-two items (50%) on the TerraNova Algebra Test (a standardized test developed by CTB/McGraw-Hill [2001]) did all six UCSMP algebra teachers indicate teaching the content needed to answer the item. If Teacher F is omitted from this analysis, still for only twenty of the thirty-two items (62.5%) did all teachers report teaching the content. So a standardized test may not be an appropriate measure of the expectations for students who have taken the same course—in this instance, first-year algebra.

We often describe variation in classroom instruction in two distinct ways on the basis of teachers' responses on the OTL forms. First, at each school where we have a pair of teachers, we note those items on which both teachers at the school reported teaching the content. Second, we look across teachers participating in the study, regardless of the curriculum being used, and identify those items on which *all* teachers reported teaching the content.

Variation in OTL on standardized tests within schools is often striking. For instance, in one school in which one teacher used UCSMP *Algebra* and another

	Test Items																															
Teacher	1	2	3	4	5	6	7	8	9	10	11	12	13	14	15	16	17	18	19	20	21	22	23	24	25	26	27	28	29	30	31	32
A																	☐											☐				
B	☐									☐					☐		☐					☐									☐	
C	☐																							☐								
D																		☐				☐										
E																																
F	☐				☐	☐				☐		☐			☐	☐						☐					☐					

Fig. 17.4. Items on the TerraNova Algebra Test for which content
was reported as taught by teachers using the field-trial version
of UCSMP *Algebra,* Third Edition. (A gray box indicates the
teacher reported teaching the content
needed to answer the item.)

used a non-UCSMP comparison curriculum, both teachers agreed about content coverage on only 62 percent of items on the Terra Nova Algebra Test. So even when students are taking the same course in the same school and eventually going to the same subsequent course, their opportunities to learn are not necessarily the same.

As reported elsewhere, we have found variability in opportunity to learn the mathematics on posttests both over time and over course level (Thompson et al. 2001, 2003; Thompson and Senk 2006). Table 17.5 reports results from this analysis of commonality on the OTL on the standardized tests used in field trials for four courses over more than a decade.

As the results in table 17.5 suggest, at the school level, for a given course little agreement (50%) or complete agreement (100%) may be found about opportunities to learn particular mathematics content. However, across all courses, all teachers in a study agreed on having taught the content needed to answer less than half the items on these standardized tests. In other words, even in studies involving fewer than fifteen teachers, little agreement is found among teachers about the expectations for middle and high school mathematics courses.

One can assume that when teachers develop assessments for their own class, they generally assess only content that they have taught. But when assessments are created at a level beyond the classroom teacher (e.g., on standardized tests or state-administered examinations), information about the extent to which students have had an opportunity to learn the content of the assessment is needed before drawing conclusions with policy implications. Even when students are enrolled in courses that might be perceived as conventional in content (i.e., first-year algebra, geometry, second-year algebra), the results cited in this section suggest that considerable variability exists in topics studied.

Table 17.5
Variability in Opportunity to Learn the Mathematics on Standardized Tests by Course

	Pre-Transition Mathematics	Transition Mathematics	Algebra	Geometry
Year of Data Collection	2006–2007	2005–2006	2005–2006	1993–1994
Number of teachers	14	10	9	8
Number of schools	9	4	5	4
Name of standardized test	TerraNova CAT Survey Mathematics, Level 17	Iowa Algebra Aptitude Test	TerraNova Algebra Test	High School Subjects Test: Geometry
Number of items on test	32	40	32	40
Percent of items common to both UCSMP and comparison teachers in the same school	50% – 97%	68% – 100%	62% – 100%	65% – 80%
Percent of items common to all teachers in the study across schools	34%	40%	48%	48%

Note: Based on Thompson et al. (2001, 2003) and Thompson and Senk (2006).

Conclusion and Discussion

In this article, we have cited data that debunk four myths about curriculum that some educators and policymakers may believe. In particular, we have shown that most teachers do not teach all topics in their textbooks; even teachers using the same textbook often teach different lessons; and even when the same lessons are taught, the questions assigned for homework may be quite different. Further, the variation in curriculum implementation noted for courses typically taught in grades 7–10 results in striking differences in how teachers respond to whether they think their curriculum has prepared students to answer questions on standardized tests.

Attempts to mandate a curriculum may be made by district or state officials or other policymakers, but the results discussed here suggest that detailed information about what happens at the classroom level is crucially important. Teachers use curriculum materials in many ways on the basis of various contextual (e.g., instructional time or state and district frameworks) and personal (e.g., their perceptions of the needs of their students, or their own understanding of the mathematics in the materials) factors (Stein, Remillard, and Smith 2007). When teachers do not teach some portion of a textbook or choose not to assign specific problems, one cannot be sure why without asking each teacher.

Such variability is not necessarily bad or inappropriate. Teachers need to be sensitive to the needs of their students and the values and learning expectations in a local community. A given curriculum may be effective in different circumstances with appropriate modifications. We suggest that the failure to acknowledge this variability in implementation is potentially problematic. For instance, because even in the same school teachers may vary in the percent of a textbook they teach, it is crucial that teachers of each course clearly articulate to teachers of the following course what material was and was not studied. Similarly, teachers of the subsequent course also have an obligation to explain to those teaching the preceding course why certain content is fundamental to success in the subsequent course. In other words, the variability that occurs in curriculum implementation necessitates articulation across the grades and courses in middle and high schools.

In the current climate of educational accountability, too often the use and effectiveness of a curriculum are discussed solely with regard to achievement. The data in this article suggest that failure to consider the implemented curriculum makes it difficult, if not impossible, to make valid judgments about the assessed curriculum. Many policymakers at the federal level argue for experimental designs in research on curriculum evaluation and accept primarily standardized assessments as acceptable measures of achievement (see, e.g., reports by Slavin [2008]). The data shared here suggest that even standardized measures may not be appropriate without information about implementation.

Collecting information about the fidelity of implementation is often difficult. Having observers in classrooms for an extended period of time is costly and labor intensive. The surveys we have used provide a relatively inexpensive way to obtain detailed information about curriculum implementation. Yet they can be burdensome at times for teachers to complete. Researchers need to continue discussions about low-cost, informative ways to solicit information about curriculum implementation that are reliable and do not require much inference on the part of researchers. They should also not place unreasonable demands on teachers and their time. We hope that the types of data and the displays we have used in this article contribute to that discussion.

REFERENCES

Begle, Edward G. "Lessons Learned from SMSG." *Mathematics Teacher* 66 (March 1973): 207–14.

CTB/McGraw-Hill. *TerraNova Algebra.* Monterey, Calif.: CTB/McGraw-Hill, 2001.

Grouws, Douglas A., and Margaret Schwan Smith. "NAEP Findings on the Preparation and Practices of Mathematics Teachers." In *Results from the Seventh Mathematics Assessment of the National Assessment of Educational Progress,* edited by Edward A. Silver and Patricia A. Kenney, pp. 107–39. Reston, Va.: National Council of Teachers of Mathematics, 2000.

Hiebert, James, and Douglas A. Grouws. "The Effects of Classroom Mathematics Teaching on Students' Learning." In *Second Handbook of Research on Mathematics Teaching and Learning,* edited by Frank K. Lester, Jr., pp. 371–404. Charlotte, N.C.: Information Age Publishing, 2007.

Kilpatrick, Jeremy. "What Works?" In *Standards-Based School Mathematics Curricula: What Are They? What Do Students Learn?,* edited by Sharon L. Senk and Denisse R. Thompson, pp. 471–88. Mahwah, N.J.: Lawrence Erlbaum Associates, 2003.

National Council of Teachers of Mathematics (NCTM). *Curriculum and Evaluation Standards for School Mathematics.* Reston, Va.: NCTM, 1989.

———. *Principles and Standards for School Mathematics.* Reston, Va.: NCTM, 2000.

Senk, Sharon L., and Denisse R. Thompson, eds. *Standards-Based School Mathematics Curricula: What Are They? What Do Students Learn?* Mahwah, N.J.: Lawrence Erlbaum Associates, 2003.

Slavin, Robert E. "What Works? Issues in Synthesizing Educational Program Evaluations." *Educational Researcher* 37 (January/February 2008): 5–14.

Stein, Mary Kay, Janine Remillard, and Margaret S. Smith. "How Curriculum Influences Student Learning." In *Second Handbook of Research on Mathematics Teaching and Learning,* edited by Frank K. Lester, Jr., pp. 319–70. Charlotte, N.C.: Information Age Publishing, 2007.

Tarr, James E., Óscar Chávez, Robert E. Reys, and Barbara J. Reys. "From the Written to the Enacted Curricula: The Intermediary Role of Middle School Mathematics Teachers in Shaping Students' Opportunity to Learn." *School Science and Mathematics* 106 (April 2006): 191–201.

Thompson, Denisse R., and Sharon L. Senk. "Methods for Controlling for Opportunity-to-Learn." In *Proceedings of the Twenty-Eighth Annual Meeting of the North American Chapter of the International Group for the Psychology of Mathematics Education,* vol. 2, edited by Silvia Alatorre, José Luis Cortina, Mariana Sáiz, and Aristarco Méndez, pp. 179–86. Mérida, Mexico: Universidad Pedagógica Nacional, 2006.

Thompson, Denisse R., Sharon L. Senk, David Witonksy, Zalman Usiskin, and Gurcharn Kealey. *An Evaluation of the Second Edition of UCSMP Advanced Algebra*. Chicago: University of Chicago School Mathematics Project, 2001.

Thompson, Denisse R., David Witonsky, Sharon L. Senk, Zalman Usiskin, and Gurcharn Kealey. *An Evaluation of the Second Edition of UCSMP Geometry*. Chicago: University of Chicago School Mathematics Project, 2003.

Valverde, Gilbert A., Leonard J. Bianchi, Richard G. Wolfe, William H. Schmidt, and Richard T. Houang. *According to the Book: Using TIMSS to Investigate the Translation of Policy into Practice through the World of Textbooks*. Dordrecht, Netherlands: Kluwer Academic Publishers, 2002.

Whittington, Dawayne. *2000 National Survey of Science and Mathematics Education: Status of High School Mathematics Teaching*. Chapel Hill, N.C.: Horizon Research, 2002.

18

Technology and the Teaching of Mathematics

Richard M. Hollenbeck
Jonathan A. Wray
James T. Fey

T HE POWER and versatility of a wide array of sophisticated electronic tools available for teaching and doing mathematics have transformed ways that we can engage students in exploring mathematical ideas and solving mathematical problems. These tools also challenge us to reconsider what mathematics is emphasized in classrooms (see Fey, Hollenbeck, and Wray elsewhere in this volume). From computer tutors, virtual manipulatives, and SMART Boards to e-books, simulation applets, and computer-adaptive testing, we have access to teaching tools that were hard to imagine in the chalk-and-talk era of only a few decades ago.

What you learn depends in important ways on how you are taught, and when electronic information technologies are applied to the tasks of teaching, they provide intriguing opportunities for transforming the mathematics learning experience. Used as a regular component in mathematics instruction, the responsible use of technology can stimulate students' interest and enhance students' learning (National Council of Teachers of Mathematics [NCTM] 2000).

The core mathematical content of the grades K–12 curriculum is drawn from the geometry and measurement, arithmetic, data analysis and probability, analysis, and discrete mathematics strands of the discipline. Very attractive tools now exist for developing important ideas in each of those strands. As new technologies constantly arrive, the challenge for educators is to create innovative ways to use technology effectively in teaching and learning mathematics. In this article, we use a variety of examples to illustrate how technology can be used to enhance mathematics learning and support effective teaching. Our objective is to help teachers understand how available technology can be incorporated as an integral component of instruction.

Geometry and Measurement

Imagine that the objective for a lesson is to develop students' understanding of the geometric principle that the area of any triangle can be calculated by using the formula $A = (1/2)bh$. With that goal in mind, present students with the task of finding the largest triangle that can be drawn inside a given rectangle. In time, students will come up with a variety of approaches for solving the problem. They may construct physical models, draw pictures, or arrive at some analytical method for making sense of the task.

After students discuss their initial ideas, they can be directed to a variety of computer applets for additional exploration or reinforcement of their conjectures. For example, the National Library of Virtual Manipulatives (http://nlvm.usu.edu) has an electronic geoboard that students can use to generate many examples of triangles enclosed within a given rectangle (see fig. 18.1).

This exploratory work can reveal or confirm the principle that for each rectangular configuration, the area of the largest enclosed triangle is equal to half the area of the original rectangle. Students can then explore the same question with a different applet available on the Illuminations Web site of NCTM (http://illuminations.nctm.org/ActivityDetail.aspx?ID=108). This applet allows students to slide one vertex of the triangle along a line parallel to the opposite side. They will quickly notice that the triangle shape changes, but base, height, and area do not.

Through combining visual images and numerical area calculations from the two applets with some analytic reasoning about the case of right triangles in a rectangle, students are likely to develop a solid understanding of the familiar area formula. At least for the case of triangles with one side along the length or width of the rectangle, they will find the area of the largest inscribed triangle.

Although physical geoboards could be used, virtual manipulatives have advantages that warrant their use. Classroom instructional time is not needed for retrieval, cleanup, storage, or maintenance. Web-based manipulatives offer visually appealing graphics that provide opportunities to highlight important relations, capture screen images, and even print students' work. Many virtual manipulatives include interactive tools, such as the capacity to measure lengths and areas, offering information not accessible with physical models. The power of these and other computer-based manipulatives lies in the way they furnish exploratory environments that give immediate feedback about consequences of mathemati-

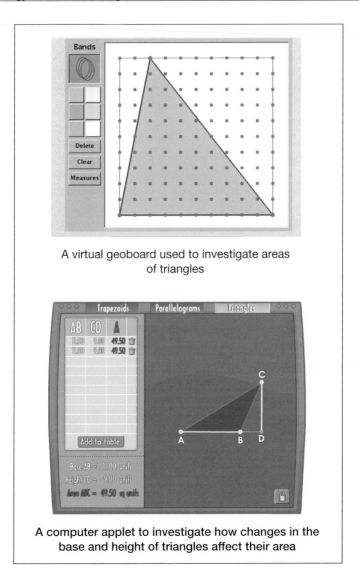

A virtual geoboard used to investigate areas of triangles

A computer applet to investigate how changes in the base and height of triangles affect their area

Fig. 18.1

cal operations. Furthermore, as access to computing becomes more and more ubiquitous, such virtual manipulatives will be available whenever and wherever students might need them.

A natural extension of the foregoing activity to the secondary school level might be to challenge students to find the area of an arbitrary triangle given the coordinates of its vertices in the (x, y) plane. Consider the following task:

Find the area of a triangle whose vertices are $A(3, 1)$, $B(12, 0)$, and $C(9, 5)$.

For students who have thought only of finding areas for triangles with their base on a horizontal line, this is likely to be a challenging task. By combining an exploration with an interactive geometry software tool such as The Geometer's Sketchpad with their earlier experience of bounding a triangle, students can be expected to arrive at strategies to find the area of an arbitrary triangle set in the coordinate plane. For example, after bounding a triangle with a rectangle, a student may use a dissection strategy to find the area of the desired triangle by decomposing three triangular areas from the area of the rectangle, or a student could apply the construction and measuring tools of the interactive geometry software tool to find the area of a rectangle whose width or length contains an edge of the triangle (see fig. 18.2).

Merely using technology to arrive at a solution gives no guarantee that the learning of a broader principle will occur. The challenge for mathematics educators is to find appropriate ways to use tools, such as interactive geometry software, to enhance the curriculum. A student who simply finds the area of the triangle by using the area measurement command is not as likely to have the same learning opportunities as a student who understands one of the foregoing strategies for solving the problem.

Number and Arithmetic

Concepts and reasoning about number relationships and arithmetic are at the heart of almost every branch of mathematics and every application to mathematical reasoning and problem solving. As a result, devices that assist in arithmetic computation have been important tools of mathematical work and learning for millennia.

At the elementary school level, for example, early childhood students can begin to explore the relationships among numbers and develop mental computational skills using five- and ten-frames. The electronic ten-frame (http://illuminations.nctm.org) helps children focus on the relationships among numbers up to and beyond ten (see fig. 18.3). The frame serves as an anchor for numbers and helps students explore methods for subitizing "building" numbers, for determining how many more are needed to build a number, for practicing identifying quantities, and for adding or subtracting numbers.

Proportional reasoning is a core subject in the number strand of middle-grades mathematics. The importance of ratios and proportions is enhanced by their use in reasoning about similarity of geometric shapes. This visual representation of proportionality in such subjects as digital photography and computer graphics provides engaging contexts for students' exploration.

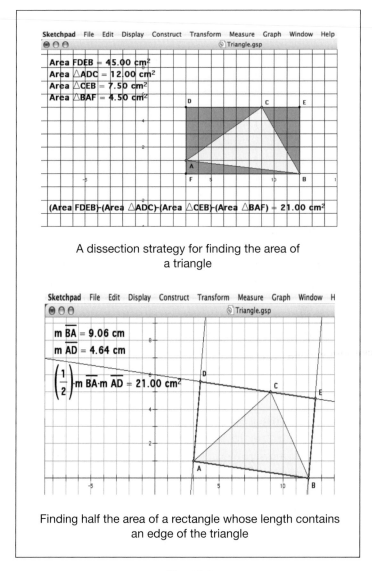

Fig. 18.2

For example, imagine presenting a digital photograph of the Washington Monument and posing the following task:

Construction of the Washington Monument started in 1848. In 1858, when the monument was 152 feet high, construction was stopped because of a lack of money and the onset of the Civil War. When the work resumed in 1879, builders had to use a slightly darker-colored

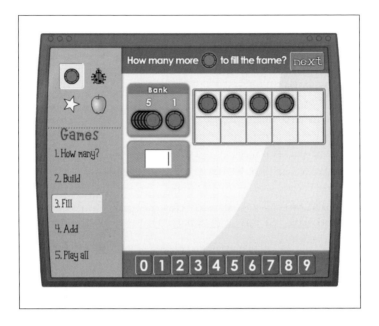

Fig. 18.3. A computer applet that helps children explore basic number facts

marble block to finish the monument. How high is the Washington Monument?

Students will probably have intuitive ideas about ways to use the known height in 1879 to calculate the height of the finished monument. Then virtual rulers can be used to measure object lengths in pixels, centimeters, or inches (see fig.18.4). Repeating the measurement with several different units of length will reveal the invariant *ratio* of the two heights. Photo-editing software allows for easy enlargement or reduction of a picture. If the two heights are measured after each size-change operation, a scatter plot of the measurement pairs will reveal a linear pattern. A spreadsheet, graphing calculator, or computer line-of-best-fit routine will show how to model that pattern with a linear function in the form $y = mx$. This function expresses the proportionality relationship in an algebraic form that can be used to answer in a new way the original question about the height of the finished monument.

Algebra

Interest in building appropriate readiness for the study of algebra has led to increased focus on development of algebraic thinking and algebraic reasoning skills as early as prekindergarten. For example, in the primary school mathematics classroom, children can use the Color Patterns virtual manipulative (http://nlvm .usu.edu) to describe a color pattern, extend a pattern, check their solution(s), and generate their own patterns (see fig. 18.5). Students should be encouraged to use their own words to describe the patterns displayed and extend the patterns by dragging the appropriate colors to the circled question marks. Afterward, children can use the Spotting Numbers Problem applet (http://www.fi.uu.nl/toepassingen/ 00299/toepassing_wisweb.en.html) to examine patterns and make and verify predictions.

Almost every secondary-school-level mathematics curriculum aims to develop students' understanding and skill in the use of algebraic equations and expressions to represent and reason about variables and relationships. Manipulating equations and expressions into alternative equivalent forms often leads to solutions for problems and insight into relationships. Computer simulations and calculation tools can help students develop understanding of the concepts and skills involved in those processes.

For example, one of the most effective ways of thinking and teaching about equations and inequalities is by analogy to the operation of a simple pan balance. Live demonstration with a real pan balance might be the best start on use of this analogy for equation solving, particularly for younger children. But exploration with a computer simulation can lead students to discover the operating principles that produce equivalent but simpler equations. Given a virtual pan balance in an applet (http://nlvm.usu.edu), students can move unknown and numeric "weights" to see which "moves" retain balance and lead to a picture revealing the value of x (see fig. 18.6).

When students are comfortable with the basic concept of solving equations and have developed some informal sense of strategy, teachers can focus on developing more general and efficient use of solving operations. Here, different computer tools can be helpful. In most computer algebra systems (CAS), once

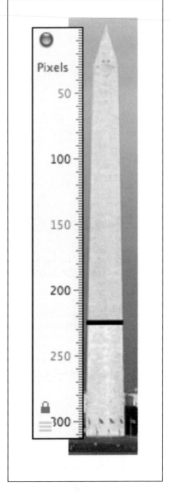

Fig. 18.4. Using a virtual ruler to measure the height of the Washington Monument

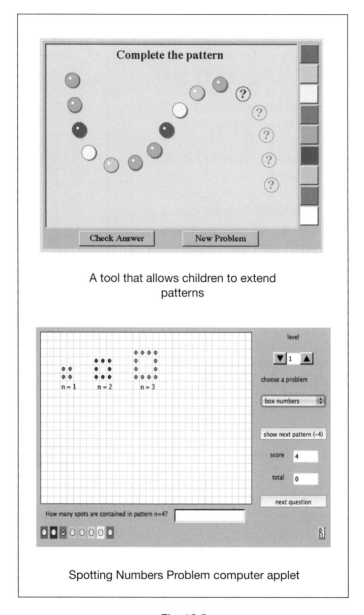

A tool that allows children to extend patterns

Spotting Numbers Problem computer applet

Fig. 18.5

an equation is entered, it is easy to perform an operation on both sides. The CAS accurately executes the directions that are given, often showing a result that is different from what students expect. For example, when beginning students are asked to solve an equation such as $5x + 3 = 18$ for x, they often try moves like "di-

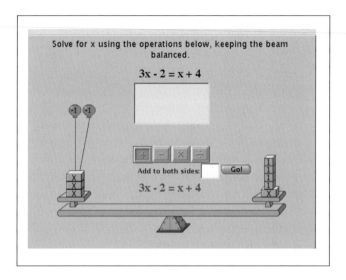

Fig. 18.6. A virtual pan balance

vide by 5" or "subtract $4x$." Of course, the CAS will show the unhelpful results of those moves:

$$\text{Divide by 5:} \quad \frac{5x+3=18}{5} \quad \rightarrow \quad \frac{5x+3}{5} = \frac{18}{5}$$

$$\text{Subtract } 4x: \quad (5x+3=18)-4x \quad \rightarrow \quad x+3=18-4x$$

Research has shown that when students explore solving moves with feedback like what the CAS gives, they quickly develop the understandings and strategic skills that are desirable goals of instruction on this fundamental topic (Guin and Trouche 1999).

Connections

One of the most valuable contributions of computers to mathematical work is in promoting multiple representations of data and relationships and connections of topics from different strands of the discipline. The following example shows how different computing tools can help students encounter the number e from a new perspective based in probability. Consider the following question:

> To help students see alternative approaches to an assignment, a teacher distributed n papers to n students at random. What is the probability that *no* student receives his or her own paper?

For most students, the first step toward solving this problem would be to generate and inspect lists of all possible arrangements in simple instances when *n* is small. The desired probability would be the ratio of the number of possible outcomes in which no student obtained his or her own paper (what might be called *derangements*) to the number of possible arrangements.

It is likely that students will quickly recognize the limitation of such a strategy for values of *n* as small as five. Although many students will realize that *n*! gives the number of possible outcomes from distributing *n* papers, determining the number of derangements is a less accessible task. A computer applet available from http://theory.cs.uvic.ca/root.html lists the derangements for *n* up to six. Ultimately, formulas for the number of arrangements and derangements, not exhaustive lists, are required for computing the probabilities. But reasoning about the situation is likely to lead to a recursive process for generating successive counts of derangements rather than a closed form rule. If $d(n)$ is the number of derangements in ordering of *n* objects, then

$$d(n) = (n-1)[d(n-1) + d(n-2)].$$

The calculation of values for $d(n)$ from such a recursive formula and the ratio $d(n)/n!$ is easy with such tools as calculators or computer spreadsheets (see fig. 18.7). If students are directed to add a column showing reciprocals of the derangement probabilities to their calculator table or spreadsheet, they will notice a surprising pattern—those reciprocals quickly converge to a highly accurate decimal approximation of *e*. So in addition to revealing a surprising result in probability, this technology-enabled exploration should pique students' curiosity about yet another amazing connection of topics from very different parts of mathematics.

N	Arrangements	Derangements	Probability	1/Probability
1	1	0	0	
2	2	1	0.5	2
3	6	2	0.33333333	3
4	24	9	0.375	2.666666667
5	120	44	0.36666667	2.727272727
6	720	265	0.36805556	2.716981132
7	5040	1854	0.36785714	2.718446602
8	40320	14833	0.36788194	2.718263332
9	362880	133496	0.36787919	2.718283694
10	3628800	1334961	0.36787946	2.718281658
11	39916800	14684570	0.36787944	2.718281843
12	479001600	176214841	0.36787944	2.718281827
13	6227020800	2290792932	0.36787944	2.718281829

Fig. 18.7. A spreadsheet that shows convergence to *e*

Conclusions

It is essential for educators to find ways to incorporate the calculating, computing, and communication power of digital-age electronic technologies into mathematics instruction. Technology engages students in the exploration of important mathematical ideas and expands the range of problems that students can solve. It supports the development of students' intuition about mathematical concepts and enhances their understanding of fundamental concepts.

At the same time, technology is not a panacea (NCTM 2000). Teachers need to carefully select and design learning opportunities for students where technology is an essential component in developing students' understanding, not where it is simply an appealing alternative to traditional instructional routines. To maximize the power of technology, teachers need access to resources and professional development opportunities to acquire a well-developed knowledge base for teaching with technology. They also need to learn about new roles for teachers and students in a technologically rich environment.

REFERENCES

Fey, James T., Richard M. Hollenbeck, and Jonathan A. Wray. "Technology and the Mathematics Curriculum." In *Mathematics Curriculum: Issues, Trends, and Future Directions,* Seventy-second Yearbook of the National Council of Teachers of Mathematics (NCTM), edited by Barbara J. Reys and Robert E. Reys, pp. 41–49. Reston, Va.: NCTM, 2010.

Guin, Dominique, and L. Luc Trouche. "The Complex Process of Converting Tools into Mathematical Instruments: The Case of Calculators." *International Journal of Computers for Mathematics Learning* 3 (October 1998): 195–227.

National Council of Teachers of Mathematics (NCTM). *Principles and Standards for School Mathematics*. Reston, Va.: NCTM, 2000.

19

Understanding Teachers' Strategies for Supplementing Textbooks

Corey Drake

RESEARCH in the past several years has examined the ways in which teachers use mathematics curriculum materials, including the ways in which teachers' uses of curriculum materials match (or not) the intent of designers (Remillard 2005), the range of ways in which multiple teachers might use the same set of curriculum materials (e.g., Remillard and Bryans 2004; Sherin and Drake 2009), and the impact of the use of these materials on students' achievement (Stein, Remillard, and Smith 2007). Several researchers (e.g., Collopy 2003; Remillard and Bryans, 2004; Sherin and Drake 2009) have found that teachers do not simply choose to use or ignore curriculum materials; instead, teachers make adaptations to various components of curriculum materials before, during, and after instruction. This finding suggests that the issue is not just one of fidelity—or accuracy—in implementation but that it also is about understanding the ways in which teachers make sense of, and interact with, new curriculum materials (Remillard 2005). Little research, however, has focused on the ways in which teachers *supplement* new textbooks with other resources for instruction. This is an important process for understanding how teachers use mathematics textbooks. These supplements include those that were part of teachers' instructional practices prior to the introduction of new textbooks, as well as those teachers continue to acquire and use following the adoption of new textbooks.[1]

---

1. Although most recent research has focused on teachers' use of NSF-funded curriculum materials, the same strategies for supplementing materials can be and have been used by

This article examines teachers' strategies for supplementing textbooks by drawing on several different data sources and addressing the following three questions:

1. Why do teachers supplement their primary textbooks with other resources for instruction?

2. What kinds of resources do teachers choose to supplement their primary textbooks?

3. What strategies do teachers enact for using multiple instructional resources in coherent ways?

To answer these questions, I use accounts previously published in research journals, newspaper articles, and curriculum Web sites regarding teachers who supplement their district-adopted textbook with other curriculum materials. I then describe some of my own research data related to early elementary school teachers' perspectives on supplementing curriculum materials. Drawing on these multiple sources of information, I conclude with a proposed framework for understanding teachers' strategies for supplementing textbooks, implications for teachers and district leaders, and some questions for future research.

Examples of Teachers Supplementing Curriculum Materials

In developing a framework to characterize teachers' strategies for supplementing curriculum materials, I turned to the research literature for prior accounts of teachers' interactions with, and decisions about, curriculum materials. Although these articles were not focused on supplementing, the descriptions of teachers' uses of curriculum materials offer frequent examples of strategies for supplementing textbooks. Some of these examples focus on the ways in which teachers supplemented new National Science Foundation (NSF)-funded materials (adopted by their school or district) with materials they used previously, whereas others focused on how teachers used NSF-funded materials to supplement their use of non-NSF-funded textbooks. For example, Lloyd (2007, pp. 338–39) describes the curriculum strategies of a preservice teacher:

> For the design of most of her mathematics lessons, Bridget used worksheets and pages from the students'… workbook in conjunction with numerous other activities that she developed or found from other sources.… As Bridget

---

teachers using publisher-generated textbooks. Therefore, in the remainder of this article, teachers' strategies for supplementing textbooks are discussed more generally, although many of the examples are drawn from cases involving the use of NSF-funded curriculum materials.

explained, "The truth is, I am trying to use what they're giving me and add to it where I think it's lacking" (Int. 1, 3/2/04). Typically, Bridget's "own stuff" extended workbook lessons to allow students to "move around" (Int. 2, 3/5/04) and use physical materials or manipulatives.

Although Lloyd (2007) focused on a novice teacher, Remillard and Bryans (2004) investigated the curriculum practices of experienced teachers. For instance, they provide a quote from Zoe Kitcher, a twenty-five-year veteran, who describes her approach to supplementing curriculum materials:

> When asked what resources she used, Kitcher explained that she used Investigations as her primary, but not sole, resource and was surprised to find an overlap between it and a resource she had used previously:
>
> > I'm using Investigations and … before we got Investigations I was using Used Numbers and doing some of those activities. I didn't know that some of those activities were actually in the Investigations book. That's fine. Sometimes I'll pick just from my memory one of the games from Marilyn Burns and do something like that (p. 368).

Remillard and Bryans then cite a quote from a second veteran teacher, Kim Reston, with a different approach to supplementing curriculum materials:

> I use a lot of Math Their Way … and I use that pretty systematically to go through numbers, but then it has been very useful to supplement it with some of the worksheets and some of the activities that are in Investigations … (p. 373).

Finally, Martin and Ambrose (2007) describe two teachers teaching the same grade in the same school with the same textbook and the same curriculum mandates. Each chose to supplement the textbook with other instructional materials, but for different reasons—one to prepare students for standardized tests, the other to support her students' conceptual understanding:

> You know, it all revolves around the [state] test, and getting their good grades for the [state] test, so we're practicing…. Usually the textbook is way over their head. And I want something that is basic, that doesn't have all this other stuff in it (p. 831).
>
> I think you can teach them the pattern of the algorithm, which is what I've been told to do by my boss, but I think that unless they start understanding what the numbers mean, that it's a crapshoot, they're going to forget it…. So I won't use any of those pages … (p. 832).

Thus, previously published research gives examples of teachers who supplement curriculum materials to address standards or standardized tests, to provide more concrete or conceptual experiences for students, and to use familiar activities from materials they have used in the past. Some supplement NSF-funded curriculum materials with more traditional materials, whereas others supplement more traditional materials with NSF-funded curriculum materials.

Although some past or current curriculum developers or publishers may have discouraged teachers from using curriculum materials from multiple sources, many publishers now produce multiple sets of curriculum materials and even provide their own guidelines for helping teachers supplement one set of materials with another. At the same time, publishers of mathematics materials now commonly offer information for teachers suggesting ways to integrate their materials with more widely adopted NSF-funded materials, including Everyday Mathematics and Investigations. For instance, the Contexts for Learning Mathematics series developed by Fosnot and colleagues (Fosnot 2007) uses "crosswalks" (http://www.contextsforlearning.com/corrCrosswalks.asp), suggesting how their materials can either replace or supplement elements of both NSF-funded and more traditional textbooks. In a sense, this strategy is similar to the use of "replacement units" that were developed and commonly used in the 1980s and 1990s. However, they do differ in that, with these newer materials, supplementation occurs not only at the level of units but also at the level of lessons and specific activities. Furthermore, the newer guidelines attempt to furnish some conceptual or mathematical coherence across the use of various materials, suggesting that it is possible to build a single coherent curriculum through the use of multiple sets of curriculum materials.

Another example of curriculum supplementation comes from an article in the *Seattle Post-Intelligencer* (Blanchard 2007). The article described an interesting compromise that had been reached by the district school board to adopt both an NSF-funded curriculum series (Everyday Mathematics) and a seemingly more traditional and publisher-generated curriculum series (Singapore Math). Especially interesting about this instance is that, in describing the district's decision, Blanchard also suggested that individual teachers had, over the years, developed their own strategies for supplementing curriculum materials, and that now the district was interested in adopting a districtwide approach to supplementation:

> Lessons will now be taught using the conceptual "Everyday Math" books, which help students discover algorithms on their own and explore multiple ways to solve problems, and the more traditional "Singapore Math" books, which help hone students' basic computation skills through repetition and problem solving. Teachers will follow the district's guidelines for the order the lessons [will] be taught.

> The move is the latest step toward the district's goal of streamlining and standardizing the math curriculum. The district has two formally adopted math programs, but over the years, teachers have had the flexibility to create their own math lessons, culling bits from various other math programs they liked.

This newspaper article supports the idea that teachers tend to develop their own strategies for using multiple sets of curriculum materials and suggests that districts might now be interested in systematizing these strategies in hopes of achieving both consistency and some measure of control over teachers' practices.

A Framework for Understanding Teachers' Strategies for Supplementing Curriculum Materials

With these examples from prior research, publishers, and newspaper accounts in mind, I turn to an analysis of two sets of interviews with elementary school teachers. The first set of interviews was conducted between 1998 and 2000 with twenty teachers piloting a university-produced curriculum, Children's Math Worlds (CMW), in the early elementary grades. These teachers were not asked directly about their strategies for supplementing the curriculum materials; however, their descriptions of these strategies became clear as we coded the data for evidence of teachers' curriculum-use strategies. The second set of interviews was conducted in 2006 with nine teachers and leaders participating in professional development focused on Cognitively Guided Instruction (CGI) (Carpenter et al. 1999). These teachers were directly asked about their experiences supplementing their use of NSF-funded textbooks with what they had learned about CGI.[2]

In analyzing these two sets of interviews, the following four major categories of reasons teachers cited for supplementing curriculum materials with other resources were identified: (1) addressing the need for different *kinds* of activities (e.g., manipulatives, games, activities that seemed fun or motivating for students), (2) addressing the needs of different *groups* of students (e.g., those struggling or needing challenge, those needing additional motivation), (3) addressing the demands of standardized *tests* and other policy mandates, and (4) a desire to *maintain the use* of activities that had been successful in previous years. These categories are quite similar to those exemplified by the teachers in the studies of Martin and Ambrose (2007), Lloyd (2007), and Remillard and Bryans (2004) described in the foregoing. Examples of representative quotes corresponding to each of the four reasons are given in table 19.1.

Implicit, and sometimes explicit, in these stated reasons for supplementing curriculum materials is a broader desire on the part of teachers to have access to multiple activities, representations, and approaches for teaching a particular

---

2. Because the teachers and leaders worked in a variety of schools and districts, they worked with different sets of NSF-funded materials, including Mathematics Trailblazers and Everyday Mathematics.

Table 19.1

Representative Quotes Illustrating Teachers' Reasons for Supplementing Curriculum Materials

Reason	Quote
Different kinds of activities	"… instead of doing the count-bys with them, I bought a multiplication tape—a rap tape—and they learned from there. So, I kind of changed it in that way for them to get their attention and get them to want to keep up with the tape. Because I found the count-bys, they would try, but they weren't putting their heart into it. So I got that and a multiplication bingo game to get their focus back in on that." (CMW Teacher)
Needs of different groups of students	"I think it [the curriculum] leaves room, if a teacher is willing to not use it as the Bible and bring in their own stuff, you can extend for high-level kids from this." (CMW Teacher) "… we're using it [CGI] as additional instruction. So the kids who need a little more time on a concept, we use CGI for that … giving them a problem or two to have them work through and figure out." (CGI Teacher)
Tests/policy mandates	"… there were certain things that I didn't get covered in the curriculum that they needed for the test… there was the measurement." (CMW Teacher) "I wouldn't be brave enough to do that [teach CGI all day, every day] right out of the gate…. I'd have to do a lot of thinking about what I'm going to collect to show that their child actually is learning these curriculum standards and benchmarks that the district has said are important…." (CGI Teacher)
Maintain use of prior activities	"I think—just like I stuck away the scrolls and stuck away the 10's and 1's from [another curriculum], I think I'll pretty much take labeled drawings with me no matter what I end up doing." (CMW Teacher)

topic, to not feel constrained in using a single set of materials rigidly, and to be supported in making the kinds of curriculum decisions, based on students' learning needs, that are crucial to the profession of teaching. One teacher summarized as follows:

> … it's a problem with any kind of program. You have to modify it for what is your present needs … that's why we had to move away from it at times and not do it because it just doesn't fit … it's all a matter of adapting. (CMW Teacher)

An analysis of the CGI interview data also suggested that teachers supplement their primary textbooks with other instructional resources in one of three ways. First, they might *replace* elements of one resource with elements of another. For instance, teachers talked about using CGI word problems to replace the problems in the textbook. Second, they might use two resources *side-by-side,* either with or without making explicit connections between the two resources. Teachers might use both resources because they address the same objective in different ways or because one addresses procedural understanding and the other addresses conceptual understanding or problem solving, as described by Martin and Ambrose (2007). Finally, CGI teachers often integrated CGI and NSF-funded textbooks by using CGI to reframe or reinterpret the textbook. In the words of two teacher leaders—

> … it [CGI] is a way of looking at the problems [from the textbook]. When you look at the way kids are struggling with problems, you can look at the problems and say, "Well, no wonder they're struggling with this one, because this is a join start unknown[3] problem," and so it allows us to deepen our understanding of the program … it really helps us to deepen our implementation of the *Standards*-based program.

> We tried to make almost every lesson last year a cognitively guided one by using what the book said you were supposed to get out of it but make it in a cognitively guided way. It was interesting and fun and more beneficial for the kids than the book was.

On the basis of these examples from my own data, as well as on the prior research and other examples cited above, the framework in figure 19.1 was developed to reflect the cyclic nature of teachers' strategies for supplementing curriculum materials.

Implications for Research and Practice

Figure 19.1 highlights four important aspects of teachers' strategies for supplementing curriculum materials, here framed in the questions teachers might ask themselves as they move through the framework:

- *Reason*
  - Why do I need additional materials?
  - What purpose will they serve that my primary textbook is not serving?

---

3. *Join start unknown* problems are a story problem type in which the starting number is unknown (e.g., "Tommy had some cookies. Emma gave him 6 more cookies. Now Tommy has 11 cookies. How many cookies did Tommy have to start?" This problem type is identified by CGI research (Carpenter et al. 1999) as a difficult problem type for children, particularly children who are trying to model the problem situation.

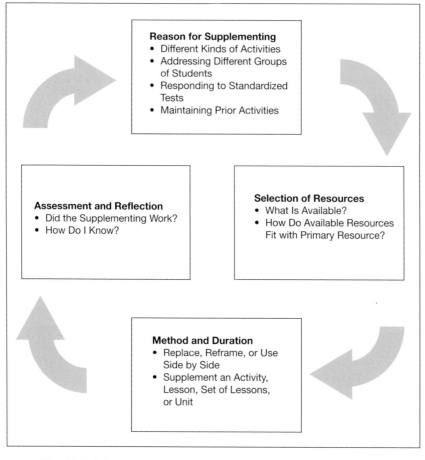

Fig. 19.1. A framework for understanding teachers' strategies for
supplementing curriculum materials

- *Selection of Resources*
    - What materials or resources are available to meet this need?
    - Do they address the same mathematical concepts as my primary textbook?
    - How do they align, or fit, with my primary textbook and with district and state standards?

- *Method and Duration*
    - Should I use the supplementary materials along with, or instead of, the primary textbook?
    - Do the supplementary materials change the way I use the textbook, or vice versa?

— Can I supplement with these materials in a way that maintains
(or increases) the rigor, quality, coherence, and equity of my
instruction?

— Would I supplement an activity, a lesson, or an entire unit?

- *Assessment and Reflection*

  — How do I, or will I, know if my supplementing was successful
  or productive for students' learning?

  — How will I use the results of this lesson, or set of lessons, to
  guide my decisions about supplementing curriculum materials
  in the future?

The number and kinds of resources available for teaching mathematics are
quite large; teachers have an almost unlimited variety of resources from which
to choose and supplement. This article, along with figure 19.1 and the questions
listed in the foregoing, offers some general guidelines and questions for teachers to consider as they contemplate supplementing their primary textbook with
one or more additional resources. However, teachers should also be cautious in
choosing to supplement their primary textbook; in particular, it can be difficult
and complex to ensure that multiple sets of instructional resources fit together in
a way that gives students coherent mathematics instruction.

More research is needed to understand the extent to which teachers' different
approaches to supplementing textbooks lead to (a) more or less coherence in the
instruction to students and (b) differences in students' and teachers' learning. At
the same time, some might argue that supplementing curriculum materials is, in
general, a less productive strategy than using a single, well-developed textbook
with minimal replacement or supplementation of lessons. At the very least, it is
clear that the practice of supplementing textbooks entails both the possibility of
significant benefits, including the ability to design instruction to meet students'
particular needs and to teach concepts in multiple ways, as well as the potential
for significant risk, particularly the danger of providing incoherent or repetitive
mathematics instruction to students.

Currently, in a few districts, district leaders have chosen not to adopt a primary or single set of curriculum materials, and thus, teachers are responsible for
identifying and using multiple sources of materials on a daily basis—in effect,
designing their own set of mathematics curriculum materials (Drake 2009). In
other districts, teachers have been instructed not to supplement their mathematics
textbooks at all (Drake 2009; Stein and Coburn 2008). Finally, many districts are
now recognizing that supplementing textbooks is an important aspect of teachers'
practices and are attempting to set up frameworks and guidance for teachers in
this process. In each of these instances, little is known about the range of ways in
which districts might guide teachers in their use of textbooks or the effectiveness

of these different guidance approaches in students' learning and mathematical coherence.

Ultimately, as a field, we need a well-developed framework, building on figure 19.1, for understanding the practice of supplementing textbooks and outlining important decision points for teachers and leaders. This framework will be an important tool for helping preservice and in-service teachers, as well as district leaders, learn to make more informed, strategic, and coherent decisions about curriculum use and supplementation in ways that effectively meet the needs of all students.

REFERENCES

Blanchard, Jessica. "Schools Streamline How Math Is Taught: Same Textbooks, Same Lessons, at the Same Time." *Seattle Post-Intelligencer,* May 30, 2007.

Carpenter, Thomas P., Elizabeth Fennema, Megan L. Franke, Linda Levi, and Susan B. Empson. *Children's Mathematics: Cognitively Guided Instruction.* Portsmouth, N.H.: Heinemann, 1999.

Collopy, Rachel. "Curriculum Materials as a Professional Development Tool: How a Mathematics Textbook Affected Two Teachers' Learning." *Elementary School Journal* 103 (2003): 287–311.

Drake, Corey. "Constructing Coherence: District Leaders' Strategies for Supporting Elementary Teachers' Use of Mathematics Curriculum Materials." Paper presented at the Annual Meeting of the American Educational Research Association, San Diego, Calif., April 2009.

Fosnot, Catherine T. *Contexts for Learning Mathematics.* Portsmouth, N.H.: Heinemann, 2007.

Lloyd, Gwendolyn M. "Strategic Compromise: A Student Teacher's Design of Kindergarten Mathematics Instruction in a High-Stakes Testing Climate." *Journal of Teacher Education* 58, no. 4 (2007): 328–47.

Martin, Heather A., and Rebecca Ambrose. "Student Needs vs. District Mandates: Teachers' Compromises in the Era of High-Stakes Tests." In *Proceedings of the Twenty-ninth Annual Conference of the North American Chapter of the International Group for the Psychology of Mathematics Education,* edited by Teruni de Silva Lamberg and Lynda R. Wiest. Reno, Nev.: University of Nevada, Reno, 2007.

Remillard, Janine T. "Examining Key Concepts in Research on Teachers' Use of Mathematics Curricula." *Review of Educational Research* 75, no. 2 (2005): 211–46.

Remillard, Janine T., and Martha B. Bryans. "Teachers' Orientations toward Mathematics Curriculum Materials: Implications for Teacher Learning." *Journal for Research in Mathematics Education* 35, no. 5 (2004): 352–88.

Sherin, Miriam G., and Corey Drake. "Curriculum Strategy Framework: Identifying Patterns in Teachers' Use of a Reform-Based Elementary Mathematics Curriculum." *Journal of Curriculum Studies* 41, no. 4 (August 2009): 467–500.

Stein, Mary Kay, and Cynthia E. Coburn. "Architectures for Learning: A Comparative Analysis of Two Urban School Districts." *American Journal of Education* 114 (2008): 583–626.

Stein, Mary Kay, Janine T. Remillard, and Margaret S. Smith. "How Curriculum Influences Student Learning." In *Second Handbook of Research on Mathematics Teaching and Learning*, edited by Frank K. Lester, pp. 319–69. Charlotte, N.C.: Information Age Publishing, 2007.

ADDITIONAL READINGS

Davis, Elizabeth A., and Joseph Krajcik. "Designing Educative Curriculum Materials to Promote Teacher Learning." *Educational Researcher* 34, no. 3 (2005): 3–14.

Lloyd, Gwendolyn M. "Two Teachers' Conceptions of a Reform-Oriented Curriculum: Implications for Mathematics Teacher Development." *Journal of Mathematics Teacher Education* 2 (1999): 227–52.

Lloyd, Gwendolyn M., and Stephanie L. Behm. "Preservice Elementary Teachers' Analysis of Mathematics Instructional Materials." *Action in Teacher Education* 26, no. 4 (2005).

Schneider, Rebecca M., Joseph Krajcik, and Phyllis Blumenfeld. "Enacting Reform-Based Science Materials: The Range of Teacher Enactments in Reform Classrooms." *Journal of Research in Science Teaching* 42, no. 3 (2005): 283–312.

20

Teachers' Perspectives on Fidelity of Implementation to Textbooks

Mary Ann Huntley
Kathryn Chval

FOR MANY years, it has been common practice for teachers to use their mathematics textbook as a starting point, supplementing from other resources to piece together a curriculum that they consider best meets their students' needs. In fact, this type of practice has been encouraged by some teacher educators who suggest that "good teachers do not use textbooks and teacher's guides, but develop their own curriculum instead" (Ball and Feiman-Nemser 1988, p. 402). However, many teachers are now hearing a different message, namely, that textbooks should be implemented faithfully to the authors' intents, with minimal (if any) alterations from what is laid out in the teachers' guides—that is, implemented with high fidelity. To further support teachers using textbooks with high fidelity, some districts have initiated the use of "pacing guides," articulating the

Both authors express appreciation to the teachers from whom they collected data. Funding for the Delaware research project came from a National Academy of Education/Spencer Postdoctoral Fellowship Award and a grant from the University of Delaware Research Foundation. Funding for the Missouri research project (the Middle School Mathematics Study) was provided by a grant from the U.S. Department of Education (no. R303T010735) and the Center for the Study of Mathematics Curriculum (NSF award no. ESI-0333879). We gratefully acknowledge Professor Óscar Chávez's assistance with compiling the data for the Missouri research project. The opinions in this article are solely those of the authors and do not necessarily reflect the policy or position of the funding agencies.

specific lessons that are to be taught each day, and have removed copies of old textbooks from classrooms to prevent teachers from using them. This message is dramatically different from that in years past, when teachers were expected to design creative lessons to augment their textbooks.

Although teachers are faced with this dramatic change in their expected role with regard to curriculum materials, they continue to receive a variety of messages—implicit, explicit, and some that are contradictory—about curriculum implementation. For example, although it is recommended that teachers faithfully implement their district-adopted materials, the National Council of Teachers of Mathematics (NCTM) emphasizes that a basic tenet of effective mathematics teaching is that teachers know and understand deeply the mathematics they are teaching and are able to draw on that knowledge with flexibility during classroom instruction (NCTM 1991). So although on the one hand, teachers are told to implement instructional materials in a certain manner, on the other hand, NCTM encourages teachers to be flexible, which teachers may interpret to mean that they need to stray from their pacing guides. As a result, teachers have struggled to make sense of how to use curriculum materials effectively and to define their roles in making decisions about curriculum implementation.

Although "implementation fidelity" is not a new concept, conversation about it has increased in recent years as policymakers and district administrators want to know which mathematics curricula "work" (i.e., positively affect students' achievement). Of course, valid evaluations of the effects of curriculum materials necessitate studying the effects of true implementation of that curriculum, yet not surprisingly, teachers continue to alter their district-adopted curriculum materials by changing the order, supplementing, or omitting portions of their curriculum materials (Chval et al. 2009). Unfortunately, a voice has been missing from these conversations about implementation fidelity. As researchers continue to think about, discuss, and study curriculum implementation, they need to consider the teachers' perspective. In this article we present research findings about teachers' views on altering curriculum materials and teachers' beliefs about implementation fidelity, present a way for teachers and those who support their efforts to think about fidelity, and discuss implications for teachers and district leaders.

An Overview of the Research

The data reported here were collected from two separate middle-grades research projects involving teachers in geographically diverse areas of the United States. One project, centered at the University of Delaware, was designed to study the implementation of three comprehensive middle-grades mathematics curricula developed with funding from the National Science Foundation (NSF)—Connected Mathematics (Lappan et al. 2002–2004), Mathematics in Context (National

Center for Research in Mathematical Sciences and Freudenthal Institute 1997–1998), and Math Thematics (Billstein and Williamson 1999–2005). For this project, data were collected from forty-one teachers; for purposes of this article we used data collected through one-on-one, tape-recorded interviews with each of the forty-one teachers, and data collected during a videotaped professional development session with eleven of those forty-one teachers.

The other project, the Middle School Mathematics Study, was centered at the University of Missouri (Tarr et al. 2008). One purpose of this project was to understand how teachers use their district-adopted textbook and other curricular resources. Although data for the Middle School Mathematics Study were collected from teachers using a variety of textbook approaches (i.e., both NSF-funded textbooks and publisher-generated textbooks), for the purposes of this article we report only data from tape-recorded interviews with thirty-one teachers using publisher-generated textbooks (Glencoe, Saxon, Prentice Hall, Houghton Mifflin, Southwestern, Harcourt Brace, and Addison Wesley).

Teachers' Voices

To understand how teachers use their assigned textbooks, teachers from both the Delaware and Missouri projects were asked about the extent to which, and ways in which, they use their textbook. In the sections that follow, we report our findings regarding teachers' views about altering a textbook's sequence, omitting content, and supplementing with other materials. We first discuss the views of teachers using NSF-funded mathematics textbooks (teachers participating in the Delaware project), and then we discuss the views of teachers using publisher-developed textbooks (teachers participating in the Missouri project). Next we report data from just the Delaware project, in which teachers were asked about the extent of their agreement (or disagreement) with four statements reflecting different ways researchers view teacher-textbook interactions. Listening to teachers' voices about why they diverge from their designated textbooks and their views about implementation fidelity provides a fresh perspective on these issues.

Teachers' Perceptions of Changing a Textbook's Sequence

Thirty-nine of the forty-one teachers using NSF-funded textbooks (95%) reported primarily going from one page to the next in order in sequential fashion and not "skipping around." They expressed two reasons for this approach. First, the most common reason they cited was the nature of NSF-funded curricula. More specifically, they said that skipping around would not make sense and would be detrimental to students' learning because the mathematical ideas build on one another. As stated by Nancy, skipping around "provides opportunities for serious holes to happen." Donna expressed this view as follows:

> It's the whole nature of the curriculum that you … start on this journey into a mathematical thought … if I want to go from Detroit to Miami, I'm not going to skip around to Denver in the process…. I'm going to go in a pretty direct line! So … the continuity is crucial—absolutely crucial. You cannot skip around.

The second reason teachers said they followed the order of their textbooks was because they respect the textbook authors' judgments. For instance, Linda said, "I have a lot of respect for the knowledge and the way the program is written and created, and their vision. So, for me … I step through it, and I don't skip around." This sentiment was expressed by Kim, as follows:

> Oh, no! Don't you dare do that [skip around]! Oh, my gosh! If you want to screw up everything, just jump around! … It's like trying to build a house and working on the floor, and then working on the roof, and then going down and working on the windows…. There's some logic and some organization behind it!

Two teachers who use NSF-funded textbooks said they did not use them in sequential fashion. They indicated that in the past they did use their books in this way, but at present they do not, because changes to the state curriculum requirements now mandate mathematical content to be taught in a certain order that does not align with their adopted textbook (*Math Thematics*). Rebecca described this situation and her resulting frustration.

> When we first started we went from front to back, and that worked out really nicely because, you know, with it being thematic it all worked together…. So that was really nice. But … the state changed up our curriculum and so now we can't go in that order. Well, that causes a problem because it's a theme. So, if you go on from unit 5, back to unit 1 and then to unit 3, well you can't do … any of those projects that are provided in there because you haven't completed any one topic…. It's a spiraling curriculum and so, you know, if it's covering decimals in that unit and we haven't done decimals yet, then we can't use that part of the lesson. So that's been frustrating for us … because the questions in the book are so good, you know, and you want to be able to use them.

Teachers using publisher-generated textbooks also followed the expected order in the majority of the cases. As articulated by John, "I do not jump around with these lessons. I use every lesson in order. Staying on track helps the students know where we are going and where we have been." Another teacher, Bob, said,

> With the spiraling, you have to follow it closely. In other books I have used before, you could skip chapter 8 and go to 12. But with Saxon you can't skip around…. If you skip a set, then kids are into problems in the sets that they have not had, [and] you would have to eliminate those problems in your assignment.

Thirty-five percent of the teachers using the publisher-generated textbooks stated that they did not follow the textbook sequentially, as articulated by Craig: "Regarding what I teach, the ideas in the text are the steppingstones for the chapters. We rearrange a lot, switching the order and ignoring the sequence in the book."

Cheri said, "You always skip around, because the text, although supposed to be set up in an orderly system, still isn't the orderly system for you."

The most common reason that teachers who used publisher-generated textbooks cited for not following their book's order concerned demands of the state test. In other words, teachers wanted to make sure that certain mathematical content was presented prior to the state assessment. Other, less common reasons included that they do not like the book's organization and their belief that their personal approach is more mathematically sound.

Bear in mind that our purpose is to report what we have learned from the teachers from whom we collected data. We acknowledge the fact that teachers using NSF-funded materials also face assessment pressures, a concern that was reported by the teachers in the Missouri study using commercially generated materials. Likewise, we acknowledge that the sample of teachers we interviewed did not identify all the reasons that others (e.g., Hix [2008]; Remillard [2005]) report for teachers' supplementing, omitting, or changing the order of the lessons in their designated textbooks. Such additional reasons included a lack of clarity in the materials about the textbook authors' intents, teachers' beliefs and prior experiences as students and preservice teachers, teachers' mathematical knowledge or understanding of the pedagogy called for in the textbook, teachers' comfort with the textbook, and the environment in which teachers work (e.g., state and district curriculum standards, testing requirements, students' prior mathematical experiences, parents' expectations, and the availability of materials and supplies).

Teachers' Perceptions of Omitting and Supplementing

Teachers reported a number of reasons for omitting material in their respective textbooks (see table 20.1). The most frequent response from teachers using both NSF-funded and publisher-generated materials was the lack of time. Other common reasons for omitting material by teachers using NSF-funded curricula included the perception that the content was redundant—or the content was optional—on the basis of what was laid out in district or state curriculum documents. Common reasons for omitting material expressed by teachers using publisher-generated curricula included the perception that students did not need to know the content or that other content was more important (e.g., problem solving is omitted because teachers believe students need to focus on skills).

Table 20.1

Reasons Cited by Teachers for Omitting Textbook Material

Reasons Cited for Omitting Textbook Material	Percent of Teachers Using NSF-Funded Textbooks	Percent of Teachers Using Publisher-Generated Textbooks
The teacher perceives that insufficient time is available.	29	23
The teacher perceives that the problem is redundant.	20	3
The content is designated as optional per district or state curriculum.	17	0
The teacher perceives that the material is confusing to the students.	10	6
The teacher perceives that students already know the content.	10	6
The teacher perceives that students do not need to know the content or that other content is more important.	7	23
The content is designated as optional per the teacher's guide.	7	0
The teacher perceives that the reading or writing load is too high for the students.	5	0
The teacher lacks access to needed equipment or materials.	5	3
The content is not on the high-stakes assessment.	5	6
The teacher is uncomfortable with the mathematical content, pedagogy, or problem context.	5	3
The teacher perceives that the mathematical content is flawed.	0	3
The teacher perceives that the book contains too much practice or review.	0	10
The teacher perceives that the book contains too much material.	0	3

As with omitting material from their textbooks, teachers reported a number of reasons for supplementing the content in their respective textbooks with material from other sources (see table 20.2). The most frequently cited reason reported by teachers using NSF-funded materials was their perception that students needed more practice or reinforcement of ideas than their textbooks offered. The second most common reason for these teachers was the fact that they did not like the book's presentation of specific content, or they merely wanted a greater variety in presentation than the book offered. The top reasons identified by the

Table 20.2

Reasons Cited by Teachers for Supplementing Textbook Material

Reasons Cited for Supplementing	Percent of Teachers using NSF-Funded Textbooks	Percent of Teachers using Publisher-Generated Textbooks
Teachers perceive that the book lacks or contains insufficient content/skills to meet students' needs—		
Practice/reinforcement	73	23
Scaffolding	12	0
Remediation	10	6
Extensions (more challenging content)	7	13
Probability and statistics	7	0
Algebra	5	0
Mental math	2	0
Area of a circle	2	0
Examples	0	6
Real-life applications	0	23
Higher-order-thinking skills	0	3
Problem solving	0	3
Unspecified student needs	0	16
Teachers perceive that they have a better way to present the specific content, or they want more variety in presentation of content.	37	52
Teachers perceive that a substitute teacher will find it easier to use a textbook with a more traditional approach.	12	0
Outside pressure (e.g., state test, state/district curriculum, high school teachers, parents)	12	42
Teachers perceive that the book is too wordy, too difficult for low readers..	5	6
Teachers perceive that the problems are not meaningful or relevant to students.	2	29

teachers using NSF-funded curricula were also prevalent for the teachers using publisher-generated textbooks. In addition, teachers using publisher-generated textbooks reported outside pressures as another common concern. These pressures came in the form of state assessments, state or local curriculum standards (e.g., grade-level expectations), and requests from high school teachers as well as parents.

Teachers' Perceptions of Teacher-Textbook Interactions

Teachers participating in the Delaware project were asked to indicate the extent to which they agreed or disagreed with four statements that reflect different ways that teachers interact with textbooks. The survey was based on a framework developed by Remillard (2005). The four questions were based on different ways that researchers conceptualize textbook use, which are grounded in different assumptions about curriculum, teaching, and teacher-textbook interactions. During the interviews, teachers were encouraged to discuss the reasons for their choices. During a professional development meeting that took place shortly after the interviews, teachers engaged in a dialogue about each of the four statements.

The survey questions, along with the teachers' responses, are shown in table 20.3. These data report only teachers using the NSF-funded curricula; we do not know how teachers using the publisher-generated programs would have responded to these items.

As indicated in table 20.3, teachers were nearly unanimous in their views on statement 1. Nearly all said they believe that teachers should implement their mathematics curriculum (Connected Mathematics [(Lappan et al. 2002–2004], Math Thematics [Billstein and Williamson 1999–2005] or Mathematics in Context [National Center for Research in Mathematical Sciences and Freudenthal Institute 1997–1998]) as the developers of the materials intended. Teachers articulated two reasons why they believe fidelity is possible and a goal of instruction. First, twelve teachers said their curriculum is research-based, and that they appreciate the work the authors put into developing the materials and trust that they "work." Second, seven teachers said a lack of fidelity results in holes or gaps in students' knowledge. Although most agreed that fidelity is possible and a goal of instruction, two teachers said it was possible only if teachers receive curriculum-specific professional development.

Table 20.3 also indicates that teachers agreed with statement 4—that the curriculum development process does not stop when textbooks are printed but continues as they teach. Kim agreed with this statement because she perceives herself to be a reflective practitioner, noting, "I think that the curriculum development process never stops.… There's always [the question] … How can I make this better?" Louise expressed this same view: "I mean, that is what teaching is. You continuously change curriculum, even from year to year—everything."

Less consistency was found among teachers regarding their agreement or disagreement with statements 2 and 3. With statement 2, teachers' views differed about whether curriculum materials are prescriptions for practice or about wheth-

Table 20.3

Percent of Responses from Teachers Using NSF-Funded Materials to Survey Items on Use of Mathematics Curriculum Materials

	Disagree or Strongly Disagree	No Opinion	Agree or Strongly Agree	No Response
1. The goal is for teachers to implement their mathematics curriculum as intended by the developers of the materials. That is, fidelity of implementation is not only possible but also the goal of instruction.	7	0	85	7
2. Curriculum materials are not prescriptions for practice; rather, they are one of many resources teachers turn to for guidance about what content to teach and how to teach it.	41	2	54	2
3. Fidelity of implementation is not possible. Teachers interpret the intentions of curriculum developers and create their own meanings of curriculum on the basis of on their personal knowledge, beliefs, and experiences.	49	5	39	7
4. The curriculum-development process does not stop when textbooks are printed, but continues as teachers are in the classroom. During instruction teachers alter, adapt, and translate what is offered in curriculum materials in ways that make the materials appropriate for their particular students.	2	0	98	0

er curriculum materials are one of many resources they use for guidance about what and how to teach. Some teachers said they agreed only with part of statement 2. For instance, Theresa said she did not agree with the second part of the statement: she believed that her NSF-funded textbook was the primary resource, not one of many resources she uses for guidance about what and how to teach. She strongly agreed, however, that curriculum materials are not prescriptions for practice, "because I don't … want to feel like I'm constrained … I'm going to follow it, and I'm going to be faithful [up] to a point. But I don't want to feel [constrained] … a prescription to me is very regimented, very scripted."

Similarly, with statement 3, many teachers agreed with the second sentence—that teachers interpret the intentions of curriculum developers. They did not, however, want to let go of their belief that implementation fidelity is possible. They also did not want their response to statement 1 to contradict their response to statement 3, which would indicate that fidelity is both possible *and* not possible. Donna articulated this tension by saying, "I can strongly agree that fidelity of implementation is the goal, but I can also strongly agree that it's pretty difficult to achieve." Below is a portion of the transcript from the professional development session highlighting participants' struggles with these issues.

Kelly: I don't know. I'm torn between it [fidelity] may not be possible, but I still think it's a goal.

Margaret: … I can disagree with both of those statements [statement 1 and statement 3], because the goal is fidelity but the reality is it's not possible! So I think you can disagree with one and three because, you know, that's your goal, you're shooting for that, but in the same breath you realize that you're never *really* going to reach that because there's just too many other variables.

Kelly: Well, you see, that's what's bothering me because … fidelity and infidelity—like adultery, you've either done it or you haven't. But, you know, there is no, like, sort of being faithful. Or sort of being unfaithful!

Margaret: Your goal could be fidelity, but then fidelity could be impossible.

Kelly: Does fidelity mean perfection?

This conversation between Kelly and Margaret highlights an important issue. Kelly's comment, in which she tries to transfer the common-day use of the word *fidelity* to curriculum use and wonders whether *fidelity* means perfection, is in contrast with Margaret's statement that fidelity is not possible owing to the dynamic and complex nature of classroom interactions. In essence, on the one hand, Kelly is wondering whether "implementation fidelity" is a dichotomous concept, that is, whether it is possible for a teacher be "somewhat faithful" to the textbook. On the other hand, Margaret is saying that a teacher can approach fidelity but never achieve it, which suggests a continuous model of fidelity, that is, that there are degrees of faithfulness. We now discuss these issues, taking into account recent research.

Defining Implementation Fidelity

Implementation fidelity has been described as the extent to which there is a match between the written curriculum, as intended by the developers, and what teachers do in the classroom. This suggests that the construct of implementation fidelity is strict and dualistic (i.e., the curriculum was either implemented as intended or not) and does not take into account the dynamic nature of classroom instruction. Indeed, teachers bring their own teaching philosophies and background experiences to their classrooms, leading them inevitably to adapt their instruction to the diverse needs of their particular students (Ben-Peretz 1990; Clandinin and Connelly 1992; Drake and Sherin 2006; Remillard 2005). It is commonly acknowledged that a written curriculum cannot capture or fully represent guidance for teaching. As stated by Ball and Cohen (1996, p. 6),

> Teachers necessarily select from and adapt materials to suit their own students. This creates a gap between curriculum developers' intentions for students and what actually happens in lessons. Developers' designs thus turn out to be ingredients in—not determinants of—the actual curriculum.

Moreover, curriculum implementation is an uneven process within and across schools (Grouws and Smith 2000; Kilpatrick 2003; Lambdin and Preston 1995; National Research Council 2004; Spillane and Zeuli 1999). Kilpatrick (2003, p. 473) explains,

> Two classrooms in which the same curriculum is supposedly being "implemented" may look very different; the activities of teacher and students in each room may be quite dissimilar, with different learning opportunities available, different mathematical ideas under consideration, and different outcomes achieved.

As described by Huntley (2009), given the improvisational nature of classroom teaching, rather than being dichotomous, we believe fidelity is more appropriately conceptualized by a continuous measure, in which instruction is characterized along a continuum from being very close to what the developers had in mind to a distant zone where what is being done is nearly unrecognizable. Consistent with this perspective, we define *implementation fidelity* as a teacher's use of a mathematics textbook as the developers intend, where adaptations are acceptable, provided they do not deviate too far from the developers' intents. This leaves us with the issue of which adaptations are acceptable and which are unacceptable. This problem has been articulated by Ben-Peretz (1990, p. 31): "How far may teachers go in their adaptations without destroying the spirit and meaning of the curriculum they implement in their classes?"

Significant adaptations that destroy the "spirit and meaning of a curriculum" are relatively easy to identify: teachers omitting entire units (or chapters) in the textbook, teachers using a NSF-funded mathematics textbook emphasizing direct instruction more than suggested by the materials, and so on. Other adaptations are more subtle. For instance, many teachers whom we interviewed outlined changing the numbers in some problems to make them "friendlier" to students (e.g., by removing decimals), occasionally changing a problem context to spark interest in their students (on the basis of teachers' experience with the textbook or of local surroundings), or modeling a particular experiment versus having each group of students perform it themselves (in situations where insufficient resources were available or when measurement errors would be likely to mask the phenomenon being studied). Laura described such changes as follows: "[I'm] not really talking about the underlying philosophy [of the materials] being changed at all." What is not clear, though, is whether these types of adaptations are "acceptable." This point is particularly salient when considering curriculum coherence. According to Trafton, Reys, and Wasman (2001, p. 260),

> Coherence refers to the presentation of mathematics so that the core ideas of the subject are highlighted and cause students to see it as an integrated whole. … *Standards*-based materials promote coherence through an initial focus on big ideas, with an emphasis on connections and links to related mathematical ideas and applications.

Curriculum coherence is important for all curricula, whether NSF-funded or publisher-generated. Thus, one must be careful about making substantial alterations.

If the developers included a problem with decimals and a teacher replaces these with whole numbers, does this make a difference? We argue that in some instances it does. Our perspective was shared by some teachers during our interviews with them. For instance, when discussing omitting material from their textbooks, some teachers said it should be done only in consultation with others (e.g., the department chairperson or the district mathematics supervisor) and only with full knowledge of the advantages and disadvantages of doing so. As stated by Ken, "You need to look at the mathematics, and have experience to know if we take something out, is that going to kill the mathematics for that unit? Are we going to skip a big step or stage they were supposed to get?" Similarly, Nancy believes that supplementation should be done in a cautious and thoughtful manner, describing her approach as follows:

> I would be very, very cautious and thoughtful about it. Teachers have to make some decisions based on the multiple demands from outside sources. So if on someone's state test they're going to be asking something that they know they have to cover, they can be thoughtful about where it's most … appropriately placed…. As an example, if I know my kids are going to have to know how to

work with positive and negative numbers, but also have worked with fractions and decimals, I build it into my Accentuate the Negative unit. I'm not going to take a week out of the beginning of the school year to review whole-number operations or assign those as drill problems on the side. I just don't think that that's effective. It's building it [in] where it works.

Conclusion

By the very nature of the profession, teachers will continue to supplement, omit problems or sections, and change the order of lessons presented in textbooks. Of course, different teachers make different decisions about when, and in what ways, they adapt their materials (Chval et al. 2009; Tarr et al. 2006). As shown from the data presented, teachers make these decisions for a variety of reasons depending on the type of curriculum materials they use. Moreover, it is clear that a number of recent influences have contributed to this decision-making process, especially the introduction of new curricula and related professional development, the nature of state assessments and when they are administered, and the introduction of state and district curriculum standards.

How can teachers be supported so that they make well-informed, purposeful decisions (that is, acceptable adaptations) to benefit students' learning of mathematics? This process is challenging and requires time for teachers to meet and discuss issues related to curriculum. During these discussions, teachers must consider a variety of issues prior to the decision-making process. We recommend a series of questions (see fig. 20.1) to guide discussions related to adapting curriculum materials and ultimately making decisions.

This series of questions demonstrates the complexity of what needs to be considered to make purposeful decisions about adapting curriculum. These decisions are crucial and ultimately can facilitate or hinder curriculum coherence and thus students' learning. As teams of teachers make purposeful decisions and evaluate their efforts, it is likely that more acceptable adaptations will result. Ultimately, this outcome will positively affect students' learning and assist district administrators, researchers, and policymakers with their efforts to evaluate the effects of mathematics curricula on students' learning.

- **Why do you want to make the change?**

- **What do you gain from making the change? What do you lose?**

- **If you are ...**
  - omitting a lesson/problem, have you considered the purpose for that lesson/problem?
  - supplementing a lesson/problem, have you considered the quality of the supplement and how it connects with your curriculum materials?
  - changing the sequence, have you considered the authors' intent?

- **How does the change impact the mathematical content ...**
  - in related lessons or unit(s)?
  - in future mathematics lessons or unit(s)?

- **How will the change ...**
  - enhance your students' opportunities to learn mathematics?
  - hinder your students' opportunities to learn mathematics?

- **How will the change impact different students, including gifted, special needs, and English language learners?**

- **In making this change, have you ...**
  - considered the school calendar, standards, and standardized testing?
  - discussed the proposed change with other teachers at your grade level (or teachers at earlier or later grade levels)?

- **How will you determine whether your change is effective?**

Fig. 20.1. Questions to guide discussions related to adapting curriculum materials

REFERENCES

Ball, Deborah L., and David K. Cohen. "Reform by the Book: What Is—or Might Be—the Role of Curriculum Materials in Teacher Learning and Instructional Reform?" *Educational Researcher* 25 (December 1996): 6–8, 14.

Ball, Deborah L., and Sharon Feiman-Nemser. "Using Textbooks and Teachers' Guides: A Dilemma for Beginning Teachers and Teacher Educators." *Curriculum Inquiry* 18 (Winter 1988): 401–23.

Ben-Peretz, Miriam. *The Teacher-Curriculum Encounter: Freeing Teachers from the Tyranny of Texts.* Albany, N.Y.: State University of New York Press, 1990.

Billstein, Rick, and Jim Williamson. Middle Grades Math Thematics series. Evanston, Ill.: McDougal Little, 1999–2005

Chval, Kathryn, Óscar Chávez, Barbara Reys, and James Tarr. "Considerations and Limitations Related to Conceptualizing and Measuring Textbook Integrity." In *Mathematics Teachers at Work: Connecting Curriculum Materials and Classroom Instruction,* edited by Janine Remillard, Gwen Lloyd, and Beth Herbel-Eisenmann, pp. 70–84. London: Routledge, 2009.

Clandinin, D. Jean, and F. Michael Connelly. "Teacher as Curriculum Maker." In *Handbook of Research on Curriculum,* edited by Philip W. Jackson, pp. 363–401. New York: Macmillan, 1992.

Drake, Corey, and Miriam G. Sherin. "Practicing Change: Curriculum Adaptation and Teacher Narrative in the Context of Mathematics Education Reform." *Curriculum Inquiry* 36 (June 2006): 153–87.

Grouws, Douglas A., and Margaret S. Smith. "NAEP Findings on the Preparation and Practices of Mathematics Teachers." In *Results from the Seventh Mathematics Assessment of the National Assessment of Educational Progress,* edited by Edward A. Silver and Patricia A. Kenney, pp. 107–39. Reston, Va.: National Council of Teachers of Mathematics, 2000.

Hix, Shirley Love. "Learning in Lesson Study: A Professional Development Model for Middle School Mathematics Teachers." Ph.D. diss., University of Georgia, 2008.

Huntley, Mary Ann. "Measuring Curriculum Implementation." *Journal for Research in Mathematics Education* 40 (July 2009): 355–62.

Kilpatrick, Jeremy. "What Works?" In *Standards-Based School Mathematics Curricula: What Are They? What Do Students Learn?* edited by Sharon L. Senk and Denisse R. Thompson, pp. 471–88. Mahwah, N.J.: Lawrence Erlbaum Associates, 2003.

Lambdin, Diana V., and Ronald V. Preston. "Caricatures in Innovation: Teacher Adaptation to an Investigation-Oriented Middle School Mathematics Curriculum." *Journal of Teacher Education* 46 (March/April 1995): 130–40.

Lappan, Glenda, James T. Key, William M. Fitzgerald, Susan N. Friel, and Elizabeth D. Phillips. Connected Mathematics series. Glenville, Ill.: Prentice Hall, 2002–2004

National Center for Research in Mathematical Sciences and Freudenthal Institute, eds. Mathematics in Context series. Chicago: Encyclopaedia Britannica, 1997–1998.

National Council of Teachers of Mathematics (NCTM). *Professional Standards for Teaching Mathematics.* Reston, Va.: NCTM, 1991.

National Research Council. *On Evaluating Curricular Effectiveness: Judging the Quality of K–12 Mathematics Evaluations*. Washington, D.C.: National Academies Press, 2004.

Remillard, Janine T. "Examining Key Concepts in Research on Teachers' Use of Mathematics Curricula." *Review of Research in Education* 75 (Summer 2005): 211–46.

Spillane, James P., and John S. Zeuli. "Reform and Teaching: Exploring Patterns of Practice in the Context of National and State Mathematics Reforms." *Educational Evaluation and Policy Analysis* 21 (Spring 1999): 1–27.

Tarr, James E., Óscar Chávez, Robert E. Reys, and Barbara J. Reys. "From the Written to the Enacted Curricula: The Intermediary Role of Middle School Mathematics Teachers in Shaping Students' Opportunity to Learn." *School Science and Mathematics* 106 (April 2006): 191–201.

Tarr, James E., Robert E. Reys, Barbara J. Reys, Óscar Chávez, Jeff Shih, and Steven J. Osterlind. "The Impact of Middle Grades Mathematics Curricula and the Classroom Learning Environment on Student Achievement." *Journal for Research in Mathematics Education* 39 (May 2008): 247–80.

Trafton, Paul R., Barbara J. Reys, and Deanna G. Wasman. "*Standards*-Based Mathematics Curriculum Materials: A Phrase in Search of a Definition." *Phi Delta Kappan* 83 (November 2001): 259–64.

part V

Impact of Curriculum Materials on Students' and Teachers' Learning

21

Developing Curricular Reasoning for Grades Pre-K–12 Mathematics Instruction

M. Lynn Breyfogle
Amy Roth McDuffie
Kay A. Wohlhuter

ALTHOUGH curriculum materials can strongly influence the nature of, and approaches to, mathematics teaching and learning (Boaler 2002; McCaffrey et al. 2001), curriculum materials alone do not determine how a lesson is implemented. While using curriculum materials, teachers need to consider the following questions.

- What are the important mathematical concepts and processes for today's lesson, this unit, and this year (the grade level expectations [GLEs])?
- What do my students already know about these ideas?
- Do the district-adopted curriculum materials align with the GLEs?
- In what ways will I need to adapt, supplement, or omit portions of the curriculum materials to meet the needs of the students and attend to the GLEs?

The decisions teachers make regarding focusing on particular problems and solutions, using important questions and prompts during interactions with students, facilitating students' discussion of ideas, assessing students' thinking about problems, and connecting ideas that emerge during discussion play a substantial role in how and what learning opportunities transpire. The thinking required for these decisions involves what we refer to as *curricular reasoning* (Roth McDuffie and Mather 2009).

Curricular reasoning refers to the thinking processes that teachers engage in as they work with curriculum materials to plan, implement, and reflect on instruction. As teachers endeavor to improve their practice, and as preservice teachers prepare to enter the profession, developing knowledge and skills to engage in curricular reasoning is essential. In this article, we discuss how we have worked with teachers, practicing and preservice, to facilitate their development of curricular reasoning so as to support their efforts to teach effectively.

In this article we focus on the implemented curriculum, that is, the aspects of curriculum that directly affect students' opportunity to learn. These include the mathematical goals that teachers focus on and the materials and plans that teachers use or develop to support students' learning of those goals. In our discussion, we refer to published instructional materials (textbooks or other sets of lesson plans) as *curriculum materials* and the mathematical goals for learning as *curriculum goals*.

Why Focus on Developing Curricular Reasoning with Teachers?

Changes have occurred over the past twenty years that directly affect teachers' professional development related to mathematics teaching. The two most prominent shifts include curriculum materials aimed at problem solving, reasoning, and students' conceptual understanding of mathematics; and the development of curricular goals and standards and associated accountability issues for instruction (e.g., state grade-level tests).

The first shift was prompted by major curriculum development efforts supported by the National Science Foundation (NSF) in response to recommendations outlined in *Curriculum and Evaluation Standards,* published by the National Council of Teachers of Mathematics (NCTM 1989; Dossey 2007). Prior to the development of these curriculum materials, U.S. mathematics textbooks typically presented mathematics to students through sample problems and exercises. In contrast, NSF-funded materials, often referred to as *standards-based curriculum materials*, were designed to nurture students' mathematical reasoning in solving and evidencing solutions, organize materials around important mathematical concepts and processes, develop knowledge from a problem-centered context, connect ideas, and develop communication and representation skills (Dossey 2007).

The recommendations of NCTM, as well as the new standards-based curriculum materials, call for teachers to think and teach differently. In planning instruction, teachers need to anticipate what prior knowledge, skills, and experiences students might use in reasoning about mathematics problems. During instruction, teachers need to be aware of students' thinking, difficulties, and progress. In assessing students, teachers need to look for valid and generalizable methods. With the shift in curriculum materials, teachers' work involves reasoning with the curriculum (curricular reasoning) that extends beyond only knowing the curriculum (curricular knowledge; see Grossman [1990]).

Another shift in the nature of teachers' work with curriculum has resulted from recent efforts to develop GLEs for students' mathematics learning. Most states now stipulate learning goals in mathematics at each grade level (Reys et al. 2006). With GLEs as policy, teachers increasingly are expected to interpret and align their curriculum materials with state GLEs. However, state GLEs vary widely from one state to another (Reys et al. 2006), and therefore no nationally developed set of curriculum materials is likely to align perfectly with any particular state's GLEs. Moreover, it could be that neither the curriculum goals (in the form of GLEs) nor the curriculum materials (district-adopted textbooks) align with the needs of a particular group of students. Consequently, developing a curriculum that considers all students' prior knowledge and experiences (including prior mathematics learning, cultural and linguistic backgrounds, and exceptional needs) is virtually impossible on a national or state level. As Darling-Hammond and her colleagues (2005) contended, "No textbook writer, curriculum developer, or department head can know exactly what it is that a particular teacher must do within a classroom" (p. 172). Thus, part of teaching is navigating these often-conflicting demands.

Recognizing the shifts in curriculum aims and the demands of teaching, we sought to develop activities that focus on developing teachers' knowledge for, and skills directly related to, curricular reasoning. Our ultimate goal is to help teachers effectively use and implement curriculum materials to support students' learning.

A Model Description for Curricular Reasoning

Figure 21.1 illustrates the relationship of our notion of curricular reasoning to other scholars' constructs about curriculum, including *curricular knowledge* (Shulman 1986; Grossman 1990), *curricular vision* (Darling-Hammond et al. 2005), and *curricular trust* (Drake and Sherin 2009).

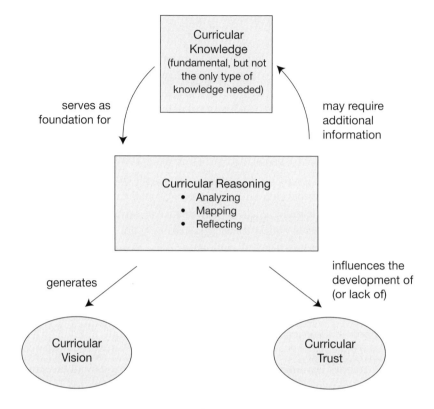

Fig. 21.1. Relationships among curricular reasoning, curricular knowledge, vision, and trust

This model is situated in a larger framework and honors the many knowledge forms (e.g., content knowledge and pedagogical content knowledge) that guide teachers' work and contribute to their curricular reasoning.

Curricular Knowledge

Grossman (1990) and Shulman (1986) characterize curricular knowledge as "knowledge of curriculum materials available for teaching particular subject matter, as well as knowledge about both the horizontal and vertical curricula for a subject" (Grossman 1990, p. 8). Curricular knowledge assumes both a familiarity with myriad curriculum materials and also an understanding of the curriculum materials' philosophical perspective. For example, teachers' guides in some contemporary textbooks contain sections that explicitly describe the authors' philosophical assumptions and rationale for design features of the curriculum. In addition, teachers' guides may focus on students' thinking and processes for engaging students in the lesson. To use the curriculum materials effectively, teachers should recognize and understand the philosophical assumptions used to create the materials.

Curricular Vision and Curricular Trust

Darling-Hammond et al. (2005, p. 177) describe *curricular vision* as a way of viewing curricular materials and their interactions with, and influence on, students:

> Well prepared teachers have developed a sense of "where they are going" and how they and their students are going to get there. They are able to create a coherent curriculum that is also responsive to the needs of students…. They have thought about social purposes for education as well as their own vision and have integrated these so that their students can be successful in the world outside of school as well as within the supportive environment of the classroom.

Curricular trust builds on curricular vision. Drake and Sherin (2009) describe it as a set of—

> beliefs and practices that reflect an understanding of the curriculum materials, [and that these materials] as written, provide a developmental trajectory that will support students in achieving the mathematical goals defined by the curricular vision.

Once teachers understand where a curriculum is going, they are positioned to decide whether they trust the materials to meet their mathematical learning goals for their students (curricular trust).

Through curricular reasoning, teachers develop curricular vision, and they also decide whether they trust the curriculum materials as written. Through curricular vision, teachers see how curriculum materials build mathematical ideas over time and what students are learning from the materials. As teachers apply curricular reasoning to plan, implement, and reflect on instruction, they use and continue to generate curricular vision (Roth McDuffie and Mather 2009). Drake and Sherin (2009) found that as teachers gained more experience with certain curriculum materials, they increasingly used curricular vision to identify the important ideas of the curriculum program and to guide their interactions with students. In doing so, they developed curricular trust for the integrity and coherence of the curricular materials, perceiving the materials as well constructed in light of students' learning needs. Thus, through curricular reasoning teachers can develop curricular vision and curricular trust.

Processes Involving Curricular Reasoning

On the basis of earlier research, we identified three processes teachers engage in that draw on curricular reasoning, namely, analyzing curriculum materials from learners' perspectives, mapping learning trajectories, and reflecting on and revising plans on the basis of experiences in teaching and learning (Roth McDuffie and Mather 2009).

Analyzing curriculum materials from learners' perspectives

Analyzing curriculum materials from the learners' perspectives takes place prior to, during, and after instruction and entails identifying and understanding the important mathematics, gaining a better sense of potential issues and approaches that learners might bring to a lesson (e.g., prior knowledge and correct or incorrect strategies that learners might employ), and considering students' background and experiences to ensure that equity principles are being addressed and met. By analyzing the materials from learners' perspectives, teachers increase their awareness of strengths and limitations afforded by curriculum materials. With this awareness, teachers can deliberately plan to leverage strengths and remedy limitations in using the materials.

Mapping learning trajectories

The process of mapping learning trajectories includes examining how mathematical understandings build over time (vertical development), analyzing how mathematics topics learned connect (horizontal development), and ensuring overall coherence in the learners, curriculum materials, and curriculum goals (GLEs). This process helps teachers prepare for, and make decisions to determine, content for which students need to develop strong understandings in a unit or grade; content for which students will develop over time, perhaps across several grades; and content that students will need to connect or apply to other areas of mathematics or other disciplines.

Reflecting on and revising plans

Teachers reflect on implemented lessons to consider implications of the immediately upcoming lesson and also for future implementation of the same lesson. Becoming a reflective practitioner is necessary for continually improving practice. For curricular reasoning to truly affect instruction, teachers need to adopt an inquiry stance during reflection and consider such questions as the following:

- Did the materials and the sequence of tasks support my students in meeting learning goals?
- Did I effectively anticipate my students' needs in preparing them to engage in the tasks?
- Did I sequence and connect ideas in the materials to solidify learning and prepare for future lessons?

Examples of Activities That Develop Curricular Reasoning

We have described three processes of curricular reasoning: analyzing curriculum materials from learners' perspectives, mapping learning trajectories, and reflecting on and revising plans on the basis of teaching and learning experiences. In this section, we illustrate activities that incorporate and help develop these processes, recognizing that the activities will cultivate multiple curricular reasoning processes simultaneously. We present three types of activities and assignments that we have used with teachers: exploring records of practice, analyzing textbooks, and developing lesson images.

Exploring Records of Practice

Using multimedia case studies (Doerr and Thompson 2004) or written episodes of classroom vignettes (Stein et al. 2000), which we refer to as *records of practice,* can help teachers situate their own learning in an authentic classroom experience. In this way, teachers have the opportunity to develop curricular reasoning by analyzing curriculum materials and, to a lesser extent, reflecting on and revising plans on the basis of teaching and learning experiences. While teachers explore records of practice (both as teachers and as learners), they develop skills to raise and answer such questions as the following:

- What are the important mathematical concepts and processes for today's lesson, this unit, and this year's GLEs?
- What do my students already know about these ideas?
- In what ways will I need to adapt, supplement, or omit portions of the curriculum materials to meet the needs of the students and attend to the GLEs?

To use records of practice effectively, we first encouraged teachers to think through the records as both learners and teachers while we facilitated the discussion, modeling the practices. To begin, we required teachers to perform the specific task(s) they would encounter in the records of practice. For example, when using "The Case of Catherine Evans and David Young" (Smith, Silver, and Stein 2005, pp. 8–31), we first had the teachers complete the Hexagon-Pattern task, in which they determine the perimeters of various trains of hexagonal pattern blocks placed side by side (see fig. 21.2). After determining the lengths of trains, they are also asked to generalize the pattern to compute the perimeter of any length of a train. Further, teachers are pressed to find as many different ways as possible to compute and justify the perimeter. This question started them on the path to understanding students' perspectives and uncovering mathematical content (Smith, Silver, and Stein 2005). This experience mirrored the practice of anticipating ways that students might solve the problems in the curriculum materials.

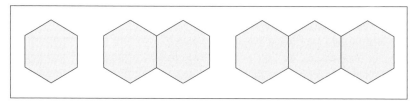

Fig. 21.2. First three hexagon trains

After they engaged in the specific problem as learners, the teachers then considered the teacher's role. They were challenged to think about multiple ways that students might solve problems and then discuss with others the responses students might offer. In this particular task, teachers anticipated that students might describe the pattern in a number of different ways that can be characterized as either visual-geometric or arithmetic-algebraic. One visual-geometric approach to determining the perimeter was to consider each hexagon in the train having four lengths of sides exposed and then the two end hexagons having one unit per end. This was represented as Perimeter = (4 units each) × (# of hexagons) + (one unit per end), or $P = 4x + 2$. There are numerous other visual-geometric approaches, such as considering the "inside hexagons" and "outside hexagons" or the number of crests or valleys in the figure. The arithmetic-algebraic approaches are based on the pattern of numbers in the table of values. Teachers using the recursive pattern of "adding 4" to the previous quantity recognized that this relationship was linear because of the constant increase of 4 and then determined from substituting values that the b in the equation $y = mx + b$ would be 2. Other arithmetic-algebraic approaches included using a graphical representation to plot the values and determine the slope and intercept from the graph.

We found that teachers had not always considered all the ways students approached problems, nor did the teachers always understand others' multiple approaches. However, as teachers shared their various solution strategies, their understanding of the content was enhanced, thus helping set the stage for understanding teachers' decisions in the records of practice.

Individually teachers read or watched records of practice, primed with some guiding questions. The questions were either furnished by facilitators' guides accompanying the records of practice or designed by the professional development facilitators to focus teachers' attention on particular pedagogical moves that support students' thinking. We found it important to teachers' development to press them to cite specific evidence (e.g., line numbers, paragraphs, or times) in the records of practice to avoid generalities. This practice allowed teachers to develop a notion of what constitutes appropriate evidence at the same time that they developed an understanding of the issues that emerged in the record. Once teachers individually thought about the records of practice, we discussed the records in small groups or whole groups to compare themes and observations.

As a facilitator, modeling good practices of guiding discussion by monitoring, selecting, and sequencing the teachers' thoughts and observations and then as a group reflecting on the process helped teachers in their role both as a teacher and learner. For example, it was important to parse out the important mathematical ideas that emerged in the students' thinking in the cases. Delving into specific examples and evidence of students' thinking that exemplified how students understood the notion of variable, or whether students saw the difference between recursive relationships versus explicit ones, are two such examples. Eventually the strength of the records of practice is the transfer to other situations through the generalizations of the practice.

Analyzing Textbooks

Analyzing textbooks to become aware of the mathematics presented is a common professional development activity for teachers. We expanded this activity into vertical textbook curriculum analyses by asking teachers not only to see the mathematics at their level but also to determine how mathematical understandings build over time. While teachers analyzed textbooks, they developed the skills to raise and answer the following questions:

- What do my students already know about these ideas?

- Do the district-adopted curriculum materials align with the GLEs?

For this activity, we directed teachers to map how such topics as multiplication, fractions, or patterns were addressed by students of different ages. The mapping process began by teachers' examining grades K–12 textbooks and identifying the scope and sequence of a topic using the following questions to guide their investigation:

- When are students first introduced to the topic?

- What relationships are students expected to learn?

- What procedures are important in the topic?

- What models are used to represent the topic?

As teachers answered the questions, they demonstrated their ability to gain knowledge about how textbooks defined the topic.

Using patterns as an example, teachers found that kindergarten textbooks asked children to identify and copy repeating patterns. As the children become more comfortable with patterns, they answer the "what comes next?" question and show how to extend patterns. Primary-school-aged children expand their pattern knowledge by creating their own repeating patterns and by exploring growing patterns. Throughout elementary school and middle school, students continue to work with patterns as they identify, copy, extend, create, generalize, and make predictions with patterns. The teachers also realized that students use various representations of patterns, such as physical, table, graphical, and symbolic, and that much of the pattern work for high school students is done in the context of functions.

In addition to having teachers identify a topic's pivotal relationships and procedures, we challenged teachers to determine how the different concepts and procedures built off one another. For example, teachers saw that children's work with doubling patterns is the basis of students' knowledge of exponential functions. Teachers also realized that children's determination of what comes next in a pattern is recursive thinking, which leads to finite differences and the connection to polynomial functions. In this way, teachers recognized how they could design instruction to build off these earlier ideas and, in the process, better meet the needs of students. Having a better understanding of students' mathematical journey enabled teachers to develop curricular vision.

Developing Lesson Images

A common pedagogical task in teacher education is to involve teachers in developing a lesson, teaching the lesson, and then reflecting on the teaching and learning that occurred. While teachers develop lesson images, they cultivate the skills to raise and answer the following questions:

- What are the important mathematical concepts and processes for today's lesson, this unit, and this year (the GLEs)?
- Do the district-adopted curriculum materials align with the GLEs)?
- In what ways will I need to adapt, supplement, or omit portions of the curriculum materials to meet the needs of the students and attend to the GLEs?

Given that U.S. teachers typically teach with published curriculum materials (Stigler and Hiebert 1999), we encouraged them to design the lesson based on published curriculum materials.

An initial task in planning was to identify the primary mathematical emphasis of a lesson or unit. Often an activity can be used to teach a range of concepts or processes. Teachers needed to determine the primary emphasis for their students' learning by considering their students' needs and alignment with their GLEs. During this part of planning, teachers relied heavily on curricular knowledge to identify and select tasks from curriculum materials and engaged in curricular reasoning by analyzing materials and mapping the learning trajectory. For example, a teacher focused on a lesson that introduced similar figures from Connected Mathematics' "Stretching and Shrinking" unit (Lappan et al. 1998). She anticipated her students' difficulties with understanding that angles in similar figures were congruent. She predicted that some students might perceive that an angle in a scaled-up figure was larger when in fact it was congruent to its corresponding angle in a scaled-down version of the same figure. The teacher recognized that understanding congruent angles in similar figures was foundational to later unit work that focused on scaling and proportionality in similar figures, and these ideas were part of her state's GLEs. So she decided that she needed to make sure that her students focused on congruent angles, and she built these understandings during the lesson. In anticipating challenges for students and using curricular vision, teachers determined how to implement the materials to meet their students' needs, align with GLEs, and ensure horizontal and vertical coherence.

Next, teachers engaged in developing a mental image of important interactions with students during the lesson. In writing a plan, teachers analyzed the curriculum materials to anticipate students' needs, questions, challenges, possible approaches, and solutions. Similarly, teachers anticipated fundamental questions, prompts, and problems they might need to provide to facilitate learning. In addition, teachers described important indicators and approaches to look for in students' work as the lesson progresses. For example, the teacher working with the lesson on similar figures acted out the lesson prior to teaching and planned to ask questions about similar figures, such as the following:

- Are the figures the same size?
- If the figures are not the same size, can the corresponding angles in the figures be congruent? How do you know?

She also planned to feature figures that were not similar and therefore did not have congruent corresponding angles. As described previously, by taking on both a teacher's role and a learner's role, teachers more thoroughly anticipated situations that might arise during instruction.

A final section of the initial plan included a written reflection on the lesson prior to teaching. Although we usually reflect on instruction *after* instruction, we suggested that teachers also reflect on a lesson's strengths and weaknesses in advance. For the similar-figures lesson, the teacher noted that students could engage in the lesson without using a protractor to measure angles. (They could test angles for congruence by laying them on top of each other). Although she did not intend for students to measure with protractors, she recognized that measuring angles was a skill that some students would need to review before they would be ready to engage in other unit lessons. Noting this possible limitation helped her be more prepared for future lessons. This early reflection helped teachers engage in inquiry and more substantive reflection during and after instruction.

Once teachers conducted a thorough thought experiment to prepare for teaching and learning, the project's next phase included teaching the lesson and reflecting on teaching and learning. As part of their reflections, teachers provided specific evidence for the nature of students' learning, understandings, and areas for further development, and for lesson aspects to change for future teaching. In addition, teachers selected three to four students for in-depth reflection on their learning. For the selected students, teachers maintained detailed records, during and after the lesson, of students' questions or comments, ways they approached problems or worked with various representations with the curricular materials, indicators of understanding or a lack of understanding, and future directions for their learning.

The teacher working on the similar-figures lesson found that many students demonstrated difficulty in seeing that angles were congruent in similar shapes of different sizes, as anticipated. By carefully thinking through the lesson in advance, the teacher felt more prepared to focus students' thinking and prompt them to cut out figures and compare angles (or measure angles) so that they could understand the relationships during the lesson. Selecting a few students pushed teachers to look for individual learning in the class and conduct deeper analysis of instruction.

In writing this report, the teachers engaged in the processes of analyzing the materials and mapping a learning trajectory in relation to their observations of students' learning, instead of only imagining how learning would progress. Moreover, this final phase provided an opportunity to connect and synthesize reflections on teaching and learning to improve future instruction. By encouraging this level of thinking and writing, we hoped to develop habits of mind and inquiry-focused dispositions that could become embedded in practice.

Summary

The benefits of helping teachers develop curricular reasoning were evident in their actions. Teachers became more aware of the purpose and philosophy of their mathematics curriculum materials. Teachers began to view teaching and learning mathematics differently than they had during their previous experiences as teachers or students. Their resulting actions showed that they not only better understood the mathematics they were responsible for teaching but also understood how students' earlier and later mathematical experiences influenced their teaching. They developed ways to structure and implement lessons aimed at facilitating students' learning through the materials.

Challenges arose after we engaged teachers in curricular reasoning activities. In some instances, teachers made curriculum-based instructional decisions in planning but did not implement their ideas in the classroom as intended. As teachers demonstrated their ability to develop and apply curricular reasoning, they also described the process as overwhelming. Our challenge now is developing ongoing support systems in schools for teachers to engage in and use curricular reasoning in planning and enacting instruction.

REFERENCES

Boaler, Jo. *Experiencing School Mathematics: Traditional and Reform Approaches to Teaching and Their Impact on Student Learning.* Mahwah, N.J.: Lawrence Erlbaum Associates, 2002.

Darling-Hammond, Linda, James Banks, Karen Zumwalt, Louis Gomez, Miriam G. Sherin, Jacqueline Griesdorn, and Lou-Ellen Finn. "Educational Goals and Purposes: Developing a Curricular Vision for Teaching." In *Preparing Teachers for a Changing World: What Teachers Should Learn and Be Able to Do,* edited by Linda Darling-Hammond and John Bransford, pp. 169–200. San Francisco: John Wiley, 2005.

Doerr, Helen M., and Tonia Thompson. "Understanding Teacher Educators and Their Preservice Teachers through Multimedia Case Studies of Practice." *Journal of Mathematics Teacher Education* 7 (2004): 175–201.

Dossey, John. "Looking Back, Looking Ahead." In *Perspectives on the Design and Development of School Mathematics Curricula,* edited by Christian Hirsch, pp. 185–99. Reston, Va.: National Council of Teachers of Mathematics, 2007.

Drake, Corey, and Miriam G. Sherin. "Developing Curriculum Vision and Trust: Changes in Teachers' Curriculum Strategies." In *Mathematics Teachers at Work: Connecting Curriculum Materials and Classroom Instruction,* edited by Janine T. Remillard, Beth A. Herbel-Eisenmann, and Gwendolyn M. Lloyd, pp. 321–37. New York: Routledge, 2009.

Grossman, Pamela. *The Making of a Teacher: Teacher Knowledge and Teacher Education.* New York: Teachers College Press, 1990.

Lappan, Glenda, James T. Fey, William M. Fitzgerald, Susan N. Friel, and Elizabeth Phillips. *Connected Mathematics.* Menlo Park, Calif.: Dale Seymour Publications, 1998.

McCaffrey, Daniel F., Laura S. Hamilton, Brian M. Stetcher, Stephen P. Klein, Delia Bugliari, and Abby Robyn. "Interactions among Instructional Practices, Curriculum, and Student Achievement: The Case of Standards-Based High School Mathematics." *Journal for Research in Mathematics Education* 32, no. 5 (November 2001): 493–517.

National Council of Teachers of Mathematics (NCTM). *Curriculum and Evaluation Standards for School Mathematics.* Reston, Va.: NCTM, 1989.

Reys, Barbara, Shannon Dingman, Travis Olson, Angela Sutter, Dawn Teuscher, Kathryn Chval, Glenda Lappan, Gregory Larnell, Jill Newton, Ok-Kyeong Kim, and Lisa Kasmer. *The Intended Mathematics Curriculum as Represented in State-Level Curriculum Standards: Consensus or Confusion?* Center for the Study of Mathematics Curriculum, 2006. http://www.mathcurriculumcenter.org (accessed April 26, 2006).

Roth McDuffie, Amy, and Martha Mather. "Middle School Mathematics Teachers' Use of Curricular Reasoning in a Collaborative Professional Development Project." In *Mathematics Teachers at Work: Connecting Curriculum Materials and Classroom Instruction,* edited by Janine T. Remillard, Beth A. Herbel-Eisenmann, and Gwendolyn M. Lloyd, pp. 302–20. New York: Routledge, 2009.

Shulman, Lee. "Those Who Understand: Knowledge Growth in Teaching." *Educational Researcher* 15, no. 2 (1986): 4–14.

Smith, Margaret Schwan, Edward A. Silver, and Mary Kay Stein. *Improving Instruction in Algebra: Using Cases to Transform Mathematics Teaching and Learning,* vol. 2. New York: Teachers College Press, 2005.

Stein, Mary Kay, Margaret Schwan Smith, Marjorie A. Henningsen, and Edward A. Silver. *Implementing Standards-Based Mathematics Instruction: A Casebook for Professional Development.* New York: Teachers College Press, 2000.

Stigler, James W., and James Hiebert. *The Teaching Gap.* New York: The Free Press, 1999.

22

Secondary School Mathematics Curriculum Materials as Tools for Teachers' Learning

Gwendolyn M. Lloyd
Vanessa R. Pitts Bannister

ENGAGEMENT with instructional materials is a commonly used and effective professional development strategy (Loucks-Horsley et al. 2003). Because many teachers' mathematical and pedagogical conceptions are deeply tied to traditional curriculum and instruction, making change—even with the support of innovative materials—can be very difficult. However, classroom instruction with innovative curriculum materials may compel teachers to become aware of and alter their conceptions on the basis of new types of classroom experiences with students and mathematics. Curriculum-based professional development for in-service teachers often aims to support teachers as they make sense of the challenging mathematical and pedagogical questions that can arise when teaching with new materials. Roth McDuffie and Mather (2009), for example, described how a team of teachers, together with a university mathematics educator, collaboratively engaged in four activities of "curricular reasoning" (p. 302) as they worked with one curriculum unit: analyzing curriculum materials from learners' perspectives, doing tasks together as learners, mapping learning trajectories, and revising plans on the basis of work with students during instruction.

The work reported in this article was funded by the National Science Foundation (NSF) under grant no. 0536678. Any opinions, findings, and conclusions or recommendations expressed in this publication are those of the authors and do not necessarily reflect the views of the NSF.

In light of the challenges of curriculum implementation, as well as the potential of curriculum materials to promote teachers' learning, teacher educators have increasingly begun to integrate grades K–12 instructional materials into preservice teacher education courses (Frykholm 2005; Lloyd 2006; Lloyd and Behm 2005). Although preservice teachers do not typically engage fully in all four activities described by Roth McDuffie and Mather (2009), preservice teacher education is an opportune time to lay the foundation for teachers' future development of productive interactions with mathematics instructional materials.

A common way that teacher educators have incorporated curriculum materials into mathematics and methods courses is by engaging preservice teachers with problems and activities with the goal of learning or relearning mathematical subject matter. As is often true for in-service teachers, preservice teachers benefit from "doing tasks together as learners" (Roth McDuffie and Mather 2009, p. 308) to revisit seemingly familiar mathematical ideas and exploring unfamiliar mathematics, such as probability, statistics, and discrete mathematics. In contrast with in-service teachers, whose past and present instructional experiences with students can provide rich data for "analyzing curriculum materials from learners' perspectives" (p. 308), most preservice teachers must rely largely on reflection on their own learning and observations of their peers' learning. As preservice teachers engage with curricular activities, an examination of their own learning processes can help them begin to recognize the significance of the mathematical development that occurs during inquiry-based, student-centered activities. With support from teacher educators and peers, preservice teachers can engage in critical analysis of the content and instructional design of different curriculum programs to begin to develop important understandings and capabilities and prepare for their future teaching.

Principles for School Mathematics

We have used NCTM's (2000) six Principles for school mathematics as a framework for designing preservice teacher education activities that involve middle and high school curriculum materials. Table 22.1 presents sample strategies corresponding to the six Principles: Equity, Curriculum, Teaching, Learning, Assessment, and Technology. In the following sections, we offer specific illustrations of selected strategies from table 22.1 (marked with asterisks). Our aim is to highlight the powerful role that activities based on curriculum materials can play in preservice teachers' learning[1] about each of the six Principles for school mathematics.

---

1. Although the focus of our work has been preservice teachers' learning, readers are likely to find the strategies in table 22.1 relevant to the learning of in-service mathematics teachers as well.

Table 22.1

Strategies for Using Curriculum Materials in Teacher Education

Principle	Strategy: Support Preservice Teachers as They …
Equity	• Evaluate the ways in which a particular textbook lesson or curriculum unit exhibits "high expectations" * • Sort tasks and problems from curriculum materials according to their levels of cognitive demand • Identify ways to differentiate within a particular curricular activity for diverse learners, including students with special needs * • Make focused observations of the material and social resources available to support the use of different curriculum materials in a variety of schools (e.g., urban schools, rural schools, high- and low-achieving schools, schools serving low-income and minority students)
Curriculum	• Create a concept map to illustrate how a particular mathematical idea builds on, and connects with, other ideas in one unit or chapter of a curriculum program • Trace the development of one mathematical concept through the grade levels of a curriculum program (e.g., How is the concept of variable developed across the grade levels in a particular middle-grades curriculum program?) • Compare and contrast the ways that two different units or chapters approach the teaching and learning of the same mathematical topic * • Identify the philosophies underlying different curriculum programs and relate them to the ways the textbook or curriculum materials position students and the teacher in the learning process • Develop criteria for evaluating curriculum materials in light of the content and process *Standards* (NCTM 2000) and apply the criteria to a variety of materials
Teaching	• Engage in solving the mathematics problems and investigations from selected curriculum materials to develop new awareness and understandings of important mathematics * • For a particular mathematical topic, compare the mathematical approaches of different curriculum materials to the *Standards* recommendations for that topic * • Watch a video of a classroom in which a particular lesson is taught; using the teacher's guide, identify the teacher's adaptations and develop hypotheses about why those adaptations were made • Use a teacher's guide from a curriculum program to plan and teach a lesson to peers * • Develop appropriate warm-up or extension activities that correspond with particular lessons and support students' learning

(Continued)

Table 22.1—*Continued*
Strategies for Using Curriculum Materials in Teacher Education

Principle	Strategy: Support Preservice Teachers as They …
Learning	• Identify opportunities for students to develop both procedural fluency and conceptual understanding within a particular lesson or activity • Sort mathematical tasks (selected from various curriculum materials) according to the opportunities the tasks provide for student learning (see, e.g., Arbaugh and Brown [2005]) • Hypothesize about typical and creative student responses to a task or problem; anticipate difficulties students might have with a task or problem; and develop possible ways to address students' difficulties *
Assessment	• Examine a variety of student work on one particular curricular task to develop a rubric or guide for analyzing student responses • Develop a collection of assessment approaches (e.g., open-ended questions *, constructed-response tasks, selected-response items, performance tasks, observations, conversations, journals, and portfolios) to determine students' learning in a particular chapter or unit
Technology	• Use technology-rich curricular tasks to learn about technological tools (e.g., Geometer's Sketchpad) and unfamiliar mathematical areas (such as discrete mathematics) • Explore computer and calculator software and activities that augment curriculum materials * • Adapt lessons to incorporate technology (calculators or computers) in ways that will enhance students' learning of mathematics *

Note: This article offers specific illustrations of the strategies in table 22.1 that are marked with an asterisk (*).

Equity Principle

The Equity Principle states, "Excellence in mathematics education requires equity—high expectations and strong support for all students" (NCTM 2000, p. 12). This vision of equity challenges teachers to raise expectations for the mathematical learning of all students and to provide instruction that responds to students' prior knowledge, academic strengths, and individual interests. For preservice teachers to enact this vision in their future mathematics instruction, they need to be supported in focused experiences that allow them to identify and explore the pedagogical implications of the Equity Principle.

Identifying high expectations in a curricular activity

It is widely accepted that teachers' expectations of students have significant impact on learning and teaching practices (Knapp 1995; Oakes 1990). In view of this outcome, the NCTM Standards emphasize high expectations for all students. To help future teachers attain this goal, we have provided them with structured opportunities to evaluate and identify facets of high expectations in mathematics curriculum materials.

For example, we have asked preservice teachers to evaluate an investigation in which students develop expressions for surface area, in "Say It with Symbols" (Lappan et al. [2005]). The preservice teachers identified several aspects of high expectations: valuing students' prior knowledge, varied approaches, and constructing knowledge. For example, one preservice teacher identified prior knowledge as an issue: "This lesson sometimes requires students to retrieve prior knowledge that they were 'supposed' to learn in a previous class or year of school. However, it is not always safe to assume that your students know something." Another preservice teacher wrote,

> This lesson is one that I would consider using in my classroom. Looking back, surface area for me was, "Here are the formulas, find the surface area." ... I love how the students are expected to find their own equations and compare them to their peers'. If the students are expected to find the equations themselves, then in the future, if they were to forget the equations, they are more likely to be able to come up with [them] again.

As this comment suggests, these preservice teachers reflected on their own learning, hypothesized about the learning of students, and developed appreciation for those activities that have high expectations for students' mathematical learning. It is noteworthy that, like the in-service teachers described by Roth McDuffie and Mather (2009), these preservice teachers "anticipated learners' perspectives, thinking, and approaches" (p. 308) as they analyzed curriculum materials from learners' perspectives.

Differentiating a curricular activity for diverse learners

The *Standards* (NCTM 2000) argue for the provision of strong support for all students. Unlike past attempts to address diverse student populations, which emphasized teacher-directed instruction and little cooperative and peer-supported learning (Knapp 1995), the *Standards* advocate instructional programs that empower all students to learn mathematics. We have asked preservice teachers to review curriculum materials with respect to their potential to meet the needs of diverse students. Consider the following excerpts from their comments:

The unit is very wordy. This may cause some difficulty for students with language or reading deficits. On page 70 of the teacher's manual there is a tip for linguistically diverse classrooms, and the use of manipulatives and symbols is language-neutral, but the descriptive sections seem prohibitive to English language learners.

I can't help but wonder about those students who cannot afford graphing calculators. I feel that the school should supply graphing calculators, this lesson should be implemented without calculators, or the teacher should use a calculator system in which examples may be visible to all students.

The group-work setup would be the main place where some students may be feeling left out. However, as Boaler (2006) pointed out, teachers need to walk around and assign competence to individuals who may not feel included in the lesson. While it is the students who are teaching, teachers must be available to assist in the learning process.

In these comments, preservice teachers identified potential equity issues related to language, technology, and cooperative learning and, in some instances, suggested ways of attending to those issues. As preservice teachers evaluated and collectively discussed particular mathematics curriculum materials, they expanded their understandings of such terms as "high expectations" and "strong support" that are central to the Equity Principle.

The Curriculum Principle

NCTM's (2000) Curriculum Principle states, "A curriculum is more than a collection of activities. It must be coherent, focused on important mathematics, and well articulated across the grades" (p. 14). For preservice teachers, this Principle can seem abstract without consideration of a specific curriculum framework, program, or set of materials. Table 22.1 suggests several experiences in which preservice teachers critically examine the content and structure of curriculum programs. Whether this examination takes place on a small scale (e.g., considering the importance of the mathematics addressed in specific problems or investigations in a curriculum unit or textbook section) or a large scale (e.g., looking at the treatment of a topic across an entire curriculum program), the goal is for preservice teachers to develop an appreciation for the role that curriculum materials can play in the design of instruction that supports students' building connections among important mathematical ideas.

Comparing and contrasting the approaches of different curriculum materials

Lloyd (2006) asked a group of preservice teachers to compare two very similar problems that appeared in two different middle school curriculum units

(*Prime Time* [Lappan et al. 1996] and *Reflections on Number* [Mathematics in Context 1998]). The Locker Problem from *Prime Time* (pp. 58–60) states,

> There are 1000 lockers in the long hall of Westfalls High…. The lockers are numbered from 1 to 1000…. Student 1 runs down the row of lockers and opens every door. Student 2 closes the doors of lockers 2, 4, 6, 8, and so on to the end of the line. Student 3 changes the state of the doors of lockers 3, 6, 9, 12, and so on to the end of the line. (The student opens the door if it is closed and closes the door if it is open.) Student 4 changes the state of the doors of lockers 4, 8, 12, 16, and so on … until all 1000 students have had a turn. When all the students are finished, which lockers are open?

In the Changing Positions Problem in *Reflections on Number,* numbered students stand up and sit down in a way similar to lockers being opened and closed in the Locker Problem.

These problems deal with the same mathematical idea (the number of factors of perfect squares[2]) but use different real-world contexts and appear in different locations in the units (at the beginning of one unit and at the end of the other). After working on the mathematics problems of both units, preservice teachers were asked to compare and contrast the two problems, identify how each problem engaged them in thinking about several mathematical ideas (factors, factor pairs, and square numbers), and consider the accessibility of the context of each problem. Because the preservice teachers were also asked to hypothesize about the curriculum authors' different decisions about where to place the problems in the units, the teachers were challenged to think about the impact of curriculum design on students' learning. This activity contributed to the preservice teachers' growing awareness that multiple ways can be used to design instruction about a particular topic.

Teaching Principle

"Effective mathematics teaching requires understanding what students know and need to learn and then challenging and supporting them to learn it well" (NCTM 2000, p. 16). As the examples of this section suggest, the use of strategically selected curriculum materials can help teachers develop new insights about mathematics and pedagogy.

Developing several different kinds of mathematical knowledge

An important part of the Teaching Principle is the notion that teachers need multiple forms of mathematical knowledge (NCTM 2000, p. 17):

---

2. Because only the square numbers between 1 and 1000 have an odd number of factors, square-numbered lockers (1, 4, 9, etc.) are the lockers that are open when the students finish.

> … knowledge about the whole domain; deep, flexible knowledge about curriculum goals and about the important ideas that are central to their grade level; knowledge about the challenges students are likely to encounter in learning these ideas; knowledge about how the ideas can be represented to teach them effectively; and knowledge about how students' understanding can be assessed.

Unfortunately, "this kind of knowledge is beyond what most teachers experience in standard preservice courses in the United States" (NCTM 2000, p. 17).

We have selected lessons and activities from a variety of secondary school curriculum materials to enhance preservice teachers' mathematical knowledge for teaching. For example, prior to their undergraduate mathematics coursework, many preservice secondary school teachers are unfamiliar with discrete mathematics. By working on and discussing discrete mathematics problems and investigations in several curriculum units, our preservice teachers have had the opportunity to gain personal experience with an unfamiliar mathematical area and consider the potential role of discrete mathematics in the secondary school curriculum. As one preservice teacher wrote,

> Right now, the curriculum seems so focused on algebra and calculus. Although I feel that algebra and calculus are important, I feel that discrete math is not given much importance. It has many applications that are just as, if not more, important than calculus.

Roth McDuffie and Mather (2009) reported that, in addition to analyzing curriculum materials from learners' perspectives, the in-service teachers in their study "act[ed] out what students might do" (p. 310). By engaging in tasks as learners, the teachers revealed issues that they "had not anticipated in only analyzing the curriculum" (p. 310). Similarly, we have found that when preservice teachers work on problems from secondary school mathematics curriculum materials, they have opportunities not only to reconsider and revise their existing understandings and views of subject matter but also to develop ideas about teaching that subject matter. For example, we have worked with our preservice secondary school teachers on the geometry and trigonometry activities from Coxford and others (2003). In some of those activities, preservice teachers built pantographs to explore and reexamine notions of similarity. Figure 22.1 shows one preservice teacher's drawing of a pantograph that she built to magnify images.

Reflecting on their learning about similarity with pantographs, preservice teachers expressed their awareness of changes in their knowledge and views about similarity as well as their developing views about teaching. Consider one preservice teacher's comments:

> The section on the pantograph changed my understanding of similar triangles and their application. Having [an early field experience] in a geometry class, I was curious why similar triangles were such a big section. Through

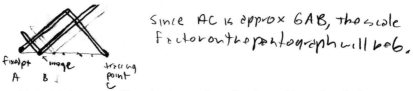

(a) Draw a pantograph that magnifies an image by 6.

Since AC is approx 6AB, the scale factor on the pantograph will be 6.

fixed pt   image   tracing
A   B   point
                   C

(b) Explain how you could use the photograph you drew in part (a) to make reductions by a scale factor of 1/6.

place the original image under point C, and your pencil at point B. Guide point c over the outlines of the image, and your pencil will draw an image w/ a scale factor of 1/6 at pt B.

Fig. 22.1. Example of a preservice teacher's work related to similarity and pantographs

the pantograph activities, I can see more clearly how knowledge of the similarity and proportionality of triangles can be transferred to similarity of other shapes. These activities are giving me a clearer understanding of how manipulatives can be incorporated into a high school classroom. The math being investigated here is sophisticated, and the use of manipulatives respects the students' maturity level.

Whereas previously our preservice teachers had a difficult time envisioning the role of real-world problems and physical materials in high school geometry classes, after working with pantographs and the concept of similarity, they possessed new ideas about how to make their future instruction engaging and meaningful for students.

Identifying content and process standards in curricular units

As we prepare teachers for their future classrooms, we aim to familiarize them with the Content and Process Standards (NCTM 2000) so that they are equipped with a coherent framework for making instructional and curricular decisions. As the Teaching Principle asserts, teachers must identify the mathematics that students need to learn and help them learn that mathematics. They must also consider the nature of the mathematical processes in which students engage. Table 22.2 shows the work of one group of preservice teachers who used the Process Standards to review a lesson (Making Purple, about using an area model to determine the theoretical probability of compound events) from the unit "What Do You Expect?" (Lappan et al. 2005). Through experiences using Content and

Process Standards to guide their analyses, preservice teachers can develop an informed basis for making comparisons between different lessons and materials.

Table 22.2
Example of Preservice Teachers' Identification of Standards in a Lesson

Data Analysis and Probability	Students compute probabilities for simple compound events using such methods as organized lists, tree diagrams, and area models. This lesson particularly focuses on the area model.
Problem Solving	Students make conjectures and solve problems in real contexts. The lesson can be adapted to include more problem-solving-based questions if necessary.
Reasoning and Proof	Students make conjectures about the spinners and "making purple." Then they test their conjectures during the activity.
Communication	Students discuss with their partners and the class why their actual probability was different from the theoretical probability.
Connections	The probability calculations in this unit build on fractions and percent.
Representation	Students create and interpret area models of probability.

Using the teacher's guide of a curriculum unit to plan and teach a lesson to peers

When in-service teachers use curriculum materials, they have opportunities to "revis[e] plans based on work with students during instruction" (Roth McDuffie and Mather 2009, p. 312). Although preservice teachers typically do not have such opportunities, in our teacher education program preservice teachers develop lesson plans and teach "mock lessons" to peers. Rather than require preservice teachers to develop or find lessons on their own, we have provided lessons from various curriculum materials and asked teachers to use those lessons to develop plans to teach their peers. Teaching—and reflecting on teaching—their peers allows preservice teachers to use curriculum materials for the design of instruction prior to student teaching and initial classroom instruction. The process of using a variety of instructional materials to teach peers offers opportunities for preservice teachers to learn not only about the Teaching Principle but also about several other principles, as illustrated in several examples in subsequent sections.

The Learning Principle

The Learning Principle emphasizes that "students must learn mathematics with understanding, actively building new knowledge from experience and prior knowledge" (NCTM 2000, p. 20). For teachers to attend to students' learning, they must develop awareness of how mathematical understandings grow through particular experiences. Frykholm (2005) described how, as preservice teachers in his courses were challenged by the mathematics activities of NSF-funded materials, they began to develop new ideas about how children learn and how instruction might support that learning. Much as Arbaugh and Brown (2005) helped high school geometry teachers analyze the mathematical tasks used in their teaching, it is also worthwhile to engage preservice teachers in *explicit* consideration of relationships between curriculum materials and students' learning.

Anticipating difficulties students might have with a curricular task

Preservice teachers should have ample opportunities to consider students' thinking, anticipate sources of common difficulties, and ultimately develop relationships between students' thinking and pedagogy. When preservice teachers examine mathematics curriculum materials, they can begin to hypothesize about students' thinking. This activity is similar to, although not as comprehensive as, what Roth McDuffie and Mather (2009) have described as "mapping learning trajectories" (p. 311) in in-service teachers' curricular reasoning.

We asked our preservice teachers to consider the challenges students might face when working on a problem about surface area in an investigation from "Say It with Symbols" (Lappan et al. 2005). The problem asks students to write an equation for the relationship between the number (n) of rods in a stack of staggered rods and the surface area of the stack. A stack consists of n equal-length rods that are staggered by the length of one unit rod. A 3-stack, using rods of length 5, is shown in figure 22.2. Whereas one rod of length 5 has surface area 22 units ($[4 \times 5] + 2$), the 2- and 3-stacks' surface areas are 36 and 50 units, respectively. In the instance of rods of length 5, an n-stack has surface area $22 + 14(n-1)$.

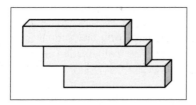

**Fig. 22.2. Stacked rods used in a surface area investigation
from Lappan and others (2005)**

Figure 22.3 presents an excerpt from one preservice teacher's hypotheses about students' work on this task. This preservice teacher suggested that instruction could focus on "building upon what the student has already done" in the table of figure 22.3 to create "a more useful table from which to construct an expression using n." Clearly $y = 1$ in each instance, and x can be replaced with the length of one rod. As this example suggests, by hypothesizing about students' thinking and difficulties with particular curricular tasks, preservice teachers can begin to develop and consider strategies for using students' thinking as a resource to guide instruction.

When writing an expression for the surface area of a staggered stack of n rods, students may feel the need to use multiple variables rather than simply using n to represent the number of rods in the stack.... An example of a table created by a student with this misconception might be as follows:

# of Rods	Surface Area
1	$4x + 2y$
2	$6x + 6y$
3	$8x + 10y$
4	$10x + 14y$
n	???

The student is using x to represent the phrase "long sides" and y to represent the phrase "short sides" or "unit sides." ...The teacher could point out that the student is capable of finding the exact surface area for 1, 2, 3, or 4 rods by finding the length of the rods he or she is using and working from there.

Fig. 22.3. A preservice teacher's hypothesis about students' work on a curricular task

The Assessment Principle

Assessment should be aligned with instructional goals: "Assessment should support the learning of important mathematics and furnish useful information to both teachers and students" (NCTM 2000, p. 22). It is often difficult for preservice teachers to appreciate that assessment should enhance students' learning *and* guide teachers' instructional decisions. Teacher educators are challenged to find ways to extend preservice teachers' views of assessment to include formative and summative assessment that occurs before, during, and after instruction.

Assessing students' understandings of particular ideas from curricular activities

Peer-teaching experiences (mentioned in our discussion of the Teaching Principle) can include attention to assessment and its role in instruction. For example, when we ask preservice teachers to use curriculum materials to design instruction for their peers, we expect them to make explicit in their lesson plans how they will obtain information about their peers' knowledge and learning. Figure 22.4 presents items that a group of preservice teachers developed to assess students' procedural and conceptual understanding of angle sums in polygons.

---

(1) What is the angle sum of an *n*-sided polygon? Use your answer to evaluate a triangle, a pentagon, and an octagon.

Why this is a foundational problem that assesses main points from our lesson:

Our lesson led students to discover the formula for interior angle sums of a polygon. This formula is extremely useful in geometry, and it is important that students know it and are able to apply it. Simply asking students to apply the formula is not necessarily useful, though, so by having them demonstrate that they can apply it to various polygons, [we] ensure that they have learned the information meaningfully.

(2) Use a visual method to show that the sum of interior angles in the polygon below is 1080 degrees. Explain the steps that you take.

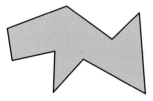

Why this is a primary problem that assesses main points from our lesson:

Memorizing the formula for sums of angles may help students to solve problems quickly, but having them demonstrate this information in a visual manner tells us how well they actually understand why the formula makes sense.

Fig. 22.4. Two assessment items developed by a group of preservice teachers

Our preservice teachers seem to have more difficulty developing assessment items that require students to communicate understandings verbally and visually (as in the second problem of fig. 22.4) than those in which numerical answers are produced (as in the first problem). This curriculum-based task has provided a fruitful context for us to encourage preservice teachers to think beyond the development of "easy to grade" problems and toward those that invite students to articulate their knowledge in meaningful, useful ways.

The Technology Principle

According to the Technology Principle, "Technology is essential in teaching and learning mathematics; it influences the mathematics that is taught and enhances students' learning" (p. 24). Most curriculum materials include supplemental resources that use technology to enhance students' learning. As the illustrations that follow suggest, work with these supplemental resources can support preservice teachers' development of an appreciation for the Technology Principle.

Exploring technological tools that augment curriculum materials

The CPMP curriculum (Coxford et al. 2003) offers a suite of Java-based applications that support the algebra, geometry, statistics, and discrete mathematics strands of the curriculum.[3] For example, for the discrete mathematics strand, tools are available for constructing, manipulating, and analyzing vertex-edge graphs and their representations as adjacency matrices. Similar technology-support materials are available for other programs. Positive experiences with such technology can support preservice teachers' development of mathematical knowledge for teaching and also influence the likelihood that preservice teachers will offer similar experiences to their future students.

Incorporating technology into lessons from curriculum materials

To help preservice teachers develop competencies with technological tools and the inclination to incorporate computers and calculators into their mathematics instruction, we encourage preservice teachers to identify ways that lessons in curriculum materials can be enhanced by the inclusion of technology (if technology is not already included). When our preservice secondary school teachers develop lessons for peer teaching, we sometimes require that they incorporate computer or calculator technology. For example, in one lesson, preservice teachers led their peers in using The Geometer's Sketchpad to develop a formula for

---

3. CPMP-Tools can be downloaded from http://www.wmich.edu/cpmp/CPMP-Tools/.

the sum of interior angles in polygons. In another lesson, teachers simulated coin tosses on graphing calculators (using ProbSim), responded to questions on the TI-Navigator system, and examined class data displayed on a SMART Board. Through activities such as these, preservice teachers can gain experience developing and carrying out technology-rich lessons while their peers have opportunities to develop facility using graphing calculators and computers to complete mathematical investigations.

Conclusion

As we have illustrated in the foregoing sections, curriculum materials can be used in a wide variety of productive ways in mathematics teacher education courses. Although our chief aim in using instructional materials in our teacher education courses has been to support preservice teachers' learning, we have found that the use of strategies such as those in table 22.1 has also fostered new insights about our students and their developing views about mathematics teaching and learning. In particular, these activities have helped us identify areas in which preservice teachers appear to need additional support to improve their pedagogical understandings and skills. In this way, teacher education activities based on mathematics curriculum materials have served as useful tools for our own learning as well.

REFERENCES

Arbaugh, Fran, and Catherine A. Brown. "Analyzing Mathematical Tasks: A Catalyst for Change?" *Journal of Mathematics Teacher Education* 8 (December 2005): 499–536.

Boaler, Jo. "How a Detracked Mathematics Approach Promoted Respect, Responsibility, and High Achievement." *Theory into Practice* 45 (February 2006): 40–46.

Coxford, Arthur F., James T. Fey, Christian R. Hirsch, Harold L. Schoen, Eric W. Hart, Brian A. Keller, and Ann E. Watkins with Beth E. Ritsema and Rebecca K. Walker. *Contemporary Mathematics in Context: A Unified Approach,* Courses 1–4, rev. ed. Columbus, Ohio: Glencoe/McGraw-Hill, 2003.

Frykholm, Jeffrey A. "Innovative Curricula: Catalysts for Reform in Mathematics Teacher Education." *Action in Teacher Education* 26 (Winter 2005): 20–36.

Knapp, Michael S. *Teaching for Meaning in High Poverty Classrooms.* New York: Teachers College Press, 1995.

Lappan, Glenda, James Fey, William Fitzgerald, Susan Friel, and Elizabeth Phillips. *Prime Time.* Palo Alto, Calif.: Dale Seymour Publications, 1996.

———. *Connected Mathematics 2.* Englewood Cliffs, N.J., Prentice Hall, 2005.

Lloyd, Gwendolyn M. "Using K–12 Mathematics Curriculum Materials in Preservice Teacher Education: Rationale, Strategies, and Teachers' Experiences." In *The*

Work of Mathematics Teacher Educators: Continuing the Conversation, edited by Kathleen Lynch-Davis and Robin L. Rider, pp. 11–27. Vol. 3, Association of Mathematics Teacher Educators (AMTE) Monograph Series. San Diego, Calif.: AMTE, 2006.

Lloyd, Gwendolyn M., and Stephanie L. Behm. "Preservice Elementary Teachers' Analysis of Mathematics Instructional Materials." *Action in Teacher Education* 26 (Winter 2005): 48–62.

Loucks-Horsley, Susan, Nancy Love, Katherine Stiles, Susan Mundry, and Peter Hewson. *Designing Professional Development for Teachers of Science and Mathematics,* 2nd ed. Thousand Oaks, Calif.: Corwin Press, 2003.

Mathematics in Context. *Reflections on Number.* Chicago: Encyclopaedia Britannica, 1998.

National Council of Teachers of Mathematics (NCTM). *Principles and Standards for School Mathematics.* Reston, Va.: NCTM, 2000.

Oakes, Jeannie. *Multiplying Inequalities: The Effects of Race, Social Class, and Tracking on Opportunities to Learn Mathematics and Science.* Santa Monica, Calif.: Rand Corporation, 1990.

Roth McDuffie, Amy, and Martha Mather. "Middle School Mathematics Teachers' Use of Curricular Reasoning in a Collaborative Professional Development Project." In *Mathematics Teachers at Work: Connecting Curriculum Materials and Classroom Instruction,* edited by Janine T. Remillard, Beth A. Herbel-Eisenmann, and Gwendolyn M. Lloyd, pp. 302–20. New York: Routledge, 2009.

23

Conducting Mathematics Curriculum Research: Challenges and Insights

Paul Kehle
Kelly K. McCormick

I N THIS article we share our reflections on large-scale evaluation of school mathematics curricula. We identify challenges facing those who do curriculum evaluation studies at any level or scale and offer insights resulting from our encounters with the challenges. We base our reflections on a recently completed five-year study of elementary school mathematics curricula.

Background: Context and Design of Study

Between 2002 and 2007, a research team based at Indiana University (IU) designed and conducted a longitudinal, comparative study of elementary school mathematics curricula. Our interest was in the relative performance of one set of curriculum materials; however, the study was conducted as an objective comparison. We conducted the research in three distinct geographical areas, and all schools were from districts whose students came from predominantly low- to average-income-level families.

Because of our desire to work with teachers experienced with the curricula they were using, we could not assign curricula randomly to create an experimental group and a control group. This constraint led us to use a quasiexperimental, matched-comparison design in which we sought comparable schools, using different curricula, that were as closely matched as possible according to their geographic locations, socioeconomic profiles, ethnic and racial compositions, and academic achievement as measured by previous state standardized tests of mathematics and reading.

The longitudinal nature of the study meant we followed two cohorts of students at each site through three years of schooling. Students in Cohort 1 entered the study in the fall of their first-grade year in 2003 and were followed through grades 2 and 3. Students in Cohort 2 entered the study in the fall of their third-grade year in 2003 and were followed through grades 4 and 5. This parallel structure, with an overlap in grade 3, allowed us to examine performance across five years of curriculum use in just three years and permitted us to compare the different cohorts' performances on the same grade 3 instruments. This longitudinal, parallel cohort structure worked extremely well and yielded much more insight than a shorter study would have.

The comparative aspect of the study focused on Cohort 2, since grade 3 is typically when students are more able to demonstrate their understanding of mathematics on written assessments. The comparisons involved students' performance on assessments designed by the IU study team and on state standardized tests. To adjust for differences in prior achievement, we also compared Cohort 2 students' achievement on the Iowa Test of Basic Skills Survey instrument (ITBS-S).

Lastly, owing to limited resources and, more important, the goal of securing active participation, the study needed to be focused in scope. We did not want to burden or intrude unduly on the normal functioning of the schools, nor did we want to overwhelm students with additional testing, given the current emphasis on high-stakes tests. By limiting our study to select content areas (i.e., number and operations, algebraic reasoning), we reduced the invasiveness of the study and made it more likely that schools would participate.

Participants: Challenges and Insights

Participant Recruitment and Attrition

We encountered our first challenge at the onset of the study. Finding comparison schools in a couple of sites was particularly difficult because of a variety of factors mostly having to do with limited time and state- or district-level priorities that precluded schools' involvement in the study. Ultimately, comparison sites were found in only two of our three sites. Success in one of those sites was due largely to the ability to work in a district where curriculum adoptions were made at the school level and to the steady support of administrators among whom there was no turnover during our study, a characteristic that was not shared at the other sites. Although we identified potential comparison schools at the third site, no schools were willing to participate in the study, because of other priorities at state and local levels, so no comparisons between curricula groups were possible for this site.

Many of the challenges we faced recruiting schools mirror those of other researchers; in the current climate of high-stakes testing, school personnel are more disinclined than ever to participate in research studies that might diminish teachers' and students' time and energy (Chval et al. 2006). For example, before data collection even began, we lost approximately one-third of our expected participant pool when a very large urban site (one of two we had planned in one geographical area) withdrew from the study because of administrative and curricular changes at the district level. Additionally, the site that participated in this area was not the one originally planned; that site also withdrew before the study began, because of changes in administrative personnel. Longitudinal studies depend highly on consistent support from teachers and administrators, and so turnover in personnel and changing local educational agendas are threats to such studies.

As challenging as participant recruitment is, attrition is the bane of longitudinal studies, especially in many of the school settings of current interest (those engaging in innovative curriculum changes). Our study suffered significantly from unavoidable attrition due to the transient character of many of the communities in which we worked (see table 23.1). For example, we lost 47 percent of the students at Site 2 in Cohort 1 over the course of the three years. Study attrition was not due to teachers' or students' withdrawing from the study; rather, it was created by students' mobility and reflects the normal changes in student-body composition faced by many urban schools owing to whole families' or children's moving from one school district to another. Moreover, the problems created for longitudinal studies by students' mobility and attrition are echoed in the National Research Council's (NRC 2004) report *On Evaluating Curricular Effectiveness.*

Table 23.1
Percent Attrition by Site, Cohort, and Curriculum: Year 1 to Year 3

	Cohort 1	Cohort 2 Curric.: A	Cohort 2 Curric.: Non-A
Site 1	27	30	10
Site 2	47	46	54
Site 3	46	42	N/A

These high levels of attrition limit the applicability of our findings, since they reflect the achievement of only the students who remained in the same school for the three years of the study. Because we did not follow students entering or leaving our study, our results do not shed light on their experiences learning mathematics. In these highly mobile environments, understanding these mobile students' learning experiences is vital. We return to this issue briefly in our concluding section.

Another form of attrition affected our ability to understand exactly how the teachers implemented the curricula in the classroom. When we considered what to require of teachers, minimizing the study's invasiveness was of paramount importance; if a teacher withdrew from the study, we risked losing an entire class of students. Still, we needed to collect information from the teachers to characterize their use of their curriculum. To gauge the nature of curricular implementation, we collected curriculum logbooks (adapted from a University of Wisconsin study conducted by Thomas Romberg and Mary Shafer) and a pedagogical survey developed by Ross and others (2003). These instruments can be extremely valuable, but only if compliance on the part of participants is high.

Although the teachers participating in our study continued to use the intended curricula and helped collect student data, the number of curriculum logbooks and pedagogical surveys they returned declined over the course of the study. Despite monetary incentives to complete logbooks and surveys, we believe that changes in local-site coordinators, administrative pressures associated with other aspects of teachers' workload, and shifting foci of attention at the school and district levels deterred teachers from completing the curriculum logs. As Chval and her colleagues (2006, pp. 161–62) indicated,

> In the current educational context, additional pressures and responsibilities, such as preparing students for high-stakes assessments and documenting alignment with state and district standards, have placed additional time constraints on teachers' schedules. It is not surprising, therefore, that participation in research activities that do not provide clear, direct, and immediate benefits for improving teachers' practice and students' learning is not at the top of a teacher's priority list.

Researchers' Responsibilities: Protecting Confidentiality and Minimizing Invasiveness

Chval and her colleagues (2006, p. 159) suggest, "The current context of high-stakes accountability and public access to information may, in fact, impede active collaboration between practitioners and researchers." Indeed, in a climate of high-stakes accountability, researchers' responsibility to protect teacher and school confidentiality becomes even more imperative. However, with the swell in public access to information (e.g., more school-performance and school-profile data available on public Web sites), this task becomes increasingly more difficult. Researchers must take significant care in protecting the confidentiality of subjects when reporting data.

Moreover, in such a high-stakes environment, teachers may be less inclined to accurately report implementation data for fear that this information will be shared with administrators. Thus, researchers have a responsibility to carefully consider what data they share with schools and likewise how schools might use the data.

In our own study, participating schools often requested classroom-level data, and we complied with these requests because these data were part of the incentive for their participation in the first place. However, we provided only the student-level data stripped of other identifiers, thereby deemphasizing the connection to individual teachers. Despite receiving unsorted, anonymous data, local site coordinators could, with some effort, reconstruct class-level data if they wished. As with all partnerships, we trusted them to not use the data to evaluate teachers—something we promised teachers and reinforced with the site coordinators.

With the current climate, and perhaps always, researchers have an additional responsibility to minimize their invasiveness in schools. Just like invasive species, researchers are nonindigenous to schools and can adversely affect the students, teachers, and schools they are trying to study. Often during our study, we asked ourselves, "Why are we adding more tests and work to already stressed teachers and overly tested children?" Researchers need to be conscious of what they are asking of teachers and students; the quality of data with respect to the quantity of data must be carefully weighed.

Curriculum Implementation: Challenges and Insights

Despite a lack of compliance with maintaining curricular logbooks and completing pedagogical surveys, we gathered enough evidence to know that none of the curriculum materials used in the participating schools was used with a high degree of fidelity. This awareness resulted in a double bind—getting only enough data to know that implementation was low actually meant that we needed even more data to pin down what curriculum students were experiencing. Such additional data are even harder to obtain.

Even though we were working with districts believed to be high implementers, we found that no site implemented the curriculum exclusively or with 100 percent fidelity to what the authors of the particular curriculum intended. The supplementing that took place was perhaps due to increased pressure to perform on state tests, resulting in more "teaching to the test" and using less of the adopted curriculum materials, teachers' personal preferences related to teaching styles, and so on. Nonetheless, the experiences of the schools in our study seem to be typical of those experienced by other researchers (Tarr et al. 2005).

In our opinion, the single most compelling reason that teachers altered the scope, sequence, and pedagogy of their curriculum was pressure associated with standardized tests, which we assume to be due in part to the No Child Left Behind (NCLB 2001) mandates. For example, in the logbooks, we regularly found evidence of teachers' using targeted worksheets in preparation for upcoming state assessments, and some teachers reported using their curriculum materials out of sequence because of approaching state tests. As Hursh (2007) indicated, because of pressure to raise test scores, particularly in urban school districts such as those participating in our study, teachers are compelled to teach the skills and knowledge that will be tested, often neglecting other, more complex aspects of the subject. Likewise, previous studies (Abrams, Pedulla, and Madaus 2003; Boyd 2008; Firestone, Monfils, and Schorr 2004) have found that high-stakes, mandated state testing can influence the content and instructional practices of teachers by narrowing the content that is taught and by changing instruction to practices that contradict those thought to be sound by teachers.

Schools are increasingly complex, busy places, and the experiences of teachers and students are complicated accordingly. NCLB increased the amount of testing and the importance placed on this testing. In turn, increased professional development and other initiatives along with an increase in school-based educational research have all reduced the availability of sites for conducting research while simultaneously changing the nature of what we wish to study.

Change Is the Norm

In hindsight, we realized that, in addition to the impact of curriculum on students' learning, a major part of what any curriculum study needs to document is change itself and how a curriculum interacts with this change, especially when rapid change is a part of school culture. For example, the following plausible sequence of changes could easily lead to a compromised implementation: more high-stakes student assessment causes more classroom use of previous state tests for practice problems, which results in more remediation and ability-level grouping; more emphasis on procedural fluency within ability groups might lead to more targeted professional development and filling of perceived curricular gaps. In the end, this professional development might be at odds with the philosophy of the curriculum. One change clearly documented since the onset of our study in 2002 is the increased stress placed on teachers due to increased testing of students, which we saw result in less time spent teaching and learning in the spirit of the adopted curriculum.

Fidelity to What?

Our thinking about issues of curricular fidelity was challenged by this study. As teacher educators, we advise our preservice students to adapt and complement the curricula they will be assigned to teach so as to effectively match their teaching styles with their students' prior knowledge, learning styles, interests, and experiences. Yet, as researchers in the midst of this evaluation study, we wanted teachers to "stick to" the intended curriculum so that we could study its impact. However, when the scope and sequence of a high-stakes state test does not fit the scope and sequence of the adopted curriculum materials, then fidelity to a curriculum is called into question.

Curriculum authors themselves (Mokros, Russell, and Economopoloulos 1995, p. 40) maintain that a curriculum—

> … is not a prescription to be followed to the letter.… It is not cast in stone; it is not the final word.… A curriculum that works is a curriculum forever in process. If the curriculum works as it should, in every classroom where it is used, that teacher and those students will make it their own in ways that the curriculum authors could not possibly have anticipated.

However, the kinds of teachers' and students' modifications the authors have in mind are ones consistent with the overall philosophy of their curriculum.

Along with these authors, and with other scholars (e.g., Remillard and Bryans 2004), we, too, believe that the primary role of a written curriculum is to support teachers as they construct the curriculum they enact with their students. We have found it useful to begin thinking about fidelity to a child's learning needs and opportunities and about fidelity to the teachable moments that arise. After all, what should matter most is that we are teaching children, not a curriculum nor even a subject. Do we really want to suppress students' curiosity or engagement because the topic of their current interest is not treated until a later chapter or because the topic will not appear on the upcoming test? As Boaler (2008, p. 88) notes, we believe that often in schools "the excitement about learning pulls in one direction; covering the material that will be on the test pulls in the other. The elimination of powerful learning experiences because they cannot be reduced to testable knowledge is damaging education."

Consider a class initially encountering multiplication and factors: who would seriously advise a teacher to ignore students who get excited about how some numbers are only the products of themselves and 1? Even if prime numbers are not on the syllabus for that class, teachers should have the freedom to table their plans to pursue students' observations. Respecting and nurturing students' ownership and interest in core mathematical ideas, whenever they arise, will have positive payoffs when it comes to other topics as well. The biggest payoff might be in increased involvement of students in their own learning—helping them take steps toward becoming more independent inquirers.

Our vision is of a classroom guided by a sound philosophy of teaching and learning but not dominated by concern for a testing schedule, fidelity to a curriculum, an obsession with one style of teaching, or a narrow focus on a child in isolation. An effective classroom will balance all these issues in a way that yields the most effective learning in the moment while connecting such moments to one another coherently.

Perhaps a more important concept than fidelity is that of integrity. In this context, *integrity* refers to the mutual coordination and support of several disparate elements in the classroom, distinct from a more exclusive concern with fidelity to one element. In discussions with other scholars, integrity emerged as a goal we now have for children's mathematics education. Beyond a simple semantic difference, we see implicit in integrity the need to attend to multiple facets of classroom teaching and learning, and among those considered must be the child. In a review of the ways researchers have defined, conceptualized, and measured fidelity of curricular implementation, O'Donnell (2008) notes that fidelity overlaps with integrity and other related constructs. What is absent in the work she reviews, and more generally in the field, is a focus on the role of the child. As only one example, researchers should consider how well a curriculum and its implementation support and connect with children's natural curiosities and ways of thinking in situ.

The appeal for us is that "integrity" implies the integration or coordination of multiple components all working together toward some end without privileging one component above the others—and certainly it implies not losing sight of the child. The intent is not that any one component—say, curriculum—should become unimportant. Certainly it is not true that the underlying philosophy of a curriculum and its broad structure should fade into the background. Instead, we believe that the effectiveness of a curriculum must be weighed in complex relation to multiple other factors. It should not be enough to assume that a curriculum is "childproof" and designed to be developmentally appropriate.

All factors need to be considered in concert with one another. If we adopt this perspective, it drives the need for much more thorough, multimethod research studies of mathematical learning and not simply of curricula in isolation. Of course, this goal creates even more complexity and tension with the desire to reduce invasiveness and increase numbers of participants. The value of such thorough studies seems to be worth careful, cooperative work on the parts of schools, teachers, and researchers.

Instrumentation: Challenges and Insights

Curricular Neutrality and Value-Added Benefits

We conducted our study with the goal of designing and using student assessments that were neutral with respect to curriculum, in the interest both of providing a fair assessment across schools and curricula and of recruiting and maintaining participants. Who would participate in a study that uses instruments that favor the use of a particular curriculum? Thus, we field-tested the potential tasks and instruments prior to use with the participants, using a range of curricula similar to that represented by the schools in our study. At the same time, we solicited feedback from teachers to confirm that the instruments were neutral with respect to curriculum. Consultation with our advisory board also confirmed that the instruments did not favor one curriculum or another and in fact tested for knowledge and skills appropriate to the respective grade levels.

One insight we gained from this study is that different curricula have different learning objectives and therefore may produce very different capabilities in students. An instrument that is neutral winds up testing only the objectives common to all the curricula being studied. Such an instrument risks missing unique, value-added benefits that a particular curriculum might provide.

In contrast with the advice of our advisory board, one scholar questioned the emphasis on instruments that are neutral with respect to curriculum. To detect evidence of the value added by a particular curriculum, perhaps assessments need to include tasks explicitly designed to elicit the sorts of understandings that neutral instruments fail to reveal. This point is well taken but challenging to implement. The challenge comes in getting all schools in a study to agree to a test that they might perceive as biased against their students and curriculum.

Obtaining and maintaining study participants was difficult enough without the additional obstacle of convincing them to administer tests that assessed knowledge not attended to in their curriculum. A challenge for future studies is to secure such permission, or to design tasks that are both neutral to curriculum and able to reveal depths of understanding that only one curriculum might cultivate. Another option would be to develop a test, for use in a comparative study, with tasks that are explicitly tied to each curriculum represented in the study. In short, in designing a test, researchers should intentionally bias different tasks in favor of different curricula so that for any one student, the test includes both items biased in the student's favor and items biased against the student's favor. Analysis could then confirm the degree to which each curriculum succeeds in its intended goals relative to similar and different emphases of the other curricula.

Thought-Revealing Tasks

Regardless of the position one takes on the role of curriculum-specific tasks in curriculum studies, one goal should be the use of tasks that reveal as much as possible about students' understanding of the mathematical concepts and procedures being assessed. Such thought-revealing tasks are difficult to write because of the tension between wanting to prompt students to share their thinking on specific concepts and procedures and the desire to not lead them to think about problems in a specific way. Field testing is invaluable in helping identify tasks that effectively capture detail about students' mathematical understandings.

Beyond this tension lies another challenge of the typical short, written assessments that most curriculum studies use in an attempt to balance data collection with invasiveness. In brief, the problem with thought-revealing tasks is that they reveal only some of the student's thinking. Many times, on coding the written work of students, we desperately wanted to interview the student to learn in much greater detail what in fact he or she was thinking about the mathematical concepts and procedures we were trying to assess. As Black and Wiliam (1998, p. 148) noted, "Sampling pupils' achievement by means of short exercises taken under the conditions of formal testing is fraught with dangers. It is now clear that performance in any task varies with the context in which it is presented." For example, consider the work of the same student on these two tasks.

> **Task A:** Jake has 6 bags of rocks, and each bag has 4 rocks in it. Rose has 4 bags of rocks, and each bag has 6 rocks in it. Who has the most rocks in all, or do they have the same number of rocks?
>
> **Task B:** River Park has 78 trees, and each tree has 324 birds in it. Lake Park has 324 trees, and each tree has 78 birds in it. Which park has the most birds in all? Or are the numbers of birds the same?

When prompted for an answer and an explanation of "how do you know?", the student replied for Task A that the numbers of rocks would be "the same" because they are "just opposite," referring to the ordering of the two factors. This response was representative of what we expected as a solid demonstration of understanding of multiplicative commutativity for a third-grade student. So you can imagine our surprise when a few pages later (on the same field-test instrument), the same student replied that in Task B the numbers of birds are "different" because "one park has 324 trees and one has 78 trees." In the midst of a large-scale curriculum evaluation study, and despite wanting to pursue this issue further, we could not take time to tease out this student's thinking. Obviously, revealing thoughts and studying them is a valuable priority, but it can complicate a "simple" evaluation study when unexpected and inconsistent thoughts are revealed.

Implications for Future Studies

Beyond raising the complex challenges identified, we offer a few, mostly practical or "hindsight" observations to guide future studies of curriculum.

- Begin with much larger initial numbers of sites and participants; larger initial numbers will yield ending numbers, after attrition, capable of delivering more statistical power. Our high attrition rates made more powerful analyses impossible, and they also limited the power of the analyses that we could perform.

- Allocate more funds for regular site visits by the study team that include observations and follow-up interviews with participating teachers to gain a more accurate understanding of the curriculum as implemented. As the NRC (2004, p. 114) noted, "Measuring implementation can be costly for large-scale comparative studies; however, . . . implementation is a key factor in determining effectiveness."

- Budget to pay participating teachers more for completion of curriculum logs, observations, and interviews to secure higher compliance with study protocols. We offered $100 for each of two ten-day logbooks and $50 for the twenty-item pedagogical survey. We would recommend $400 per logbook, $200 per class observation and follow-up interview, $100 for the pedagogical survey, and $50 for each test administration. Per teacher, this would total $1,400 a year (two logbooks staggered with two observations or interviews, a year-end survey, and two test administrations). On the basis of conversations with teachers, we think that this increased compensation will more likely ensure compliance and serious participation in the study. The daily life of teachers is so demanding that a significant investment is needed to honor them as professionals and simply to attract their attention.

- Limit the scope of the study even further in content examined, commit to increased days of testing, or use a sampling approach where students do not all take the same test. Our tests were long, and the use of free-response items in a culture where students are being asked more often to "show their work" and to show more of it leads to longer tests. An alternative would be to include some multiple-choice tasks; however, these kinds of tasks dominate state standardized tests, and a study would probably not want to duplicate such data.

- Combine a study of achievement with a study of professional development and pedagogy; information could be gathered to guide both types of studies for the same investment of overhead (each study would be working with the same participants). Such a comprehensive study of teachers, students, curricula, professional development, and so on would go a long way to answering the criticism of not using a randomized design, because it could gain validity through being a study of thoroughly natural situations. Such a comprehensive study also would capture the authentic environment in which curriculum implementation is embedded and with which it interacts.

- Most of our assessment tasks worked well for our purposes; however, some stood out as being particularly useful for large-scale studies of curricula. In determining a task's effectiveness, we considered the task's topical and developmental appropriateness, its ability to reveal students' reasoning, and the feasibility of reliably coding the students' work it elicited. All three of these criteria are vital in maintaining a study's worth and feasibility.

Additional Insights: Coordinating Curriculum Implementation with Professional Development

Although our study did not focus on issues of professional development or on the details of curricular implementation, we can offer some perhaps obvious but vital observations about these issues as they relate to curriculum adoptions by school districts similar to those we studied.

- To the extent that legislation such as NCLB maintains pressure on teachers to "teach to a test" and to the extent that state tests are developed independently of the curriculum adopted at the district or school level, curriculum authors should consider the necessity of rearranging the sequence of units, both within and across grade levels, and provide guidance accordingly.

- In districts with high student mobility, teachers need plans for helping new students who are also new to the curriculum adjust to mathematics lessons that might appear to be review or completely disconnected from their previous work. As obvious as this need is, it forcefully asserted itself on us through the high rates of attrition in our study.

- Be alert for before- or after-school mathematics "enrichment" programs. Such programs might or might not be true enrichment, and in either instance, the philosophy that guides them might not be consistent with that of the students' curriculum or classroom instruction. Work with teachers and curriculum coordinators in the district to ensure that the primary mathematics instruction, remediation, enrichment, and tutoring approaches do not work toward conflicting goals.

- The active, quickly shifting, and increasingly demanding contexts of teachers' work make both longitudinal studies and professional development difficult to sustain. In such turbulent environments, the turnover of just one primary advocate for a curriculum can have schoolwide and districtwide consequences. To keep pace with accelerating rates of change, professional development must be sustained even as it responds and adapts to changes in the local school or district environment.

REFERENCES

Abrams, Lisa M., Joseph J. Pedulla, and George F. Madaus. "Views from the Classroom: Teachers' Opinions of Statewide Testing Programs." *Theory into Practice* 42 (Winter 2003): 18–29.

Black, Paul, and Dylan Wiliam. "Inside the Black Box: Raising Standards through Classroom Assessment." *Phi Delta Kappan* 80 (October 1998): 139–44, 146–48.

Boaler, Jo. *What's Math Got to Do with It: Helping Children Learn to Love Their Least Favorite Subject.* London: Viking, 2008.

Boyd, Brian T. "Effects on State Tests on Classroom Test Items in Mathematics." *School Science and Mathematics* 108 (October 2008): 251–62.

Chval, Kathryn B., Robert Reys, Barbara J. Reys, James E. Tarr, and Óscar Chávez. "Pressures to Improve Student Performance: A Context That Both Urges and Impedes School-Based Research." *Journal for Research in Mathematics Education* 37 (May 2006): 158–66.

Firestone, William A., Lora Monfils, and Roberta Y. Schorr. "Test Preparation in New Jersey: Inquiry-Oriented and Didactic Responses." *Assessment in Education Principles Policy and Practice* 11 (March 2004): 67–88.

Hursh, David. "Assessing No Child Left Behind and the Rise of Neoliberal Education Policies." *American Educational Research Journal* 44 (September 2007): 493–518.

Mokros, Jan, Susan Jo Russell, and Karen Economopoulos. *Beyond Arithmetic: Changing Mathematics in the Elementary School Classroom.* White Plains, N.Y.: Dale Seymour Publications, 1995.

National Research Council. *On Evaluating Curricular Effectiveness: Judging the Quality of K–12 Mathematics Evaluation.* Washington, D.C.: National Academy Press, 2004.

No Child Left Behind Act of 2001. Public Law No. 107-110, 115 Stat. 1425 (2001).

O'Donnell, Carol L. "Defining, Conceptualizing, and Measuring Fidelity of Implementation and Its Relationship to Outcomes in K–12 Curriculum Intervention Research." *Review of Educational Research* 78 (March 2008): 33–84.

Remillard, Janine T., and Martha B. Bryans. "Teachers' Orientations toward Mathematics Curriculum Materials: Implications for Teacher Learning." *Journal for Research in Mathematics Education* 35 (November 2004): 352–88.

Ross, John A., Douglas McDougall, Anne Hogaboam-Gray, and Ann LeSage. "A Survey Measuring Elementary Teachers' Implementation of Standards-Based Mathematics Teaching." *Journal for Research in Mathematics Education* 34 (July 2003): 334–63.

Tarr, James, Óscar Chávez, Aina Appova, and Troy Regis. "Discordant Implementation of Mathematics Curricula by Middle School Teachers." In *Proceedings of the 27th Annual Meeting of the North American Chapter of the International Group for the Psychology of Mathematics Education* (CD-ROM), edited by Gwendolyn M. Lloyd, Melvin R. Wilson, Jesse L. M. Wilkins, and Stephanie L. Behm. Eugene, Oreg.: All Academic, 2005.

24

The Influence of Curriculum
on Students' Learning

Mary Kay Stein
Margaret S. Smith

THE PURPOSE of this article is to review research that fosters insight into the influence of curriculum on students' learning, often called *curricular effectiveness*. For a variety of reasons, the past decade has witnessed growing interest in the question of curricular effectiveness. First, the accountability provisions of No Child Left Behind (NCLB) have made administrators keenly aware of every dip and rise in students' performance and eager consumers of programs that "work." Second, NCLB has restricted the use of federal monies to instructional programs backed by scientific evidence of students' learning (NCLB 2001), leaving many curriculum developers and publishers eager to prove that their materials can be counted on to produce increases in students' performance. Last but not least, more varied curricular materials are available to select from than ever before. National Science Foundation (NSF)-funded curricula—embodying a different vision of what it means to learn mathematics—vie for adoption committees' attention alongside publisher-generated

This article draws on an article prepared for the *Second Handbook of Research on Mathematics Teaching and Learning* (Stein, Remillard, and Smith 2007). The work herein was supported with a grant from the National Science Foundation (IERI Grant REC-0228343). The content or opinions expressed herein do not necessarily reflect the views of the National Science Foundation or any other agency of the U.S. government.

textbooks. Although both NSF-funded and publisher-generated curricula aim to develop some conceptual understanding and some procedural competence, they place different emphases on the two. NSF-funded curricula generally include more focus on conceptual development and the development of reasoning, problem solving, and communication skills, whereas publisher-generated curricula generally include more focus on the development of procedural fluency.

The wider variety of curricula now on the market means that schools and districts, perhaps for the first time ever, actually have a choice among different approaches to *what* mathematics is taught and *how* it is taught in their classrooms. *If* curricula are actually effective in developing the kind of knowledge and skills they endorse, then it would follow that decisions about what curriculum to adopt should depend on an organization's values with respect to the kinds of student outcomes they wish to promote.

Despite this ripe environment for definitive answers to the question of curricular effectiveness, determining the impact of curricular materials on students' learning has proved to be a deceptively challenging task. The framework illustrated in figure 24.1 (Stein, Remillard, and Smith 2007) helps explain why.

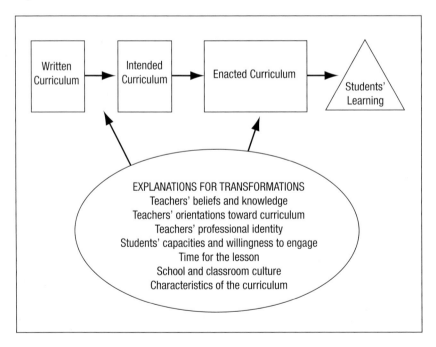

Fig. 24.1. Temporal phases of curriculum use

As shown in figure 24.1, curriculum does not influence students' learning directly but rather, unfolds in a series of temporal phases from the printed page (the written curriculum), to the teachers' plans for instruction (the intended curriculum[1]), to the actual implementation of curriculum-based tasks in the classroom (the enacted curriculum).

The curriculum that students experience in the classroom is different from the curriculum that appears on the pages of a textbook. That is because between and within the phases shown in figure 24.1, interpretative and interactive processes transform the nature of the curriculum. *Between* the written and intended phases, teachers bring their own understandings, beliefs, and goals to their reading of the written curriculum and, in the process, transform it into a plan that they believe will work in their classroom. *Within* the enactment phase, the teacher and the students, in interaction with one another, bring the curriculum to life and, in the process, create something different from what could exist on the pages of the book or in the teacher's mind or lesson plan.

We believe that the best way to understand how a curriculum influences students' learning is to observe its unfolding through the various phases, paying particular attention to how the curriculum is enacted in the classroom as the proximal determinant of students' learning. Researchers, however, generally do not have the resources to do so. Although some studies have examined transformations between two adjacent phases or during the enactment phase (see studies in sections 2, 3, and 4 of Stein, Remillard, and Smith [2007]), we know of no published studies that have traced curriculum materials through all phases and on to students' learning.

Because such comprehensive studies do not exist, we examine two types of available research that may be informative. First, we focus on research studies that aim to identify a direct relationship between curriculum materials and students' learning. Returning to figure 24.1, the reader might imagine a line drawn between the "written curriculum" and "students' learning" as a way to characterize most of these studies. Although some of the studies in this category acknowledge the fact that curriculum materials are not self-enacting, they do not highlight directly the enactment process; instead they focus on the relationship between the adoption of written materials and student outcomes. Second, we review a smaller set of studies that have examined the relationship between the enacted curriculum and students' learning. As we shall see, these studies provide information regarding *how* curriculum influences students' learning

---

1. Note that the phrase "intended curriculum" is used differently than in other sources; here, it means what the teacher *intends* for the lesson (i.e., the teacher's plan).

and, by doing so, shed additional insight into the question of curricular effectiveness.[2]

The Relationship between the Written Curriculum and Students' Learning

Few studies have been conducted of the effectiveness of publisher-generated curricula (NRC 2004). The earliest studies to appear regarding the effectiveness of NSF-funded curricula came from the curriculum developers who had produced the materials. On the whole, these early evaluations were promising, suggesting that students taught with these materials demonstrated at least comparable levels of computational learning as students taught with publisher-generated curricula and superior understanding of concepts and problem solving (Senk and Thompson 2003).

That said, critics raised a host of concerns regarding these early studies, the biggest of which was the fact that the curriculum designers themselves were often the primary evaluators of their curricula, raising issues of conflict of interest. In addition, critics noted that many of the studies were carried out in unusual circumstances. For example, the study of one curriculum included primarily teachers who had received professional development from the curriculum developers themselves. Also, in many of the early studies, the materials were not always in their final forms or had not been used long enough to establish stable implementations. All these concerns meant that drawing strong conclusions based on any one of this early wave of studies was not possible, although the number of studies and the diversity of approaches represented in the Senk and Thompson volume might—for some readers—increase confidence in the general patterns that emerged. Others, however, demanded that independent researchers develop more rigorous methodologies with which to examine students' learning, a discussion to which we now turn.

---

2. In preparing this article, we started with the review of studies that appeared in an earlier review of how curriculum influences students' learning prepared for the *Second Handbook of Research on Mathematics Teaching and Learning* (Stein, Remillard, and Smith 2007). Because studies published through 2005 had been reviewed for that publication, we then conducted a search of articles published from 2005 to late 2008. We used such search terms as *standards-based curriculum and students' achievement, curriculum and students' achievement, mathematics curriculum materials and students' achievement, written curriculum and students' achievement,* and *research review of curriculum materials* to search the databases of Google Scholar and JSTOR. We also conducted a hand search of particular journals from 2005 to the present, including *Journal for Research in Mathematics Education, Mathematical Thinking and Learning, Educational Studies in Mathematics,* and *Journal of Mathematics Teacher Education.*

Comparative Studies Conducted by External Researchers

Questions of curricular effectiveness are best addressed through comparative studies, that is, studies designed to answer the question "Is curriculum X effective *compared with* curriculum Y?" Although it may seem simple to evaluate whether one curriculum is better, worse, or no different from another, designing a study to do so is fraught with pitfalls and complications, leading a National Research Council (NRC) panel convened to examine evaluations of mathematics curricula to conclude that "comparative evaluation study is an evolving methodology" (NRC 2004, p. 96).

To start, each curriculum's objectives must be well specified, and credible measures of students' learning aligned with those objectives must be readily available. This can be particularly problematic with NSF-funded curricula that focus on conceptual understanding, thinking, reasoning, and problem solving—outcomes for which the field has limited measures. Even when curricular objectives are well specified and appropriate measures are available, comparative studies between NSF-funded and publisher-generated curricula face another dilemma: Does one assess only the goals and topics that the two kinds of curricula have in common, or does one assess all students on all goals and topics, regardless of which curriculum they were exposed to?

Another issue is determining how the curriculum materials were actually implemented in classrooms. One cannot say that a curriculum is or is not associated with students' achievement unless one can be reasonably certain that it was implemented as intended by the curriculum developers. Nevertheless, claims about the effectiveness of one curriculum over another are commonly made, citing students' achievement data but providing little or no data on the degree of implementation.

Given the limitations associated with comparative studies, the question naturally arises: What claims can be made about the impact on students' learning of various curricula? This question sits at the heart of the charge given to the NRC panel, and their conclusion was (NRC 2004, p. 3) that—

> the corpus of evaluation studies as a whole across the 19 programs studied does not permit one to determine the effectiveness of individual programs with a high degree of certainty, due to the restricted number of studies for any particular curriculum, limitations in the array of methods used, and the uneven quality of the studies.

The report goes on to caution that the inconclusive finding of the panel should not be interpreted to mean that these curricula are ineffective, but instead that problems with the data or study designs—or both—prevented the panel from making confident judgments about their effectiveness.

Although cautions regarding the effectiveness of a *particular* curriculum may be warranted, one can observe interesting patterns across several large-scale studies comparing achievement in classrooms using NSF-funded curricula with achievement in classrooms using publisher-generated curricula. Despite the differences in methodologies, grades, and curricula examined, many of these studies have produced fairly consistent findings. The first is that students taught using NSF-funded curricula, compared with those taught using publisher-generated curricula, generally exhibited greater conceptual understanding and performed at higher levels with respect to problem solving (e.g., Boaler 1997; Huntley et al. 2000; Thompson and Senk 2001). Second, these gains did not appear to come at the expense of those aspects of mathematics measured on more traditional standardized tests. Compared with students taught using publisher-generated curricula, students who were taught using NSF-funded curricula generally performed at approximately the same level on standardized tests that assess mathematical skills and procedures (e.g., Riordan and Noyce 2001; Thompson and Senk 2001). The differences that occurred were usually not significant, and some show students in classrooms using NSF-funded curriculum doing slightly better, whereas others show students in classrooms using publisher-generated curriculum doing slightly better. For example, students using the Core Plus Mathematics Project (an NSF-funded high school curriculum) outperformed others on tests of algebraic concepts set in real-world contexts, but the students taught using publisher-generated textbooks outperformed those in a Core Plus classroom on tests of algebraic skills set in questions without contexts that did not allow calculators (Huntley et al. 2000). Unsurprisingly, students tend to do well on tests that match the approaches through which they have learned.

Comparisons among NSF-funded curricula

More recent studies have compared different NSF-funded curricula with one another under realistic conditions offered by districtwide adoptions. For example, Harwell and his colleagues (2007) studied students' learning in six districts, three of which used the Core Plus Mathematics Project, two of which used Mathematics: Modeling Our World, and one of which used the Interactive Mathematics Program (all NSF-funded high school curricula). They found that, once background variables were taken into account (e.g., socioeconomic status, prior mathematics achievement), no differences were found in students' scores across the three curricula on the multiple-choice and open-ended sections of the SAT-9. Similarly, Post and his colleagues (2008) found no significant differences between districtwide implementations of Connected Mathematics (three districts) and Math Thematics (two districts), both NSF-funded middle school curricula.

The similarity between the patterns of findings reported in Senk and Thompson (2003) and the findings of the larger-scale studies conducted by external reviewers is striking: Students taught using NSF-funded curricula tended to hold their own on tests of computational skills and to outperform students taught with publisher-generated curricula on tests of thinking, reasoning, and conceptual understanding. This pattern of findings—not the findings of any one study—has prompted some to point to the overall effectiveness of NSF-funded curricula (e.g., Schoenfeld 2002).

Limitations of existing research

Despite these emerging patterns, it is important to acknowledge the questions that the foregoing studies cannot answer. Returning to the framework depicted in figure 24.1, the majority of the comparative studies cited did not collect data on how the various curricula were enacted in the classroom (the third box in the framework); none examined the way in which teachers engaged with the materials to create the intended curriculum (the second box in the framework). When implementation measures are included, the findings can become less clear. For example, Boaler and Staples (2008) studied algebra classes across three high schools, approximately half of which used publisher-generated textbooks and half of which used NSF-funded materials. On tests of algebra at the end of their first year of high school, students in the two groups performed at the same level, both in skills and in conceptual understanding. However, this was not an indication that the curricular approach did not matter, only that there was a need to look beyond curriculum to the ways in which teachers implemented them. Indeed, the most significant factor in comparisons of algebra achievement in this study was *the teacher,* with large variations between teachers *within* the same curriculum. The importance of individual teachers and their particular teaching decisions was also reported by Huntley and her colleagues (2000), who found that different classes using the same curriculum varied to a large degree in classroom implementation and students' achievement.

As noted earlier, many scholars and policymakers have (implicitly) conceptualized the question behind student-outcome studies as the testing of a (causal) relationship between curricular materials (the written curriculum—the first box of fig. 24.1) and students' learning (the final triangle in fig. 24.1). Our framework, together with findings associated with most of the studies discussed herein, suggests, however, that such a conceptualization—although useful for some reasons—is incomplete. Although studies that focus on student outcomes can reveal *whether* a particular curriculum or type of curriculum achieved superior outcomes, they cannot shed light on *how*. However, a knowledge of how an effect was achieved is crucial for enhancing the field's understanding of teaching and learning mathematics, for others who wish to implement the curriculum, and for designers hoping to improve the curriculum.

How the Enacted Curriculum Influences Students' Learning

In this section we examine the impact of curriculum on students' learning by looking at the relationship between the enacted curriculum (the third box in fig. 24.1) and what students appear to learn from their instructional experiences (the final triangle in fig. 24.1).[3]

Although a host of studies have analyzed the ways in which teachers and their students have enacted mathematical tasks or curricula (see Stein, Remillard, and Smith 2007), few studies have connected the curriculum (or tasks) *as enacted* to students' learning or achievement. Several studies, however, provide evidence that the cognitive demands experienced by students, related to the instructional tasks with which they engage, shape students' learning.

Maintenance of Cognitive Demand Matters

Evidence gathered across scores of classrooms in QUASAR middle schools has shown that students who performed best on a project assessment designed to measure thinking and reasoning processes were more often in classrooms in which tasks were enacted at high levels of cognitive demand (Stein and Lane 1996), that is, classrooms characterized by sustained engagement of students in active inquiry and sense making (Stein, Grover, and Henningsen 1996). For students in these classrooms, having the opportunity to work on challenging mathematical tasks in a supportive classroom environment translated into substantial learning gains.

The results of the 1999 TIMSS video study (Stigler and Hiebert 2004) provide additional evidence of the relationship between the cognitive demands of mathematical tasks and students' achievement. In this study, a random sample of 100 eighth-grade mathematics classes from each of six countries (Australia, Czech Republic, Hong Kong, Japan, Netherlands, Switzerland) and the United States were videotaped during the 1999 school year.[4] The 1999 study revealed that the higher-achieving countries implemented a greater percent of tasks that focused on concepts and connections among mathematical ideas (i.e., making connections) in ways that maintained the demands of the task. With the exception of Japan, higher-achieving countries did not use a greater percent of high-level tasks than in the United States. All other countries were, however, more successful in not reducing these tasks into procedural exercises. Hence, the primary

---

3. We have limited our discussion to studies that involve observational measures of instructional practices instead of those that rely solely on self-reported data.

4. The six countries were selected because each performed significantly higher than the United States on the TIMSS 1995 mathematics achievement test for eighth grade.

distinguishing feature between instruction in the United States and instruction in high-achieving countries is that students in U.S. classrooms "rarely spend time engaged in the serious study of mathematical concepts" (Stigler and Hiebert 2004, p. 16).

More recently, Boaler and Staples (2008) reported the results of a five-year longitudinal study of 700 students in three high schools. Students at one high school, Railside, used a curriculum designed by teachers around fundamental concepts (e.g., what is a linear function?) that featured group-worthy tasks drawn from such NSF-funded curricula as College Preparatory Mathematics and the Interactive Mathematics Program, as well as a textbook of activities that use algebra manipulatives. The students at the other two high schools used publisher-generated curricula. By the end of the second year, Railside students significantly outperformed all other students in a test of algebra and geometry. An important factor contributing to the success of students at Railside was the high cognitive demand of the curriculum and the teachers' ability to maintain the level of demand during enactment through questioning.

Learning environment matters

The results of a study of middle school curricula provide additional evidence of the importance of the learning environment in students' achievement. In this study, Tarr and his colleagues (2008) investigated the impact of three factors on students' achievement: curriculum type (publisher-generated versus NSF-funded), the fidelity of curriculum implementation, and the nature of the learning environment.[5] The study included more than 4200 students in grades 6–8 from eleven middle schools across six states. The curricula included both NSF-funded curricula (i.e., Connected Mathematics, Mathematics in Context, and Math Thematics) and publisher-generated curricula (e.g., Addison Wesley, Glencoe, Harcourt Brace).

The study's findings suggest that students' achievement in mathematics cannot be predicted solely by the type of curriculum used or by the fidelity of implementation of a curriculum. However, students' achievement in mathematics can be predicted by the nature of the classroom environment. Specifically, a standards-based learning environment (SBLE) was associated with higher performance on an assessment of thinking, reasoning, and problem solving regardless of the curriculum being used. An SBLE, however, was more frequently found in classrooms that used NSF-funded curricula. Particularly interesting is the finding that achievement was highest among students who experienced an NSF-funded

---

5. The authors use the term *standards-based learning environment* (SBLE) to describe classrooms where students make conjectures and explain responses, and where teachers use students' thinking as the basis for instruction and encourage multiple perspectives and strategies.

curriculum in an SBLE over two consecutive years. These findings suggest that NSF-funded curricula are particularly effective when normative practices are in place that promote understanding, that is, when learning is viewed as problem solving, alternative strategies and perspectives are discussed publicly, and explanations are given to support conjectures and approaches. Interestingly, these same practices have been found to be present in classrooms in which high cognitive demand is maintained (Henningsen and Stein 1997).

Evidence appears to be accumulating, then, that specific classroom-based factors mediate the ways in which curriculum affects students' learning. In particular, NSF-funded curricula (or high-cognitive-demand tasks such as those likely to be found in NSF-funded curricula) can be implemented in a manner very different from the intentions of the developers. By focusing on tasks, discourse, and students' opportunities to learn—rather than, or in addition to, the written curriculum—the studies reviewed in this section uncovered *the mechanisms by which* curricula improve students' performance. Moreover, they offer explanations for *why* two different classrooms using the same curriculum might result in different levels of student performance and thus are a necessary complement to the studies reviewed in the first section of this article.

Summary and Conclusions

The pattern of findings associated with the comparative, mostly quantitative research discussed in the first section suggests that the differences between NSF-funded and publisher-generated curricula matter, at least with respect to how much computational and conceptual knowledge that students gain relative to one another using the two kinds of curricula. Students taught using NSF-funded curricula tend to "keep up" with their publisher-generated counterparts with respect to computational knowledge but to surpass them in conceptual knowledge and their ability to solve nonroutine problems. However, all students tend to do best on tests that align with the way in which they have been taught, leading to a slight edge for students taught with a publisher-generated curriculum on traditional standardized tests and a more considerable edge for students taught with NSF-funded curricula on measures of thinking, reasoning, and problem solving.

These findings point to the role that healthy discussions of values must play in decisions to adopt one curriculum over another (Hiebert 1999). Administrators and teachers need to pose to themselves such questions as the following:

- What kinds of knowledge and skills will best prepare our students for their most likely futures?
- How much repetition and diligent practice do students need to become procedurally fluent?

- What is the best way to ensure that students can recognize and deal with complexity?

The findings on curricular enactment and students' achievement point to the crucial role of the teacher in successful implementation of NSF-funded curricula. Thus, adoption committees need to take into account how teachers will be supported for teaching in more complex ways, posing such questions as the following:

- What kinds of resources is our district willing to contribute to professional development?

- In particular, how will our teachers be supported through the long, often arduous process of trying out and refining new practices in their classrooms?

Developing truthful and agreed-on answers to questions like these can be challenging but worthwhile because the answers furnish a compass for decision making.

The framework presented in figure 24.1 can provide a lens through which to consider the enactment of curriculum, its impact on students, and the factors that can influence the ways in which the curriculum can be transformed as teachers plan for and enact instruction in their classrooms. The framework serves as a reminder that the way in which the curriculum is used matters most and ultimately determines what is learned.

REFERENCES

Boaler, Jo. *Experiencing School Mathematics: Teaching Styles, Sex, and Setting.* Buckingham, U.K.: Open University Press, 1997.

Boaler, Jo, and Megan Staples. "Creating Mathematical Futures through an Equitable Teaching Approach: The Case of Railside School." *Teachers College Record* 110, no. 3 (2008): 608–45.

Harwell, Michael R., Thomas R. Post, Yukiko Maeda, Jon D. Davis, Arnold L. Cutler, Edwin Andersen, and Jeremy A. Kahan. "*Standards*-Based Mathematics Curricula and Secondary Students' Performance on Standardized Achievement Tests." *Journal for Research in Mathematics Education* 38 (January 2007): 71–101.

Henningsen, Marjorie, and Mary Kay Stein. "Mathematical Tasks and Student Cognition: Classroom-Based Factors That Support and Inhibit High-Level Mathematical Thinking and Reasoning." *Journal for Research in Mathematics Education* 28, no. 5 (November 1997): 524–49.

Hiebert, James. "Relationships between Research and the NCTM Standards." *Journal for Research in Mathematics Education* 30 (January 1999): 3–19.

Huntley, Mary Ann, Chris L. Rasmussen, Roberto S. Villarubi, Jaruwan Sangtong, and James T. Fey. "Effects of *Standards*-Based Mathematics Education: A Study of the Core-Plus Mathematics Project Algebra and Functions Strand." *Journal for Research in Mathematics Education* 31, no. 3 (May 2000): 328–61.

National Research Council (NRC). *On Evaluating Curricular Effectiveness: Judging the Quality of K–12 Mathematics Evaluations.* Washington, D.C.: National Academies Press, 2004.

No Child Left Behind Act of 2001. Public Law No. 107-110, 115, Stat. 1425 (2001).

Post, Thomas R., Michael R. Harwell, Jon D. Davis, Yukiko Maeda, Arnold L. Cutler, Edwin Andersen, Jeremy A. Kahan, and Thomas Norman. "*Standards*-Based Mathematics Curricula and Middle-Grades Students' Performance on Standardized Achievement Tests." *Journal for Research in Mathematics Education* 39 (March 2008): 184–212.

Riordan, Julie E., and Pendred E. Noyce. "The Impact of Two Standards-Based Mathematics Curricula on Student Achievement in Massachusetts." *Journal for Research in Mathematics Education* 32 (July 2001): 368–98.

Schoenfeld, Alan. "Making Mathematics Work for All Children: Issues of Standards, Testing, and Equity." *Educational Researcher* 31, no. 1 (2002): 13–25.

Senk, Sharon L., and Denise R. Thompson, eds. *Standards-Based School Mathematics Curricula: What Are They? What Do Students Learn?* Mahwah, N.J.: Lawrence Erlbaum Associates, 2003.

Stein, Mary Kay, Barbara W. Grover, and Marjorie Henningsen. "Building Student Capacity for Mathematical Thinking and Reasoning: An Analysis of Mathematical Tasks Used in Reform Classrooms." *American Educational Research Journal* 33, no. 2 (Summer 1996): 455–88.

Stein, Mary Kay, and Suzanne Lane. "Instructional Tasks and the Development of Student Capacity to Think and Reason: An Analysis of the Relationship between Teaching and Learning in a Reform Mathematics Project." *Educational Research and Evaluation* 2 (1996): 50–80.

Stein, Mary Kay, Janine Remillard, and Margaret S. Smith. "How Curriculum Influences Student Learning." In *Second Handbook of Research on Mathematics Teaching and Learning,* edited by Frank K. Lester, pp. 319–70. Greenwich, Conn.: Information Age Publishing, 2007.

Stigler, James W., and James Hiebert. "Improving Mathematics Teaching." *Educational Leadership* 61, no. 5 (2004): 12–16.

Tarr, James E., Robert E. Reys, Barbara J. Reys, Óscar Chávez, Jeffrey Shih, and Steven J. Osterlind. "The Impact of Middle-Grades Mathematics Curricula and the Classroom Learning Environment on Students' Achievement." *Journal for Research in Mathematics Education* 39, no. 3 (May 2008): 247–80.

Thompson, Denisse R., and Sharon L. Senk. "The Effects of Curriculum on Achievement in Second-Year Algebra: The Example of the University of Chicago School Mathematics Project." *Journal for Research in Mathematics Education* 32 (January 2001): 58–84.